Understanding
SEX

Marshall Cavendish

Editor: Sandy Carr
Art Editor: Graham Beehag

Published by Marshall Cavendish Books Limited
58 Old Compton Street
London W1V 5PA

© Marshall Cavendish Limited 1985

ISBN 0 86307 321 2

Printed and bound in Hong Kong by
Dai Nippon Printing Company

Introduction

In spite of greater openness and more liberal attitudes to sex education in the last twenty years or so, sexual matters are still surrounded by a great deal of myth and misunderstanding. Many people, even now, find it difficult to speak frankly about their feelings on sex even with their sexual partners. As a result, they not only become prey to needless anxieties about their own sexuality, but also remain ignorant of, and insensitive to, the needs of their lovers. Yet many of their fears are shared at one time or another by most of us and problems can often be resolved once this reticence has been overcome.

Understanding Sex *is a first step towards better loving relationships. The basic, most up-to-date information about sexual development in childhood, what happens in puberty and the facts about male and female sex organs, about orgasm, and the ways in which the body responds to sexual stimulation are here in straightforward, non-prudish language. Some of the questions people often ask are answered simply and clearly, for example, how can you tell if you're gay, how do gay relationships differ from those of heterosexuals, what makes some people sexually deviant, what is normal in sexual behaviour and is it possible to continue to enjoy a rewarding and fulfilling sex life as you get older? Sexual relationships involve our deepest emotional as well as physical needs so it is not surprising that there are sometimes difficulties. Throughout the book some of the commonest fears and phobias are explored by means of case studies in which a counsellor attempts to get to the root of the problem, to allay groundless anxieties and, if necessary, suggest solutions. The knowledge that a problem is not unique can, in itself, be reassuring to those in similar situations. This, together with a deeper understanding of their sexuality, will help caring couples to a happier and more satisfying sex life.*

Contents

Sexual Development in Childhood and Adolescence

Sexual development begins much earlier than most people think, long before the obvious physical changes that take place at puberty. Yet many parents find it difficult to come to terms with this aspect of a child's growing up. They are often unable to talk about sex to their children either through embarrassment or simply because they cannot find the right words. However, sympathetic, informed understanding from parents is crucial to healthy sexual development.

Child sexuality

Some parents are shocked and worried when their small children begin to masturbate, play games of 'mothers and fathers', or ask questions about sex. But there is no cause for alarm — interest in sex is a natural, healthy part of a child's development.

Childhood is popularly supposed to be a time of innocence and purity, uncorrupted by worldly desires, 'unspoiled' by sex. It comes as quite a surprise to many parents when they discover that their infant sons and daughters have definite sexual urges, if only because, as adults, their own notions of sex are often mixed up with feelings of shame and guilt.

Many parents are shocked and frightened when their children ask questions about sex, or when they discover them masturbating or playing games like 'mothers and fathers'. But sexuality does not suddenly awaken at puberty, and masturbation and sexual curiosity are perfectly natural and healthy ways for children to express the sexuality which is a part of them from birth.

Masturbation

Some adults still believe in the old myths about the harm that can result from masturbation and, when they find their children playing with their genitals, they might well be disgusted or very angry. But there is nothing harmful about masturbation and the vast majority of children, including babies, touch and play with their genitals. There is another myth that girls don't masturbate, but it probably only arose because some girls can stimulate themselves simply by clenching their thighs together.

Many parents are also upset when they see that their small son has an erection (a girl's excitement is not so obvious) and believe him to be in some way 'abnormal'. But they have no need to worry for children do experience sexual excitement, although this is usually for non-sexual reasons. Baby boys often have erections shortly after birth — after all, birth is probably one of the most exciting experiences any of us will ever have. Rough-and-tumble games, sitting quietly reading with a parent, being washed and dried, or just simply being hugged — all these activities can be arousing to a young child.

Children don't tend to think of their genitals as being special parts of the body and so don't see any harm in playing with them in public — that is, until their parents teach them otherwise. They must, of course, be taught that, while masturbation is nothing to be ashamed of, in our society it is something to be enjoyed in private. But parents should explain this calmly and simply — anger and disgust may make children ashamed of their genitals and may inhibit them in later adult relationships. Also, some children may too readily believe adult lies about withered genitals and blindness and consequently become very frightened and unhappy.

Questions about sex

Children are naturally very curious, and parents may often find it difficult to answer their constant questions, especially when they begin to ask about sex. Parents should try to answer these questions on sex as they would about any other topic: honestly and simply, and by consulting one or two easily understood books with the child when parental knowledge fails. Evasions or the wrong information can only mislead and may result in sexual difficulties in later life.

'Mothers and fathers'

While many parents are willing to answer questions about sex, they may be shocked if they find out that their children are playing games of sexual

exploration like 'mothers and fathers' or 'doctors and nurses'. These games seem to have been re-invented by each generation of children and are perfectly natural. Games of exploration with the same sex are also quite common and there is no need for parents to fear that their children are abnormal. It's best just to ignore this kind of play; the games won't do the children any harm and can be an excellent way for them to learn about the differences and similarities between the sexes. The world of adults can sometimes be very puzzling to children, but by acting out adult be-haviour, these games may also help children to cope with any worries they may have.

9

Nudity

Young children may also be curious about what parents or older brothers and sisters look like without clothes. This curiosity is normal and there is no evidence that it will lead to voyeurism in later life — on the contrary, there is evidence which suggests that peeping Toms have had fewer opportunities than sexually healthy adults of seeing members of the family or other people without clothes. There is also no evidence to suggest that children will suffer any harm in families that take nudity for granted.

However, this does not mean that previously modest parents should suddenly invite their children into the bedroom or bathroom. This may only confuse children and make them think that nudity is something special. Equally, parents should not be overstrict about privacy and make a fuss if children accidentally burst in while they are bathing. Again, children will only think that nudity is special or even that the naked body is ugly or something to be ashamed of.

It certainly does not harm children either if they come into their parents' bedroom occasionally, but it's much better for this to be a special treat rather than something that happens every day. Small children, especially, may feel rejected when their parents do want to be alone in the bedroom together. Children are unlikely to

feel unloved, however, if parents have a lock on the bedroom door and explain that adults sometimes like to be private and that children should knock on bedroom and bathroom doors.

Toilet training

Some people are surprised when toilet training is discussed as part of child sexuality, but some psychologists believe it is an important stage of a child's sexual development. It is also sometimes the case that those parents who find it hard to deal with their children's sexuality are also anxious about toilet training.

Some parents worry a great deal about training their children to use the pot or lavatory, and feel that children who are not 'clean' at an early age are either being deliberately disobedient or stupid. These worries arise because of the different attitudes adults and children have: to adults, faeces are disgusting, while children find them interesting — they will even touch their own faeces.

Because of their feelings, some parents put their children on the pot, occasionally as early as three months of age, and claim that their children are toilet trained. However, until the age of about 15 months to two years, children cannot control their bowels, simply because the nerve pathways from the brain do not mature until then. So these parents have not really

trained their children; instead they have trained themselves to put the children on the pot when bowel movements are likely — after a feed, for example. Problems arise when children are old enough to control their bowels and, like adults, want to empty them when they choose to, not when they are told to. Parents, used to 'cleanliness' are angry and disgusted at these lapses, while children become frustrated and confused.

It's much better to begin toilet training at a proper age, and in a relaxed fashion. Parents should not expect overnight success or compare their children's progress with that of others (which may, in any case, be exaggerated by boastful parents). Children should be praised when they succeed, but parents should never be angry at failures. Also children, like adults, are best left alone when on the lavatory, as they can understand even silent anxiety.

Phases of sexual development

We owe much of our understanding of child sexuality to Sigmund Freud, who suggested that there are three phases of sexual development — oral, anal and phallic — and that if children experienced difficulties with one phase, they would find it hard to progress on to the next.

The oral phase

For approximately one year after birth, according to Freud, children gain most pleasure from sucking. At first this is due to the satisfaction derived from feeding, but later, because of the feelings of love and security they get from the feel of their mothers' bodies while feeding, they come to associate sucking in general with pleasure. So babies suck their thumbs, dummies, and, in some instances, even blankets and toes.

The anal phase

From the age of approximately one to three years, babies discover that defecating is enjoyable and that pleasure is increased if they wait until their bowels are full. Young children regard their faeces as a gift which gives pleasure, and so Freud believed that, if parents show anger at soiled pants or try to hurry toilet training, behaviour problems can result in later life.

The phallic phase

Freud called the time between approximately four and five years the phallic rather than genital phase because at this age, he thought, girls begin to envy boys' penises. If a girl fails to resolve her so-called 'penis envy', Freud believed, she would find it difficult to cope with her future feminine role. During this phase all children are sexually curious, asking questions and playing games of sexual exploration. Freud counselled parents not to punish children for their curiosity, warning that making a child feel guilty could only cause harm in future relationships.

When experts disagree . . .

Though Freud's theories are accepted by many psychologists, others disagree. They point out that Freud based his ideas on those people he treated in Europe at the turn of the century, and that while his theories might have been correct for that society, they may not apply to societies in other parts of the world where parents bring up their children in a different way.

Some psychologists say that, while we may think sucking is most pleasurable for a young baby, we can never be quite certain because babies cannot tell us what they are thinking. After all, babies defecate and touch their genitals and they may find these activities as enjoyable as sucking. Others have suggested that if girls do envy boys, they are not envious of their penises but of the lives they lead. In some families, boys still receive more food, are allowed to be lazy or play while their sisters have to help with the housework, or are encouraged to play rough and noisy games. Perhaps it is not surprising if some girls are dissatisfied with being female.

. . . what should parents do?

Although doctors, psychologists and other experts may disagree about the theories of child sexuality, most agree that in practice the majority of children masturbate, are sexually curious and play sexual games, and that these activities are a natural and healthy part of growing up.

Of course, if parents are concerned about their children's development, they should speak to a doctor, teacher or a child psychologist at a child guidance clinic. Parents quite naturally worry about their children — although they might worry less about childhood sexuality if they recalled their own early years — but most children follow the example of their parents and grow up to enjoy happy sexual relationships.

'My child masturbates'

Because some terrifying myths still surround masturbation, many parents are alarmed to see their small children feeling their genitals. There is, however, no need for such worry, and a calm reaction is by far the best policy, both for the peace of mind of the parent and for the future happiness of the child.

All children masturbate — that is, they at some time touch their genitals in a way that gives pleasure, though very young children rarely masturbate to the point of orgasm. Many parents find it difficult to accept their young children's sexuality as natural; even if they don't believe the myths that masturbation is harmful, many adults feel uncomfortable if they see their children touching their genitals, and do not know how best to react.

Christine, age 24, has recently become very concerned about the behaviour of her 11-month old daughter, Diane. The child's masturbation not only embarrasses, but also shocks her mother, who does not know how to deal with what she sees as a very serious problem. Fearing to talk to her husband, who 'thinks the world of' their baby, Christine has come to a local clinic to ask the advice of a counsellor:

Natural exploration

'I am frightened that Diane might be over-sexed. Ever since I brought her home after she was born, she has been touching herself when I change her nappies. Sometimes it's as if she can't wait for her nappy to come off to start. I'm frightened she is starting to masturbate.

Of course, she knows I don't like it — I've smacked her hand and told her to stop often enough — but as soon as my back is turned, she starts again. When I discover her touching herself, she looks very guilty indeed. Surely it's not normal for a child of Diane's age to want to feel her genitals.'

Masturbation at an early age is, in fact, completely normal. If you were to compare notes with other parents, you would find that they had similar stories to tell. For instance, baby boys touch their penises from the earliest age: indeed, some can have erections immediately after birth.

A baby naturally wants to explore the world around itself — everything, including its own body, is new and exciting — and just as a baby will handle its fingers and toes, so it will touch its genitals. You have told me that you always keep Diane's nappy on, except when you are bathing or changing her. This means that she has little opportunity to get to know what her genitals feel like, thus increasing her curiosity.

The effects of guilt

Your obvious disapproval when she touches herself has also increased her curiosity, although her masturbation is not simply the result of her need to explore her body. Touching her vulva also gives her pleasure, though your disapproval and her own guilt mean that already her feelings are probably mixed. The clitoris doesn't suddenly become sensitive when a girl is in her teens or at the start of her first sexual relationship. It is always a part of the body that feels good when it is touched, as your daughter has found out for herself.

'But doesn't the fact that Diane looks guilty prove that she knows that what she is doing is wrong?'

All her reaction demonstrates is that you have made her feel guilty. A baby is quick to react to disapproval from her mother, and so her guilt is only a reflection of your anger. If you were to smack her every time she put her foot in her mouth, she would soon respond by looking guilty

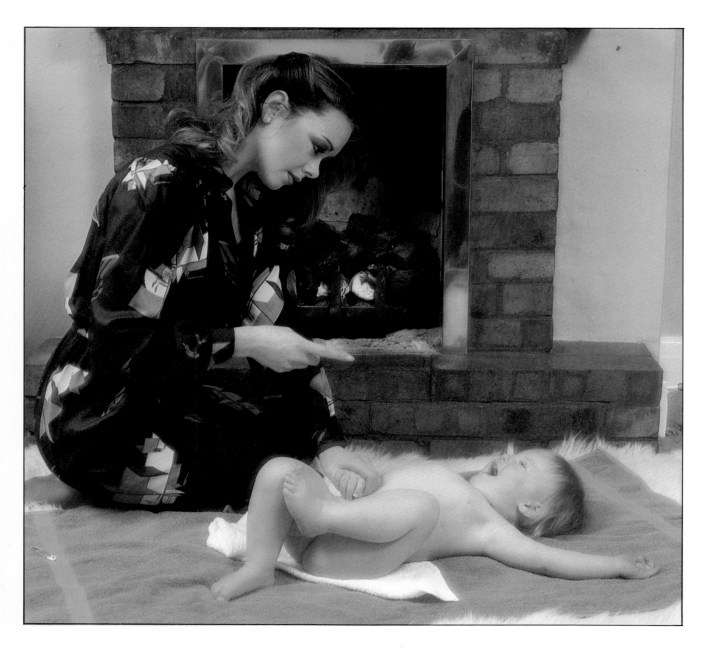

whenever she did that.

You are not doing her, or your cause, any good by showing your disapproval. Firstly, it will draw her attention to what she is doing. Secondly, her first sexual feelings will be accompanied by fear and the belief that something natural is naughty. And finally, your disapproval will certainly not stop her masturbating; she will just make sure that in future she does it secretly and defiantly.

'How can I stop her masturbating when she gets older?'

You can't, and you shouldn't. Most normal children touch their genitals, but as they get older they become more secretive about it, especially if they know their parents disapprove. An older child who

continues to masturbate openly is often showing signs of a problem — but not a problem caused by masturbating as a young child. Such a youngster may masturbate because he or she has no friends or has outgrown babyish toys. A child who is feeling unhappy or is deprived of love may use masturbation as a comfort. Clearly, if a parent punishes an older child for masturbating, he or she has failed to tackle the underlying problem, and will have added guilt to the child's other worries.

Can masturbation be harmful?

'But masturbation does have harmful effects, doesn't it? Nowadays people don't say it sends you blind or mad, but there's often a grain of truth, even in old wives'

14

tales. My sister works in a mental hospital, and she says masturbation is more common there than normal.'

You are drawing the wrong conclusions. All that your sister's observations can tell you is that patients in mental hospitals have few other sexual outlets. If your sister were to tell you that the patients cried more frequently than is usual, you wouldn't suppose that crying had caused their mental problems.

Masturbation itself does not cause physical or mental illness. Problems arise only if a child has been taught to believe that it is wrong. After puberty, when masturbation is more frequent, some adolescents suffer agonies, feeling that what they are doing is wrong, and not knowing or really wanting to stop themselves. Tiredness and an inability to concentrate on schoolwork can be caused by this conflict of emotion, not by the act of masturbation.

What 'innocence' really means

'I appreciate that a certain amount of masturbation is common at puberty, but surely young children should be innocent, and not always thinking about sex.'

You are expressing a common worry, which is based on a misunderstanding. You are projecting adult thoughts into a child's mind. When adults masturbate, they are most likely to be daydreaming about making love or other sexual fantasies. A masturbating child — even a five-year-old who is acquainted with the facts of life — is thinking no such thing. However, she or he will be experiencing her first immature sexual sensations, and the atmosphere in which these feelings arise is important. If it becomes furtive or tainted with guilt, the child's attitude to sex in later life may be affected. Parents who react to their children's masturbation unemotionally and with common sense are much more likely to rear adults with a healthy and unhibited attitude to sex.

'That sounds like a recipe for promiscuity.'

On the contrary, obsessively promiscuous people are precisely those who *don't* have a positive and happy attitude to sex.

Remember too that masturbation has practical benefits. Ignorance about the female genitals in particular is widespread. Adolescent girls who masturbate, however, learn about the responses of their bodies, and so, when the time comes, will be able to explain to their partners the best way to arouse them properly.

Do girls masturbate?

'I thought my daughter was abnormal because people rarely talk about girls masturbating, only boys.'

Boys' sexuality is more obvious than girls'. As I said earlier, baby boys can have erections, and when they masturbate this always takes the form of handling their penises — simply for physical pleasure. Later on, at puberty, parents will see the evidence on the bed sheets of wet dreams.

So some parents expect their sons to masturbate — though they may disapprove and try to discourage the practice. However, boys also suffer from masturbation taboos. They are sometimes told that their penises will fall off if they continue to masturbate, or indeed that their parents will cut off their penises — which of course can create great fear and worry.

Although almost all boys masturbate, the proportion of girls who do so is lower. However, this could be because signs of sexual excitement are less obvious in girls. Many parents who see their daughters touch themselves — like yours — simply do not connect it with masturbation, or else turn a blind eye. Later on, young girls may masturbate in many different ways without anyone being aware of what they are doing. They may discover that they get pleasant sensations from wriggling, rubbing against furniture or merely pressing their thighs together. Others may discover pleasurable feelings when they wash themselves in the bath and may not even realize that they can produce the same sensations at other times. All this means that many girls may masturbate without anyone else — and sometimes themselves — ever knowing.

Why parents worry

'But if masturbation is so normal and harmless, why do so many parents feel as I do — that it is wrong when their children do it?'

The myths about masturbation still flourish. Generations of parents have told their children that masturbation makes you blind or mad, or that it is evidence of a deeply immoral character. Even when parents have the evidence from their own experience of masturbation that none of this is

true, the fear still lurks, and they don't want to take any chances with their own children's well-being.

As well as repeating their own parents' warnings against masturbation, adults often remember those myths circulated by children themselves — for example, that masturbation causes acne. Both masturbation and acne are very common in adolescence — which certainly does not mean that one is the cause of the other — but the first crop of spots might well cause a parental lecture, even if earlier sexuality had gone unnoticed.

Turning a blind eye

'Can preventing a child from masturbating cause real harm in the development of their sexual life?'

It can't be good to make any child feel doubtful about something both natural and pleasant, and it certainly would be better to adopt a very cool approach. In some cases, scolding or smacking a child for touching his or her genitals can cause problems later on.

The people I see tend to be those who have been most affected by parental disapproval. For instance, one father hated the idea of his son masturbating. He did not repeat any of the myths, but tried to discourage his son by threatening that 'no one would like him' if he continued. The boy was sensitive and nervous in any case, and certainly could not control his natural wish to masturbate. However, he felt so guilty that he became sullen and anti-social — just as if his guilt led him to prove his father's warning to be true.

'So how do you suggest I should deal with my own daughter masturbating?'

I hope that you are no longer worried that masturbation is harmful. The best thing you can do now is to ignore it when your daughter touches her genitals. If you can accept that this is quite normal, you will be able to be unemotional. Certainly, you will be doing her a great favour if you allow her to be happy and relaxed about her body — without fear that a part of it is bad or shameful.

Playground myths

Most people probably remember the strange ideas they had about sex when they were young. Despite more widespread sex education, today's children are little different. Here are some modern 'playground myths' — and the possible reasons why they arise.

Some people feel that today we are rather too open about sex and believe that children miss out on their childhood in some way by learning the facts of life too early. However, children often think they know more about sex than they really do, and frequently have very odd ideas. In fact, the most important reason for giving children a proper sex education is that, if they are not told about sex when they are fairly young, they may pick up incorrect information from other sources.

How myths begin

For some children, the first real knowledge of sex comes from their own bodies: a boy will have 'wet dreams' and a girl will start her periods. Others will ask friends at school. Children always share this sort of knowledge, so as soon as one child hears something he or she will tell friends.

Children have vivid imaginations and, if they haven't been told anything, will make guesses which are often absurd; or, if they have been told only half the story, will make up the rest. Sometimes children will tell their wildest flights of fancy to others as fact in order to impress their friends with their knowledge.

Dirty jokes are another way in which children get to know about sex, and they are an important means of passing on information as the laughter stops the knowledge from being stressful. However, jokes can cause worries for children who only pretend to understand and are afraid to ask.

Sadly, even when they feel able to talk to adults about sex, children's confusion is sometimes made worse. Adults are themselves sometimes embarrassed or ignorant when it comes to answering questions about sex and so fob children off with evasive answers. Sometimes parents, teachers and other adults believe that telling children the truth will lead them into 'immorality', and so instead circulate scare stories designed to frighten them into chastity. Even when adults try to be honest about sex, children can become confused if they don't understand how their own bodies work, or if technical terms are not explained clearly.

Even now, it is common for young children to be told that they were brought by the stork or the doctor, or that they were found under a gooseberry bush. Some children are doubtful from the outset: one girl said, 'I only half-believed this. Where was I before I was found?'

Children are frequently told that they came from 'Mummy's tummy', but are not told how they got

there and so supply the details themselves. Some end up thinking that babies are made out of the food their mothers eat. Others believe that their mothers swallowed them, and this can lead to the idea that they have lived before.

Other common myths about conception are that Father Christmas makes babies as if they were toys, or that parents go to a hospital to buy one. Some children believe that a woman only has to want a baby to become pregnant, or that a couple are given a baby during the wedding ceremony. This idea is widespread among children who are told, 'You can't have babies until you're married.'

By the age of 10, girls tend to know more about sex than boys do, since they usually have periods explained to them before they start. However, they often are not told how sperm reach the womb, and make guesses which are logical but a long way from the truth: one girl thought that sperm walked like ants in a trail, across the sheet, and used to inspect her parents' bed for the tell-tale line.

Many children are told about 'making love' without being told exactly what happens, and so usually decide it means kissing. This leads to the myth that kissing can make a woman pregnant. One boy, who had been told he came from 'a seed in Daddy's willy', decided that the seeds worked their way up his father's digestive tract, passed into his mother's mouth and down to her stomach.

Parents are often embarrassed about explaining how a baby is born, presumably because they feel ashamed of their own sex organs, and so children have to guess. It is a common belief that a baby comes out of its mother's navel. One girl was told she came out of a hole 'which opened at the appropriate time', another that babies 'swim round in water and then tap on the door to say they're coming'. Some children cannot see how a baby can possibly get out and think that the doctor cuts a hole in the mother's abdomen.

Scare stories

Rumours go round the playground about the harm that can come from sex, especially from masturbation, contraception and abortion, and these stories undoubtedly originate from adults who are convinced that the truth about sex will encourage children to 'get into trouble'.

Boys, especially, often believe dreadful things about masturbation. Some myths are that masturbation can make a boy deaf, blind or mad; that it can give him anything from spots (a particularly cruel story since so many teenage boys have spots anyway) to headaches, stomach aches or even cancer; and that in later life it can make him sterile, ruin his marriage and wither his sex organs. Above all, masturbation is supposed to be 'debilitating' — though it uses about as much energy as walking upstairs — and drains the body's 'vital juices'. This last myth is probably based on the idea that men have a limited amount of semen to last their entire lives, which is of course quite untrue.

Boys are sometimes warned against 'self-abuse' and 'beastliness' but have no idea what is meant and so carry on masturbating as before. What they should be told, and usually aren't, is that masturbation can do good by relieving tensions and helping children to get to know their own bodies.

Most of the horror stories directed against girls are designed to protect them from pregnancy by making them afraid of intercourse. Girls are told that losing their virginity produces some kind of unspecified change that everyone can 'see at a glance', or that by Government order there is a hole in every twentieth sheath to prevent a decline in population. This is quite false, and all reputable manufacturers test each sheath individually. Another very common rumour is that an abortion will inevitably stop a woman from having other babies — again untrue.

At the same time, because they are not told the full truth, girls often believe that it is more difficult to conceive than it really is. This belief may arise because most girls under the age of about 14 don't ovulate every time they have a period. So sexually active young girls may mistakenly think that they won't get pregnant if they jump up and down, urinate or have a hot bath immediately after sex. Unfortunately it is possible for young girls to get pregnant, and some find out the hard way.

Getting the wrong idea

Because adults often say 'stomach' when they mean abdomen, children often get the idea that babies grow in the stomach, especially if they also think that babies develop from food that the mother eats or that sperm enter the woman's mouth during kissing. Consequently, some children also believe that periods come from the stomach. One girl, whose periods began fairly late, was told by a friend that if they didn't start soon, all the blood would come up through her throat. This horrifying belief was fortunately put right when she asked her mother about it that evening.

Because of taboos against masturbation, girls are warned against touching their genitals — for instance, they are told that tampons will take away their virginity — and so many young girls, and some adult women, have never examined themselves in a mirror and have no idea of what their genitals look like. As a result, a common belief is that a woman urinates through her vagina.

Boys are less likely to be so ignorant about their genitals because they are so clearly visible, but they can have odd ideas. One boy thought that sheaths were worn not over the penis, but on the testicles to act as a tourniquet and prevent sperm getting out. He simply did not realize how painful this would be.

Sex education

Some playground myths can arise from sex education itself if it introduces children to a lot of technical terms which are then not fully explained. As a result, words which sound similar — conception and contraception, orgasm and organism — are often confused. Menstruation and masturbation are often mixed up for the same reason, and also perhaps because they both involve a flow of liquids from the body. Consequently, wet dreams can be mistaken for periods.

Some sex education films and books try to simplify technical terms by using, for example, 'egg' for ovum and 'seed' for sperm. Unless this is done very carefully, however, it can lead a child to expect something like tiny real eggs and seeds. Some girls assert quite confidently that they produce something like a miniature egg yolk with red or blue veins because they don't want to seem ignorant. The term 'seed' can lead both boys and girls to believe that the man produces a minute baby and that the woman's womb is simply the place where it grows.

Other myths arise because children don't like to admit they can't understand what something means and don't feel able to ask adults. 'I used to think,' said one boy, 'that copulation was when you were sick and adultery was when you got engaged.' Even when children try to clear up their confusion by themselves, perhaps by looking up words in a dictionary, they are often none the wiser. If a child has heard adults swear by saying 'bugger' and finds it defined as 'sodomite', he or she is unlikely to be any clearer.

Some parents do answer children's questions but don't explain in enough detail. One girl asked her mother what a prostitute was and was told it was a woman who sold her body. The girl then took this to mean that a prostitute sold her arms and legs. A boy who was told that vasectomy meant sterilization thought that it involved dipping the penis in boiling water. Both ideas seem ludicrous but were quite logical to the children because things hadn't been fully explained.

The importance of honesty

Playground myths frequently begin because adults themselves are uneasy about sex, believing it to be dirty or unnatural. Children can be very sensitive to adults' attitudes, and if they sense embarrassment will be reluctant to ask questions or confide their fears. Myths instilled in childhood can cause unhappiness in later life, so it is important that adults — whether at home or at school — answer children's questions honestly and simply. Books and films by themselves are not enough and there is really no substitute for calm discussion between an adult and child.

Explaining sex to children

Children's questions about sex can make even an enlightened adult feel struck dumb with embarrassment. A sensible and simple approach is often all that's needed to satisfy children's curiosity

Most parents worry about what they are going to tell their children about sex and how they are going to tell them, but it can be especially difficult for those people who could not talk naturally to their own parents. Perhaps they picked up what they knew from other children or dirty jokes, or perhaps the whole subject was surrounded with mystery and guilt. Some people will remember a stern or embarrassed lecture about the 'facts of life' or the 'birds and the bees'. These were usually given when the child had already reached puberty and was full of mixed-up biological facts and warnings.

This kind of experience has made many of today's parents even more anxious not to make the same mistakes as their own mothers or fathers.

Learning about sex is a continual process, which starts from the moment a child becomes aware of its own and other people's bodies — a child can absorb attitudes towards sex, before the questions begin. Even baby boys have erections, and little girls have pleasant feelings when they touch their clitoris. If children are smacked and told not to touch themselves 'there', they will learn something about their parents' attitudes.

It is important for parents to understand that the first questions a young child of three, four or five asks about babies and sex are no more significant to the child than any of the thousand and one other questions he or she asks in a day. The right time to answer the questions is when they are asked — the earlier and more frankly questions are answered the better adjusted the child's feelings about sex.

There are times when it is more difficult to answer these questions simply and naturally. In a crowded store, for instance, on top of a bus, or in front of relatives or friends who do not share the parents' views. In these cases it is probably best to say, 'There's a lot to tell you about that, and there isn't time at the moment. Remind me to talk with you about it at bedtime.'

The sooner you do talk about it the better. It is important not to put the child off yet again, when he or she does remind you. If the child thinks you are angry he or she might not dare to put the question again. If this happens it is often a good idea for the parent to bring the subject up again.

Listen to the question

Often parents are so keyed up about answering a child fully and frankly, that a simple question becomes the cue for a lecture on the body and its workings. If a child asks: 'Why can't tea be made with cold water?' no one would give a factual account of the origins of tea in India, how it is grown and harvested, transported and packaged. A question about sex is just the same.

Sometimes a child will ask further questions, but if every one is answered simply the child will be able to find his or her own level and will stop asking questions when they have all the information they want for the moment. A mother of a four year-old boy was asked, 'Where did I come from?' She drew the child onto her knee, took a deep breath, and described in great detail, conception, pregnancy and childbirth. The little boy was fascinated and said so, but then he added: 'What I meant was, my friend was born in France and I thought I came from Liverpool.'

Avoiding the issue

Many children become worried and suspicious about babies and sex, because their parents avoid answering questions. Often parents say they are 'too busy', or carefully distract the child with a game or the television, so that he or she forgets the question. At best a child will think that the subject is taboo — not to be talked about. At worst he or she will invent a peculiar explanation or get inaccurate stories from other children.

Children who know that babies grow inside the mother's tummy can dream up all sorts of explanations which may be frightening — they might

decide that the mother ate the baby!

Many parents feel that their child is too young for the truth and will not understand it. In these cases parents often make up stories that they think are more suitable for a young child. It is surprising how many children still think that the stork brought them; that they were found in Daddy's beer; bought in a shop — or brought over by the doctor in his bag.

Some children will accept these stories for a time, but they are often shocked when they discover the truth. Usually it is not the facts that a child finds shocking, but the idea that his parents have lied to him. Parents probably feel that it was just a 'white lie' but for a child it is an important lie, which can reinforce the idea that sex is unmentionable and shameful.

Some children will assume that their parents lied because they did not know the facts themselves. As a result they will think that it is no good asking their parents anything else about sex as they know nothing about the subject.

Not knowing the right answer

As a child grows older and the questions become more involved, parents often worry that they do not know the answer. However, as long as the basic facts are right you need not worry over small details. Children soon learn that their parents do not know everything. So if you do not know the answer to a child's question about sex it is always better just to say so. You can always help the child find the right answer by looking in a reference book or asking a doctor.

The child who doesn't ask

Parents are sometimes worried as the years go by that their child shows no curiosity about sex. If this happens it is usually a good idea for the parents to take the initiative. Sooner or later a child will talk to other children and learn about sex in a way that parents may not like. The child could also be approaching puberty with little, or no, idea of how the human body works.

Try to bring up the subject naturally by relating it to a relative or friend who is pregnant. This could start a discussion and the child may well bring out questions or worries that he or she has been keeping secret.

If a child has never mentioned babies or sex it is rarely because he or she is just not interested. Some sensitive children might have been put off at an early stage by a sharp answer to a question and decided not to risk raising the subject again. Others might have sensed their parents' embarrassment and feel they should not talk about it. Others still might have difficulty in talking to busy parents about anything at all and decided that they are not a good source of information.

Keeping it in the family

If you have encouraged your child to talk frankly and openly to you about sex, it is likely that sooner or later he or she will want to share their knowledge with friends. Problems can arise with the parents of other children who perhaps don't think their children should know the truth and have either avoided the questions or answered with a 'white lie'. These parents can often be upset and angry when they discover that their child has been discussing sex with another child.

Some parents could take their feelings out on your child, telling him or her that it is rude and naughty to talk about such things. In one extreme case of this kind, a little girl who had been the source of the knowledge was excluded from her best friend's birthday party — the other children were warned to avoid her because she 'talked about dirty things'. This can be extremely upsetting for a child.

The best way to avoid this situation is to explain to your child that although you think that the facts about how babies are made are interesting, some parents don't think the same way at all. You can explain that these parents may get angry if they think that their own children are talking about sex.

This kind of explanation may not stop your child talking but would at least prepare him or her for any unpleasantness.

Help for the parent in difficulties

With the best will in the world, some parents find it impossible to talk to their children about sex without suffering great embarrassment. Inevitably the child will sense their parents' feelings and will also feel awkward and shy.

Some parents hope that a child will learn all he or she needs to know from sex education at school. But, although more and more school timetables include a sex and relationships course which is generally sensitive and of a high standard, it often comes too late. The lessons tend to be given at secondary schools at about the start of puberty, although some primary schools do have lessons for 10 or 11-year-olds. Even at this age there are few children who have not thought about babies and sex, or talked about it with other children.

If parents cannot talk to their children, then buying a simple storybook about sex is probably the best alternative. There are several books available and it is a good idea for parents to look at a selection before buying. This way they can choose a book that is written and explained in the way that they would have liked to talk to their child, if they could have found the words themselves.

If a child is old enough to read, the parents often feel that it would be simplest to let him or her read the book on their own. If you do this, make sure that the child understands that you will answer any questions that arise. Many parents find it easier to answer a child's questions when he or she knows the basic facts. However, it is often better if the parents read the book to the child themselves, and then talk about it afterwards, together. It is surprising how talking about something you find embarrassing can be much easier when the words are given in the form of a book.

However you decide to approach the subject, it is important to be patient and allow your child to ask questions as he or she feels ready. If you have explained about sex simply and warmly your child will feel able to talk to you freely throughout adolescence. This will give you a real opportunity to help with some of the difficult problems of growing up sexually.

SOME QUESTIONS AND ANSWERS

Here are some questions that a young child is likely to ask when he or she first shows interest in sex and babies. Simple answers are suggested but you will need to adapt these for your own child.

Where do babies come from?
A baby grows in a special place inside its mother's body.

How does a baby start to grow?
The baby starts to grow when a tiny egg inside its mother joins up with an even smaller thing called a sperm from the father.

How does the sperm get into the mother's body?
The sperm live in a liquid which comes out of the father's penis (this is not the same as urine). The penis is just the right shape to fit inside the mother's vagina. The father and the mother cuddle together when they are alone and the father slips his penis gently into the mother's vagina. The sperm comes out of his penis near the egg.

How long does the baby stay inside the mother?
The baby grows inside the mother's body for nine months, when it is big and strong enough to come out.

How does the baby get out of the mother?
The baby comes out through a special stretchy passage in the mother. It is called the vagina.

Can the baby drop out into the toilet?
No, because when the baby is growing it is held firmly inside the mother. When the baby is ready to be born the mother lies safely in bed and pushes the baby out with her strong muscles. A doctor or nurse will be there to help her.

Does it hurt the mother when the baby is born?
Yes, part of the time it hurts like a stomach ache, but the doctor and nurse can help. After the baby is born it stops hurting the mother and she forgets the pain.

The Oedipus complex

Having an Oedipus complex is considered a normal part of a child's development: a boy may love his mother but resent his father, and a girl adore her father but be jealous of her mother. However, if this emotional conflict is unresolved before adolescence, it causes problems. Recognizing an unresolved complex and helping children overcome it is vital to their well-being as adults.

Many parents worry if their shy young child clings to mother or father, shrinking from opportunities to mix with other children at school or on social occasions. And since Sigmund Freud and his theories of child sexual development, it has been fashionable to assume that such a child has an 'Oedipus complex'. But what exactly is an Oedipus complex?

Origins of the Oedipus complex

Freud identified and named the Oedipus complex. He pointed to the ancient Greek myth of King Oedipus, who unknowingly killed his father and married his mother. Freud saw a vital human truth in this story: all children want to dispose of the parent of their own sex and possess the parent of the opposite sex.

In girls, the equivalent is the Electra complex, also named after a figure from a Greek legend. Electra was the daughter of King Agamemnon and Queen Clytemnestra, and the sister of Orestes. Clytemnestra and her lover had Agamemnon murdered and then treated Electra as a slave. Electra saved her brother's life by sending him away; then, when he returned, she persuaded him to avenge his father by killing her mother and her mother's lover.

Sexual development

Freud considered it foolish to believe that sexual feelings develop at puberty. Sexual feelings (what Freud called 'organ pleasure' — the ability to feel physical and emotional pleasure from bodily sensations) are, he argued, present from birth.

Freud defined the child's development further: as the child grows, he moves into a second stage, discovering that he does not need another body to give him these sensations but can give them to himself by handling and stroking various parts of his body, for instance, by sucking his thumb. In the next stage, he discovers the world outside cot and playpen, and returns to the first object of his love — his mother. She becomes the first and most important object of his love, and as he revels in the love and attention he receives, he recognizes that he has a rival — his father. Freud explained that the child's rival was not only there first, he could do so many things the boy envied. He was bigger, stronger, more knowledgeable than the boy. So in the normal run of events the father was both rival and hero. Freud's theory was that the boy not only wanted to take his place in the mother's affections because he wished to monopolize the mother's attention, but because he wished to emulate, to *become* the admired father. Freud's concept of the child's sexual development has been criticized by some anthropologists and psychologists who argue that children are more likely to be influenced by the culture of their particular society than by such direct family relationships.

For a girl, the Electra complex process is more complicated, for she has to transfer her affections from the first love object — her mother — to her father. But essentially the picture is the same.

What are the problems?

A child's strong loving attachment, envy and its wish to take the parent's place, are *normal* stages in any child's development. But Freud maintained that problems arise when the complex is not 'resolved' as a matter of course; that is, when one stage of development is not completed, to become the foundation and jumping off point for the next stage. This resolution usually occurs around the age of five. At this point, the child moves on from the phase where the home and parents are the most important boundaries and relationships. Sexual

Children see their parents as the all-powerful centre of their world, but problems can sometimes arise in later life if adult partners are expected to live up to this childish ideal.

development consists of exploring and testing his or her own body and perhaps those of similar and dissimilar friends (for instance, in games of doctors and nurses or, more important, mothers and fathers), to the stage called latency, where sexual development is said to become less important.

Latency is an exciting and enjoyable stage. School starts with new things to learn, new friends, new responsibilities and new adventures. For the child who does not move satisfactorily on to this stage, recognizing the problem of an 'unresolved' Oedipus complex may not be as easy as diagnosing measles or a broken leg. All sorts of behaviour

problems can result and many of them, in a moderate way, would be normal.

Recognizing an unresolved complex

It is often difficult for a parent to decide when the expressions of love and the young child's natural desire to be cuddled become instead an excessive need for security with signs of timidity and a tendency to cling. Most children have occasional bouts of sleep disturbances or nightmares and anxieties. Some go through phases of having rituals; that is, sets of behaviour they *must* perform. They might even occasionally wet their beds, or demand to be allowed to sleep with their parents. Children during their early school years can still have the occasional food fad or tantrum, tell lies, be shy, be over-tidy — behaviour more common in a pre-school child. All these are normal *in moderation*. More serious would be a child's inability to make friends or to settle down to work and school achievement. These may not seem like the usual signs that a child has an unresolved complex, but if they are too persistent, they could be. Freud maintained that when a child does not progress, but functions at an inappropriate or babyish level, these could be danger signs. Where such signs are particularly pronounced and worrying in a child, parents would be well advised to seek an expert specializing in child problems.

It is a mistake to believe that a young girl marrying an older man, or a young man marrying an older woman, is proof of an Oedipal fixation. To a certain extent, we quite normally choose our partners partly on the basis of our experiences in childhood, but why we do this is complex. In lots of different ways, we may react against characteristics we dislike or imitate ones we like. Some psychologists believe that we are more likely to choose our partners on the principle that 'like attracts like'. But the reasons why we select a certain partner, and the ways in which we go about it, are so complex that we should avoid jumping to simple conclusions about relationships.

Relying on expert help

When can a psychologist confidently claim that the choice of a partner is the result of an unresolved Oedipal complex? A psychologist would look, for example, into the reasons why a choosy young woman refuses all suitors.

Take Claire, for instance. Her mother was al-

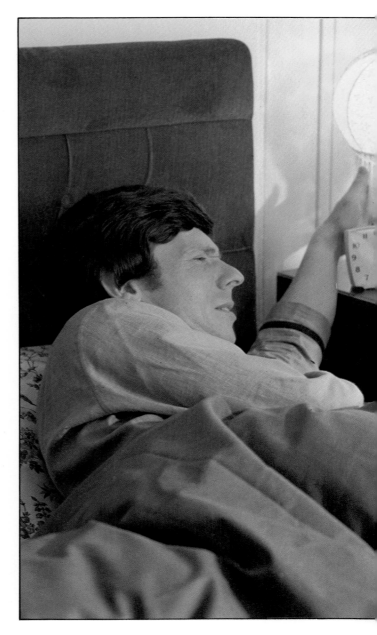

ways proud and pleased that she was a 'good' child, a tidy child. She would always do as she was told and never wanted to play and get dirty with the neighbourhood children or schoolmates. She was mummy's 'pet' and her daddy's 'little girl'. Both her parents were relieved when she refused dates with boys during her teenage years, pleased that she preferred to stay at home. But in her late twenties, Claire was still at home, rarely mixing with members of the opposite sex, becoming withdrawn, for none of the men she met ever came up to her mental image of what a man should be. In Claire's case, what she did not want to admit to herself was that her model was based on what four-year-old Claire thought of her father — the big, strong and all-knowing hero

react with concern, wishing, they think, to prevent their offspring from being hurt. A sheltered child's boy or girl friends are discouraged or criticized. But in fact, unconsciously, these parents' true feelings are often of hurt or even anger as they are supplanted as the first and most important love object.

How parents can help

Don't have children until both of you are able to cope with all the stresses and strains of parenthood and are able to give your child a stable and loving home. Having two parents is not just a luxury or an asset but can be very important to some children. Where a mother or a father is absent, through death or other reasons, during the important stages of a child's development, some children can have difficulty in progressing through these important stages. Many psychologists' studies show, however, that a child from a broken home is just as likely to develop into an emotionally well-adjusted adult as a child from a harmonious home.

There are cases of boys without fathers who find it hard to resolve conflicting feelings of jealousy and admiration, or learn to cope with the fact that they cannot monopolize their mothers, or perhaps marry them when grown up. Similarly, some girls equally have great difficulty if they do not have a father there so that they can experience the natural rivalry they should have with a mother. In some young girls, the result can be neurosis. This does not mean that children brought up by a single parent or a lesbian couple are unavoidably going to have problems — an Oedipal relationship can be found outside the immediate home in grandparents, uncles or adult friends. And the benefit of two parents of opposite sexes does not necessarily mean that a child is going to develop to maturity normally.

Parents have been known unwittingly to create problems for their children. Take Stephen and Debbie, for instance, who carefully planned their two children and who desperately wanted to do their best for them.

Stephen lived for his two children and did everything he could for them, but one day he confided to a friend at work that he was at the end of his tether. He was tired, not only from working overtime so that he could afford a good holiday for his family, but from spending all his free time in building an extension to his home. And now he was getting hardly any sleep because his four-

who could do everything and knew everything. What real man could compete with that? Claire may have grown up, but her emotional world was still that of a child.

Problems in adolescence

The results of neglecting such a state of affairs in a child's early life can be disastrous for its future. Adolescence brings with it enormous stresses and strains. The teenager must become accustomed to a changing body and finally achieve independence. This is the final resolution of the Oedipal tie as the unconscious Oedipal drives are, with luck, redirected on to a new love object.

Often when this starts, over-protective parents

year-old daughter woke him up every night with nightmares and demands for stories, glasses of water, or to come into bed with him because she felt cold or lonely.

Stephen saw his problem just as one of not getting enough sleep. He was lucky in having a perceptive and honest colleague able to suggest that the one with the problem was his four-year-old daughter. She never saw her father. He only entered the house after the child was in bed. It didn't matter to her that this was all supposed to be for her sake. All *she* knew was that she wasn't seeing daddy, but mummy was having him alone to herself in bed at night. Stephen began to under-

stand what he had been doing and took a cut in pay to be home at a normal time to read bedtime stories and to play with his daughter at weekends. As a result, the night-time interruptions stopped because she no longer felt neglected.

Every child is an individual and, as such, should be treated as one — there is no guaranteed, universal formula for bringing up a child successfully. While it is all too easy to over-react to a child's problems or tantrums, a sympathetic, caring, aware parent — with the advice of a trained, experienced child psychologist — can do much to help the difficult child to reach a well-adjusted and happy adolescence.

Growing up sexually-girls

Puberty can be a confused and unhappy time for girls with so many physical and emotional changes affecting them. Sympathetic and informed advice – preferably from the girl's mother – can help.

Sexual development is something people tend to associate with adolescence — the time between childhood and adulthood — because this is when the most visible changes occur. But, in fact, the biological sex of a child is determined long before it is born — at the moment of conception. For the first few weeks of life in the womb, the male and female foetus have identical sexual 'furrows' between their legs, but by the twelfth week, they will have developed male or female sex organs.

Reaching physical maturity

Physical maturity or puberty is a gradual process rather than a single event. It begins and ends at different times for each individual. The changes occur between the ages of 11 and 18, even though some children may start earlier. The process takes about four years to complete.

Puberty tends to start later in boys than in girls, so that around the age of 12 to 13, girls tend to be more physically developed than boys of their age. Early or late starting in puberty may be hereditary but general health and nutrition can also play an important part.

Unfortunately, young people often regard physical development as a race and comparisons with friends may cause anxiety for those who are late developers, so reassurance from parents is often necessary. It is only when puberty has not begun by the age of 16 or 17 that medical advice should be sought.

Increase in height and weight

A girl's body prepares for puberty a couple of years before menstruation: when she is 10 or 11. The pituitary gland, which controls the growth of the body, releases hormones into the girl's bloodstream and she may grow several inches in a short time, put on weight and find she is bigger than boys of her age. She may suffer from 'puppy fat' and if this is the case, she should be reassured that in time her body will probably regain more even proportions, as otherwise she may diet obsessively at a time when her body needs nutrition.

Girls may find that their hands and feet also grow disproportionately to the rest of their body; one foot or breast may also enlarge faster than the other. This is only temporary and the girl should be assured that it is normal.

Menstruation

The hormones from the pituitary gland will also stimulate the ovaries to produce the female hormone 'oestrogen', which, in turn will cause the egg cells, dormant since birth, to mature.

The egg is encased in a 'follicle' and as it matures it pops out of this. If the egg remains unfertilized by a male sperm, it will pass out of the body unnoticed, as it is the size of a pinhead. A period is not the egg being shed but the lining of the womb — which would have been used to feed a developing baby if the egg had been fertilized. The lining breaks down and passes out of the vagina in the form of menstrual blood, which is thicker and darker than blood from a cut on the body.

For the first few years, girls often have irregular menstrual cycles. This is because it takes time for the body to produce a regular pattern of egg producing (*ovulation*). It is quite common for a girl to have a gap of a few months after her first period before the second and she may have sparse periods for over a year.

If a girl is unprepared for menstruation the experience may be traumatic: she may think she is bleeding to death, that she has cut herself or has

some dreadful disease. It is essential that a parent or teacher explains what will happen to her at puberty, why and how. Mothers and sisters should not keep their own periods secret from her, since this is the most natural way for a young girl to learn about them.

The maturing female figure

The same oestrogen hormone produced by the ovaries causes a girl's nipples to grow and her breasts to 'bud'; her pelvis will widen and her hips and buttocks become fatter.

Breasts — their size and how quickly they develop — are often a source of anxiety to young girls. If a girl has well formed breasts at 11 or 12, she may be embarrassed and self-conscious. If she is a late developer, she may feel she is unattractive and will envy her more physically mature friends. It is a great status symbol for a girl when she first wears a bra.

However, the size and shape of breasts can vary as much as facial features and a woman may never be entirely satisfied; women are particularly obsessed with their breasts because they see them as a measure of their femininity. There are no muscles in the breasts, so exercises will not increase them; nor will dieting necessarily reduce

their size and shape in any significant way.

The maturing sex organs

Both internal and external sexual organs develop in puberty. The outer genital lips become fleshier and inside they develop oil and sweat glands to help keep the area moist. The inner lips develop scent glands which become active when a woman is sexually aroused.

Pubic hair grows in a triangular shape, tapering to a point between the girl's legs: it appears on the outer lips and sometimes back towards the anus and around the top of the thighs. It is darker, coarser and curlier than the hair on the head.

Inside, a girl's womb grows and becomes pear-shaped with muscular walls; the walls of the vagina also thicken and become muscular. Natural secretions, which cleanse and lubricate the vagina, are produced and girls may notice some whitish discharge. This is quite natural but, if there seems a great deal of discharge or it smells offensive, check with a doctor.

Other changes

At the same time that underarm and other body hair appears, the sweat glands under the arms become more active. Underarm hair can trap sweat, so it is necessary to wash more often and a deodorant may be helpful.

The vagina cleanses itself naturally with secretions and these do not have an unpleasant smell in a healthy girl. The external genitals should be washed regularly with mild soap and water but nothing else is needed. Vaginal deodorants can be dangerous — the chemicals they contain may irritate and damage the delicate skin.

As well as sweat glands, other glands in the skin become more active at this time, which may mean that a girl's skin and hair tend to become more greasy. This can lead to the bane of many teenagers' lives — spots and acne. Keeping the hair and skin scrupulously clean and using mild, non-abrasive soap and shampoo is the best way to combat the problem, particularly if a girl is experimenting with make-up.

Psychological changes

The apparent changes in personality adolescents display can be explained as reactions to physical changes and to the social pressures of having to behave 'like a lady'. A girl's intellectual and emotional development may be out of step with her physical appearance — she may look like a woman but act, and want to be treated, like a child much of the time.

Adolescent rebellion against authority figures such as parents can be understood more easily when the gap between physical and social adulthood is realized — together with the personality changes that come with puberty. Often parents find it as difficult to cope with the changes of puberty as do teenagers: there may often be clashes of personality and opinion. Parents may not be able to accept that their children are growing into independent adults. But if they can develop supportive and relaxed relationships with them, it helps greatly.

Sexuality

Sexuality is many sided and can be expressed in many ways. Feelings about sex and sensuality begin to be formed in early childhood. At a young age, children become aware of getting pleasure from their bodies but these feelings will be influenced by parental attitudes, education and social taboos.

As girls reach puberty they become aware of their sexuality, and touching their genitals will cease to be merely a comforting, pleasurable experience but a way of learning about their capacity for sexual response and arousal. They may have the urge to masturbate frequently, to relieve sexual tension, and they may experience orgasm for the first time.

Far from being harmful, masturbation is an enjoyable, relaxing activity in its own right. It provides important preparation for sex with others. Most adults continue to masturbate throughout life when sexual activity with a partner is impossible for one reason or another.

By the time they reach adolescence, girls will probably have begun to 'fancy' other people. Sex with others is more complicated as it involves emotional as well as physical feelings. Falling in love usually happens for the first time during the teenage years.

Often girls have crushes on an older woman teacher or schoolgirl when they are growing up. They may also have very intense relationships with a best friend, from whom they are rarely separated. This doesn't necessarily mean that they are 'gay'. There may not be any sexual activity.

What is most important is that a girl be allowed to develop and discover her own sexuality without parental or any other 'outside' pressure. Despite sex education in most schools, parents still have an important part to play. If the parents are shy, they may find books and leaflets help get a discussion started but they should make every effort to be relaxed and frank about the subject.

If there is a relaxed relationship between parents and their daughter, it makes it easier for them to discuss contraception and the responsibilities of having sexual intercourse. A girl must know before she makes love that she will need to use a contraceptive to avoid becoming pregnant and she should be encouraged to visit a family planning clinic.

During adolescence a girl will find conflicting pressures being exerted on her: the hopes and fears of her parents, the ideas of her friends, the images from magazines and television of what is good and desirable. She may find she has little opportunity to work out what she would like to be herself.

Some girls do go through adolescence without problems but there are few who don't feel confused and insecure some of the time. Understanding what is going on inside and outside their bodies and realizing the social pressures that exist can help both teenagers and parents.

Growing up sexually-boys

Growing up can be a mixed-up, unhappy time for boys with
so many physical and emotional changes affecting them.
Sympathy and understanding can help the adolescent through
this important stage of his life.

'I don't think my voice has ever broken. I've just started shaving a month ago. All my mates' voices have broken, and their parents say it's because they're becoming adults. So everyone's waiting for the changes, to become a man. They expect as soon as their voice is broken, or they grow a moustache or something, they're going to walk out of school, walk into a job, go into a bar . . .' *Paul (17)*

'Legally, although I'm nearly 17, I'm still a child, though I could be a father as well. But I cannot buy myself a drink, although I could be earning a full-time wage alongside other adults. So where do I fit in?' *Matthew (16)*

Adolescence — the time between childhood and adulthood — is a time of great change but even greater expectations. Paul and Matthew are fully aware that they are neither children nor adults, and this 'in-between' status often produces frustration and disappointment.

Growing up sexually does not just mean maturing physically (puberty). It also involves changes in emotions, behaviour, dress and attitude. Physical differences between men and women are to do with their biological sex, but it is useful to have a separate term, 'gender', to describe the psychological and cultural factors which give meaning to the words masculinity and femininity.

Your biological sex — whether you are male or female — is almost always clear, although there are a few people who have the physical characteristics of both sexes and they are called *hermaphrodites*. How masculine or feminine you are is determined primarily by the balance of hormones in the body, but it is also determined by the society you live in and the way you were brought up in that society. So adolescence is a time when the individual undergoes the biological changes of puberty and also the time when society expects the individual to conform more rigidly to its particular definitions of what is considered masculine or feminine.

Male or female?

Sexual development tends to be associated with this time in our lives, because this is when the most visible changes occur. But, in fact, the biological sex of a child is determined long before it is born, at the moment of conception. From the ninth week onwards, the specific organs for each sex begin to form and by about the twelfth week the sex organs are formed, although they continue to mature until early adulthood with puberty as the main period of development.

Reaching physical maturity

Puberty is a gradual process rather than a single event. It begins and ends at different times for each individual. The changes occur between the ages of 12 and 18, even though some may start earlier, and the process takes about four years to complete.

Puberty tends to start later in boys than in girls, so that around the age of 12 to 13, girls tend to be more physically developed than boys of their age. Puberty occurs much earlier today than it did 100 years ago and the main reason seems to be better nutrition.

Unfortunately, some boys look upon physical development as a competition, and comparisons with friends who are early developers may cause unnecessary worry: Reassurance from parents is often needed. It is only when puberty has not begun by the age of 16 of 17 that you should seek the advice of a doctor.

Here is a list of the changes that happen to boys at puberty. The order may vary, and some changes will be more noticeable in some boys than others:
● the penis, testicles and scrotum begin to enlarge;
● body hair increases, particularly around the penis and scrotum, under the arms and on the upper lip and chin. This hair gradually gets coarser and thicker;
● height and weight increase in what is known as the 'growth spurt';
● the *larynx* (voice box) grows and makes the Adam's apple larger. This causes the voice to deepen and 'break';
● ejaculation begins. This may occur for the first time when he is masturbating or when he is asleep and has a 'wet dream'.
● the skin becomes more oily;
● some boys may notice a swelling beneath their nipples — this disappears within a couple of years;
● the armpits, genitals, and often the feet begin to produce characteristic smells.

To help prevent spots and other reactions to oil and sweat, regular washing becomes more important and a boy who has not been circumcised should be taught to wash his penis underneath the foreskin by pulling it back gently. A white substance called *smegma* develops here and it can cause irritation and infection if it is allowed to build up.

Other changes

Not much is known about why puberty starts when it does, but it seems that a part of the brain called the *hypothalamus* acts as a 'biological clock', which sparks off a chain reaction. First it passes a signal to the very small pituitary gland in the brain. The pituitary starts to produce two hormones — chemical messengers — Follicle Stimulating Hormone (FSH), and Luteinizing Hormone (LH), which are then secreted into the bloodstream and carried to the testicles. Inside the testicles two things occur: the production of sperm and the production of testosterone — which triggers off the visible changes in the male body. Once the testicles have started to produce sperm, the boy is capable of making a woman pregnant.

Psychological changes

The 'psychological changes' of adolescence — the apparent alterations in personality — are usually reactions to the physical changes and social pressures involved in becoming a man.

A boy's emotional and mental maturity may not be in tune with his physical appearance. He may bewilder parents and teachers by looking like an adult but often behaving like a child. This might well be the case for a boy who begins puberty earlier than his friends. The reverse is often true as well. When a boy is a 'late developer' physically, he has changed his interests and outlook on life in keeping with other boys of his age.

Boys who feel uncomfortable and gangly because they have grown so suddenly, or those who feel embarrassed about remaining small, may become withdrawn and shy as a result of the comments others make about them. Although many of these boys appear sullen and uncommunicative, often they really want a chance to talk with a sympathetic person.

A hundred years ago, puberty seemed to coincide with the time when the young person started working and got married — in short, had the status and responsibilities of an adult. Today, puberty occurs earlier, but childhood has been prolonged because of a longer period of compulsory education and changes in employment legislation.

Adolescent rebellion against figures of authority such as parents can be understood more easily when the gap between physical and social adulthood is realized. Often parents find it difficult to accept this — when one minute their son is demanding to stay out late and the next minute he wants to be treated like a small child.

Sexuality

Awareness of sensuality and sexuality begins in early childhood, and at a very young age children get pleasure from their bodies. The way an adolescent's feelings towards sex develop depends not only on self-discovery but also on the attitudes and inhibitions of his parents and the society he lives in.

For instance, those maturing young children who have baths with their mother or father, and who see their parents hug and kiss each other, are much less likely to feel inhibited about their own bodies and feelings than children whose parents' behaviour instils the idea that sex is somehow dirty and shameful.

When do boys start to have sexual feelings? They get erections as babies. Unlike girls, their sexual organs are easily visible and accessible and they will automatically touch and play with their penis as well as other parts of their bodies. When boys are toilet trained, they learn to handle their penis, whereas girls are usually discouraged from touching themselves 'down there'.

Coming to terms with sex

Boys also discover their sexual feelings from the touching and exploring games they play with their brothers and sisters. By the time they become adults the majority of boys will masturbate regularly and it is likely to be their main form of sexual activity in their teens.

Parents who discover their child masturbating are often embarrassed, worried or disapproving. If these reactions are openly expressed, the child will probably not stop masturbating, but will be more secretive, shameful and guilty about it. What a parent should do is to help the child understand that, like other forms of sexual activity, masturbation is regarded as private, like going to the toilet, and should not be done in public.

Masturbation is not harmful: in fact, it is an enjoyable, relaxing activity in its own right. Familiarity with one's own body can also provide an important preparation for sex with others. It should not be seen as merely an 'adolescent phase' since most adults masturbate throughout life.

Adolescent boys will probably have begun to focus their sexual awareness on others. But sex with other people is more complicated since it involves strong emotional feelings too.

The type of attraction depends on a boy's sexual identity, which is not necessarily fixed and may change at different times of his life. The term sexual identity refers to whether a boy is attracted to girls (heterosexual), to girls and boys (bisexual), or to boys (homosexual or gay).

Whatever their sexual identity, many boys will continue to spend most of their time with a group of friends of the same sex during adolescence, and only as they approach their late teens may they start forming serious relationships with girls.

During this time of hormonal change and sexual confusion many boys cling together in gangs or

groups, feeling too uncertain about their sexual roles to get involved with girls, who can seem so far removed from what teenage boys understand that they could be from another planet!

Little wonder then that many boys form strong emotional attachments to each other; with boys they feel on 'safe' emotional territory, on familiar ground. Some of these intense friendships may involve physical contact or some form of sexual expression. *Almost all boys go through this phase during their adolescence and it is not necessarily a permanent homosexual attachment.*

Most of them finally adjust to a heterosexual relationship but some do not, remaining predominantly or wholly homosexual. Even in these 'enlightened' times it is often a shock to the boy's parents to discover this type of sexuality. But there is no 'cure' because it is not an illness — nor is it a perversion. It is just the way he is and the only way his family can make him happy is by trying to understand and accept his emotional and sexual preference.

Grown-up problems

It is most important to make it clear to boys that from the moment they begin to ejaculate they are capable of making a girl pregnant, and that it is their responsibility as well as the girl's to ensure that this does not happen unless they both feel ready for the responsibilities of parenthood. Boys should also be told that there is a possibility that pregnancy can occur during heavy petting if semen gets on the outside of the girl's vagina.

So far, the sheath is the only method of contraception available to men — except for the rather drastic step of sterilization by vasectomy, which is unsuitable for young men who may want children. The sheath is easily available and, when used properly and with a spermicide, is safe.

By far the most common anxiety boys and men have is the size of their penis. It is as if the penis becomes a symbol of how big a man he is. In fact, the size of the penis has nothing to do with the ability to satisfy a partner sexually. The sexual excitement a woman experiences depends on how sensitively her partner is able to stimulate her — still penis size is a worry that plagues otherwise rational men throughout their adult lives. A man must be truly mature to realize that sexuality is not simply physical, not a competition or a performance but a gift to be treasured, respected and enjoyed by both himself and his partner.

Coping with adolescence

One of the most difficult times for both children and parents is adolescence. No one is sure whether the adolescent is a child or an adult, and this can complicate a period during which there is already a great deal of change.

Adolescence is the twilight zone between childhood and adulthood; it includes puberty, the period of physical maturation, and most of the teenage years. But it also covers the time when a young person has to cope with the emotional and social changes which mark the move from childhood to adulthood.

Adolescence is a new concept. A hundred years ago girls reached puberty at about the age of 17, although many of them were working by the time they were 13 or 14 and so had time to adjust to being adults socially and emotionally long before they were adults sexually.

Conflicting roles

Today the process is reversed, and physical maturation precedes the social and emotional changes and this contradiction is reflected in laws and social attitudes. For example, the age of sexual consent in a country may be 16, but to vote, get married or buy alcohol may not be allowed until a person is 18 or 21. This can make the adolescent even more confused about who he is — child or adult.

The first indication of the change from child to adult is at the start of puberty, when the whole body prepares for its full adult appearance and function. This is not a dramatic chrysalis-to-butterfly transformation but a very gradual change which takes several years to complete.

Changing relationships

Adolescence is a time of conflict: teenagers do not know if they are adults or children — at school they are told to behave like adults, at home they are treated like children. These years can seem like a war and each argument a battle, with no winners and no losers. Adolescents feel they are ready for responsibility while their parents feel they need supervision.

If a teenager's friends are allowed to stay out until the early hours of the morning and he isn't, there can be a full-scale argument with the adolescent saying, 'All my friends can stay out late, but I'm treated like a baby,' and the parents replying, 'You are not one of the bunch, and as long as you are living under our roof you will do what we say.' Tempers fray until the teenager runs to his room and the parents shake their heads in despair.

Parents should constantly keep in mind that, although this is a difficult time for them, it is doubly so for their child. These are the years when the adolescent suffers from physical problems like puppy fat, spots and oily skin as well as having to cope with bodily changes like menstruation, breaking voices and facial hair. Parents should let their children know they care, and while they may not understand why their sons or daughters feel the way they do, they are there to help them.

Parents may also find themselves applying double standards to their male and female children, which also cause tension. Parents naturally want to protect their daughters from the risks of sexual exploitation and unwanted pregnancies. But if they do not explain to their daughter why they are strict with her and not with her brother, problems can arise — not only in the parent-child relationship but also in the brother-sister relationship as well.

Relationships between brothers and sisters often change during the teenage years. Brothers and sisters are usually close and happy companions during childhood, but as one or both mature they may grow apart — their interests and friends change and they may resent having a younger brother or sister 'tag along' after them when they go to a party or the cinema or even to meet friends. Adolescents may even begin to be more possessive about belongings and refuse to let younger children play with them. Parents can make this situation worse by insisting that teenagers maintain their former close relationship with younger brothers and sisters, which can cause further family strain.

The 'gang'

During adolescence, teenagers often feel compelled to join a particular group of young people their own age. This group may have a unique identity — for example, they may all follow a particular fashion or have the same hairstyles. Or the group may be formed because the members have similar interests or activities.

Whatever the reason for its formation, the group's main importance lies in the security it gives its members. Within the group, they are not alone, they do not stick out in a crowd: they belong. Often the need to belong is so strong that teenagers will suddenly adopt a style of dress or behaviour which they are not happy with but follow because they don't want to be left out.

Parents often find this 'group identity' threatening, especially if they feel that their own child suddenly becomes a stranger to them. What they do not understand is that in most cases adolescents benefit from the security and strength of the group and at the same time learn social skills they will need in adulthood.

Teenage rebellion

For many young people, expressing ideas that are different from those of their parents is part of their attempt to assert their independence. Young people may develop interests in unusual religious or political groups, but this is usually a genuine attempt to decide what *they* believe is right.

Parents often dread the possibility of their sons or daughters becoming involved in the kind of group which they think will 'lead them off the rails' and tempt them into delinquency, drug abuse or promiscuous sexual behaviour, or cause them to drop out of work or studies. There is a small proportion of teenagers to whom this does happen, often causing a great deal of hurt and distress to all concerned. However, most teenagers remain largely unscathed by 'undesirable' influences even if they do make casual contacts with them.

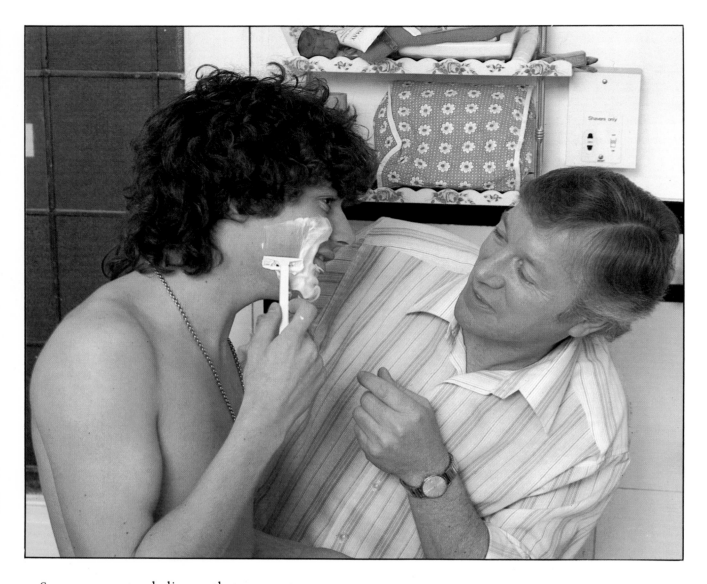

Some experts believe that parents may unwittingly tempt their children to use extreme forms of behaviour as a protest. This may be because young people sometimes feel that their parents are not really taking into account their wishes or personal feelings in planning their future. Parents may hope that their sons or daughters will go on to higher education, take up a particular profession or avoid involving themselves in serious relationships until they are mature. It may be a bitter disappointment to parents if their children choose not to follow the hopes and ambitions that they have for them. But it is vital for parents to understand that young people need to be allowed to make their own choices, hopefully with the advice and encouragement of their parents.

Adolescents often use this period as a time for experiment, for testing out new ideas, and it can be important to their intellectual development.

Developing sexuality

An important part of any young person's development will be a growing interest in the opposite sex, and sometimes the same sex. Parents may feel anxious if their sons or daughters start to 'go steady' in their early teens, fearing that they may tie themselves down and restrict their social circle. Dating, going out and getting to know a number of different boyfriends or girlfriends is usually a learning experience. This is the way that most people discover the qualities they find attractive in other people. Sudden infatuations, and acute depression over romantic disappointments, are common emotions for the adolescent.

Adolescents may seem to take these setbacks as crises out of all proportion, but it is important to realize that confidence and self-esteem are likely to be very fragile at this early stage. We all use our experiences to build our hopes and ambitions on,

and if failure or rejection is the result of tentative experiments in relating to other people this is naturally going to be a setback. Happily, most adolescents have enough good and bad experiences to help them develop mature and loving relationships as adults.

Part of any relationship with the opposite sex will invariably involve some sexual experimentation, as both sexes explore their own and each other's physical and emotional responses to sex.

There is, of course, no guaranteed formula that parents or teachers can adopt to ensure that teenagers do not find themselves involved in premature sexual relationships. But good sex education both at home and at school may be a way of ensuring that adolescents do understand about sex, responsibility and birth control. This means that parents and teachers have to be sympathetic and accessible, not to mention sensitive and able to discuss sexuality in a forthright and caring manner. Sex plays an important part in the lives of most adults; if adolescents have good, clear education and can appreciate their own as well as others' sexuality, this can help provide them with the basis for a happy and fulfilled adult sexual life.

Adolescence is a complex and important time in most people's lives, from the early stages when puberty begins to late adolescence when young people have finished their education and are working, developing interests and relationships or perhaps setting up their own homes and families. Because adolescence encompasses enormous physical, social and emotional changes, it is often a period of tremendous ups and downs, not only for young people but for their families and friends. The pressures of growing up sometimes seem overpowering, but with sympathetic guidance and friendship from parents and other adults, most adolescents emerge as happy and successful people.

Adolescent resentment

Rivalry and resentment between parents and children often starts when the child is very young. But is usually takes a family crises to bring it to the surface and when this happens the depth of feelings involved can come as a surprise.

Rivalry and resentment between parents and children can be one of the most difficult problems many families have to cope with. Most of the time it is buried deep within family relationships. It is rarely seen for what it really is by either side, often expressing itself as bouts of emotional behaviour alternating with moodiness — especially during adolescence. And it usually emerges only when some serious crisis occurs either within the family or to an individual member. Then, the hatred, bitterness and jealousy expressed may come as a surprise to everybody concerned.

Natural feelings

Both parents and children have to learn to adjust to their respective roles. Children must grow up and accept the responsibilities of adulthood: and, equally, parents must learn how to let go, accepting that eventually their children will want to leave home and lead independent lives. It is often in this dual process of maturing that resentment of the children for their parents and their way of life shows itself most clearly. During this period the children become more able to form reasoned judgements which may not necessarily agree with their earlier, automatically loving, instinctive feelings — a fact that may bring about feelings of foolishness that they didn't have the ability to see the more human side of their parents before.

The form the crisis may take depends very much on individual family circumstances. A father may experience impatience with his children for not being able to grasp things that he sees clearly. In fact, he is probably subconsciously jealous — seeing his children grope towards adulthood and remembering his own lost youth. This idea of repressed feelings of rivalry between parents and children is often at the heart of many family crises. The children, for instance, feel resentment at the privileges their adult parents have which they are impatient to acquire. Hence both sides — parents and children may consciously or subconsciously see each other as rivals in different ways.

As with most other complex human emotions, it is not possible to point to any one reason and say that it accounts for these competitive feelings — there are a multitude of reasons, ranging from general social attitudes and customs to very specific issues within any family. But it is important to understand how natural these feelings of competition are, and to work together to develop a mature approach to dealing with them.

Sexual rivalry

Rivalry plays a large part in the early developing relationship between parent and child. Parents normally regard their children's very early expressions of sexual rivalry with nothing more than amusement. If a male child says: 'I'd like daddy to go away so that I can marry mummy', it's usually treated as a clever statement to be repeated to admiring friends. But what the child may really be saying is 'I feel jealous of my father because my mother loves him and is affectionate to him and that interferes with her loving me'.

Many parents find that their pre-pubescent child may follow this up by trying to interfere with or interrupt when they openly demonstrate physical affection towards each other. If this happens, it is best dealt with gently but firmly. On the one hand, the child's need for security must be recognised; on the other, he or she must be made to understand that parents, too, have a right to express their feelings openly within the family.

When open competition occurs

Sometimes the sexual rivalry existing between children and their parents may break out into open competition. This usually expresses itself as an attempt by the young child to prove that he or she loves the parent more than their rival does. A girl may try to look more beautiful and more desirable than her mother; a boy may challenge his father to tests of strength; or he may go out of his way to help with the housework and spend more time with her, trying to show in this way that he can be a better male companion than his father.

This type of competitiveness should never be encouraged, because if it is not dealt with in the family situation, it can spill over into areas of social life. The child may end up having a competitive attitude to people in general, particularly to others of the same sex, always striving to prove sexual, social or physical prowess. And when the child finally begins to break away from the family the guilt feelings at how foolishly he or she has behaved can be emotionally limiting.

Children and the generation gap

The other main cause of parent/child rivalry is simply the age difference. Many children show early jealousy because their parents knew each other before they were born.

And it comes as a shock to many children to realize that they never 'catch up' with their parents. At first they may well feel envy that their parents will always lead them in experience. Nevertheless, later in adolescence the realization that they will almost certainly die earlier, may change their feelings to one of sadness that their parents will not be there forever.

Many children may well feel a deep resentment at the age-advantage their parents have, for, in their eyes, age brings all sorts of priveleges, from being able to stay up late, to choosing which TV programmes to watch, or having their own money and being able to go out and enjoy themselves without restriction.

This resentment is most likely to be openly displayed during adolescence, when a young person feels especially insecure about their identity —

halfway between childhood and adulthood. They no longer have the joys of childhood such as complete security and lack of responsibility, but they are not yet considered by their parents to be ready to join in adult life.

Sexuality is an area where the resentment may be felt most bitterly. The adolescent groping towards sexual awareness may deeply resent his or her parents' easy attitude to sex, and their ability to be happy together.

Together with the many other problems of adolescence this may well be the cause of stormy rows between the parents and children, or withdrawal and moodiness on the part of the developing adult as he or she struggles to come to terms with growing up. And parents must try to react with sympathy, readily offering advice when help is requested — though generally this is a time when children retreat sharply from any hint of interference in their lives or relationships. It may be hard for the parents, but they have to learn to let go gracefully and to sometimes be content to sit back and watch the growing process, intervening only when they are sure it is absolutely necessary. It may well help if parents and children sit down and discuss the problems together, particularly if the parents try to remember what their adolescence was like and how they felt at the time.

Parents and the generation gap

On the other side, parents too may feel jealousy towards their children as they start to show signs of adulthood. It's easy to love a young defenceless child, but a prickly 'almost-adult' can be a different proposition altogether, particularly when they may be a constant reminder to the parents' of their 'lost youth'.

Recognition by the parents that their child is becoming aware of his or her own sexuality, and a realization that the child has many years of enjoyment and fulfillment ahead, often awaken jealous feelings in the parents. Nowadays, parents may feel this even more keenly than in the past because, for the most part, today's adolescents are better informed about sex and better able to experiment openly than they were in their parent's day.

So the parents may react with what will almost inevitably appear to the child as an old-fashioned puritanism, placing restrictions on their going out or continually demanding to know who they are with. Of course, this is basic common sense on the part of the parents — adolescents are not yet able, in many cases, to make wise and responsible decisions about sex, and may need some protection. But parents must therefore be extremely careful that behind any parental restrictions and warnings there does not lie a jealousy that their children are doing what they were never allowed to do, and maybe would still like to do if they were not married with responsibilities and 'too old' to enjoy themselves.

Missed opportunities

Apart from sexual rivalry, the main reason parents may feel competitive towards their children is that they regret the missed opportunities in their own lives. They may feel especially bitter if they think they have been prevented in their life ambitions because of their children.

This is a very sad situation, but the children cannot be held responsible for decisions made in the past by their parents, nor can they be expected to act out their parents' frustrated ambitions, such as becoming a lawyer, doctor, etc. The happier the parents in their own lives and the more fulfilled and appreciated they feel in their own right, the less likely they are to put any unnecessary pressure on their children.

Many parents, particularly mothers, feel jealousy if they believe the children to be more attractive than they are (or were) or have had more educational opportunities than they did. This jealousy may well be caused by a fear that if the child is successful in life, he or she may grow away from the parents, and ultimately come to despise them.

It is important at this point that parents realize that it is inevitable that their children will eventually grow away from them. But they will only despise their parents' lack of achievement if the parents themselves feel dissatisfied or feel that they have not made the most of their lives.

If you are constantly in competition with someone else, it's hard to see their good points or to allow yourself to have any sympathy with them. Rivalry between parents and children can destroy all the happiness of family life and poison relationships within the family circle. It can also effect the child's attitude towards the rest of the world, possibly for life.

Since the capacity for happy relationships with others is developed and nurtured within the family, it is essential that this rivalry is confronted as soon as it shows itself, and not allowed to develop into bitterness or resentment.

Know Your Body

People are surprisingly ignorant about their bodies, and this is often the cause of many unnecessary fears and anxieties. This is particularly true as far as their sex organs are concerned since these are 'private' parts of the body that are usually hidden from public view and there is less opportunity for reassuring comparisons. This is made worse in many cases by taboos on touching and self-exploration instilled by upbringing or social pressures.

The female sex organs

*A woman's knowledge about her own body is often
surprisingly limited. Much anxiety about her 'normality'
can be dispelled if she knows what her female organs
do and where they are located.*

However familiar women are with their
faces, they probably wouldn't recognize
their own external sex organs. Many women were
brought up to think that this important part of their
bodies had to be kept secret and private, even from
themselves. So their genitals are a mystery, and
some women spend years worrying that they are
not 'normal' because they have never had a chance
to understand how each part works or what it looks
or feels like. And when something *does* go wrong it
is difficult to describe the problem to a doctor.

Outer genitals

People learn what their faces look like by seeing
them in a mirror, and although it may seem a
strange thing to do at first, this is the best way to
learn about sexual organs too. Women should do
this at a time when they can be quiet and undisturbed, so they can have enough time to relax.
Make sure there is plenty of light, then sit on the
floor or the bed. Sit with your legs apart, and get as
comfortable as possible. It is best to use a large hand
mirror, preferably the kind that magnifies on one
side. What you will learn by looking at your own
body for half an hour will teach you more than a
dozen medical textbooks.

First you will see the *vulva,* the outer genitals,
surrounded by *pubic hair.* The pubic hair grows out
of the outer lips and varies from woman to woman
as much as the hair on their heads. Some will have
sparse hair on the outer lips and mons, others will
have hair that curls around from the inside of their
thighs or around the *anus,* the opening of the
rectum, or large intestine.

A woman's pubic and underarm hair probably
started to appear close to the time she started to
menstruate, when her body began to produce a
large amount of the hormones oestrogen, from the

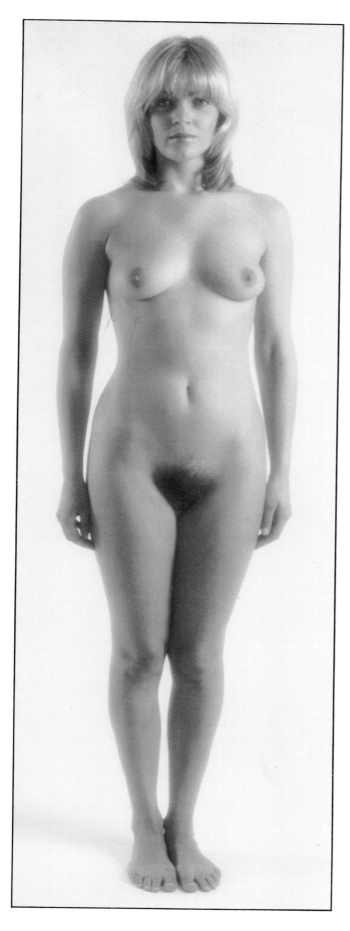

ovaries, and androgen, from the adrenal glands. When a woman is sexually aroused, scent glands in the pubic and underarm area give off an odour, which although neither partner is aware of, is designed to stimulate her partner. The hair therefore acts as a kind of scent trap. Because of the influence of these special hormones the pubic hair is usually coarser and darker than the hair on the head and may be a different colour altogether.

The *mons,* the only part of the genitals visible when you stand naked in front of the mirror, is soft, fatty tissue which cushions the *pubic bone* underneath it and is sometimes called the Mound of Venus — after the Greek goddess of love.

The hair-covered area between your thighs forms the outer lips, *labia majora.* Like the mons, they are made of fatty tissue and act as a pair of pillows to protect the clitoris lying underneath them. Some women, particularly those who have not had children, have outer lips that almost meet in the middle. Other women will see either the whole of the inner area, or that the inner lips, the *labia minora,* protrude past the outer ones. Every woman has her own personal variation of outer organs, so no two women are the same. The inner lips may even vary in size from each other. They are folds of soft tissue which range from light pink to brown in colour. They may be smooth or ridged and wrinkled. Unlike the outer lips they are hairless and have no fatty tissue. The inner lips are rich in scent and oil glands, well supplied with blood vessels, very elastic and very sensitive.

The inner genitals

Once the inner lips have been identified you will be able to find the clitoris. Trace the inner lips upwards to the point where they join, just below the mons, and you will see that they form a hood, which is fleshy and sensitive. Most of the clitoris is hidden under this hood, but you may be able to see its small pink tip protruding from the hood. The *clitoris* is about the size of a pea, and plays a very important role in the female orgasm. When you are aroused, the clitoris, its hood and the inner lips fill with blood. The clitoris becomes erect, in the same way as its male equivalent, the penis, does. If you are still not sure where your clitoris is, gently press your genitals with your finger until you touch the most sensitive spot — this is the clitoris.

Once you are familiar with the mons, the outer and inner lips and the clitoris, look more closely at the inner area. This is the part surrounded by the inner lips. It is lined with delicate mucous membrane, and has a texture similar to the one inside your mouth. In it are two openings: the *urethra* and the *vagina.*

The urethra is the small passage that runs out from the bladder and you urinate through the urethral opening. It can be difficult to see this opening as it is much smaller than the vaginal opening. So imagine a straight line running from your clitoris down to the vagina. Look carefully, and you will see the urethra, a small dimpled area closer to the vagina than to the clitoris. Since the urethra is so close to the vaginal opening, it can become irritated by intercourse.

Now move down from the urethral opening to the entrance to the vagina (*vaginal introitus*). Whether you are a virgin or not you may be able to see the *hymen,* a small semi-circle of membrane lying across the lower part of the vaginal opening. It can either be quite obvious or hardly visible. Some women, especially those who have not had children, may have small uneven fringes of tissue instead of a hymen — this tissue used to be joined together to form the hymen but was destroyed in some way. In a virgin, the hymen may cross the vaginal opening, but if it doesn't, it is *not* an indication that she has had intercourse. The hymen can be broken by vigorous exercise — tennis, horseriding, swimming — or by using tampons. There is no way that a man can tell whether a woman is a virgin or not. The hymen rarely covers the entire vaginal opening, and some virgins may have no visible hymen at all.

If you look at the area between the vaginal opening and the anus, you will see the *perineum.* It is smooth, and very elastic since it has to stretch a great deal in childbirth.

It is possible to see just inside the vagina. If you look carefully at the *vaginal opening,* you may be able to see two small bumps on either side. These are the *Bartholins glands,* and are often quite difficult to see. They produce a small amount of mucus, but do not really contribute very much towards lubricating the vagina during lovemaking. They are important only because they may become infected and swell up — in much the same way as the appendix.

A woman may have never touched or examined her vagina, so it is worth pointing out that it is not a dangerous or immoral thing to do. Gently insert two or three fingers into the vagina. You will notice that it is not as sensitive as the clitoris since it does not have as many nerve endings — only the outer third is sensitive.

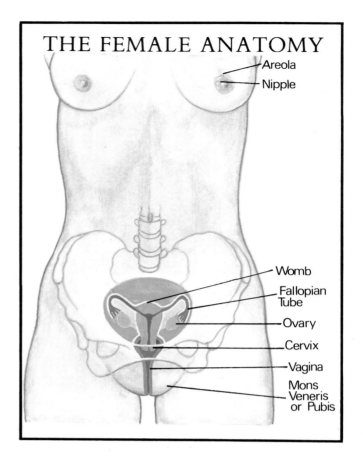

THE FEMALE ANATOMY

Areola
Nipple
Womb
Fallopian Tube
Ovary
Cervix
Vagina
Mons Veneris or Pubis

The flexible vagina

It is very important to understand how the vagina works. Like the rest of the genitals, it changed and matured during puberty. The vagina is a flexible, stretchy passageway about three to five inches long and you can probably insert two or more fingers into it. When you insert your fingers into the vagina you can feel how the soft folds of skin hug them. These folds enable the vagina to mould itself around whatever penetrates it.

During sexual arousal the vagina widens and lengthens by about two inches. It needs to be very elastic as it will open to a diameter of about five inches during childbirth.

The vagina will probably feel moist, and how moist it is varies from woman to woman. The moistness depends on the stage of the menstrual cycle and how sexually aroused the woman is. This natural lubrication means that the vagina can constantly clean itself and maintain a delicate balance of acid/alkali to keep the tissue healthy.

The vaginal discharge has a musky smell, and each woman has her own individual scent. Some women may worry about vaginal odour, and feel they should wash themselves frequently during the day or use vaginal deodorants. This can upset the delicate self-cleaning mechanism, and it is better just to gently wash the outer organs daily.

The discharge is usually whitish, although when a woman is sexually excited it may be colourless and more profuse. This extra discharge is produced by a kind of sweating action from the walls of the vagina. During intercourse some women may want extra lubrication so that the vagina can enclose the penis more easily. If it is not produced naturally it may be helpful to use a lubricant jelly to make the vagina less dry.

If you gently push your fingers as far back into your vagina as you can, you will notice that your fingers go towards your back at an angle and the vagina feels closed: this is the end of the vagina — the *fornix*.

The vagina is surrounded by a series of *vaginal muscles*, which are very powerful and extend around the uterus, down around the urethra and anus. You may be able to tense the vaginal muscles around your fingers. One of the internal muscles in this area is the *pubococcygeus*, which controls the flow of urine. This is the muscle that you use to control urinating. All the muscles work together to support the lower organs, and are strong and elastic so that they can 'push' in childbirth.

Once you have gently explored the inside walls of the vagina, move your fingers up and back towards the *cervix*, the neck of the womb. It is possible to touch the cervix, although you may have to squat and push down with your muscles to feel it properly. The cervix is the opening or base of the *uterus*, or womb, a thick-walled muscular organ shaped something like an upside-down pear. The uterus is responsive to pressure but has no nerve endings on its surface. Its lower part is compressed and protrudes into the upper part of the vagina — that is the only part of the uterus you can feel.

Gently press the cervix with the end of your finger. If you haven't had a baby, it will feel a bit like pressing the end of your nose. If you have had a child, it will be softer, more like the flesh of your chin. In the middle is a small dimple, the centre of it is called the *os*, the entrance to the uterus. It is a hole about the diameter of a thin straw, which acts as an important gateway since it lets the sperm travel upwards in their search for an egg to fertilize, allows the passage of menstrual blood from the uterus and can enlarge to four inches in diameter during childbirth. The uterus changes position during the menstrual cycle, which means that the cervix will be in a slightly different place depending at what time of the month you feel it.

The uterus lies between the bladder and the rectum. It is about the size of a woman's clenched fist and its inside walls are pressed together. In most women, the uterus is tilted forward to form a right angle to the vagina. Some women have what doctors call a *retroverted uterus*, which means that the uterus is tilted backwards, towards the rectum. This does not alter a woman's chances of becoming pregnant.

The uterus is lined with a thin membrane rich with blood vessels which can receive a fertilized egg and protect and nurture it until childbirth.

The two *fallopian tubes*, which look something like curved horns extend out and back from the upper sides of the uterus, and are about four inches long. The opening connecting the uterus and fallopian tubes is very small. The other end of the tubes, *fimbria*, is funnel shaped with fringes at the ends. The *ovaries* are held on to the fringed ends with delicate strands of tissue and are protected with fat. They are sometimes described as being about the size of unshelled almonds and are located somewhat behind and on either side of the uterus. Besides producing eggs, the ovaries produce the sex hormones — oestrogen and progesterone, which are so important in the maturing process.

The breasts

The breasts are composed of fat and a gland which produces milk (the *mammary* gland). The size of the breasts is determined by the level of hormones — during adolescence the increase in sex hormones determines the size of the breast. Menstruation and pregnancy can also affect the shape and size of the breast. Most of the breast consists of fat surrounding the mammary gland and it is the amount of fat which makes breast size vary in women.

In the middle of the darker part of the breast, the *areola*, is the nipple which may or may not stick out. When exposed to the cold or sexually aroused, the nipple may become more erect than usual. Ducts inside the breast may cause a slight secretion periodically, which is quite normal. The surface of the areola may have small bumps — these are glands which, during pregnancy, secrete a lubricant that protects the nipple. A common occurrence is hair growing around the areola; this is caused by changes in hormonal balance.

Knowledge of the structure and function of the female organs is important for every woman. It will give her more confidence and a better understanding of her own sexuality.

Vaginal problems

A surprisingly large number of women worry needlessly that their genitals are in some way abnormal. However, it is never too late for a woman to learn about her own body, and the facts are usually enough to reassure her that she has nothing to fear.

In literature the female genitals have often been compared to the most beautiful and sensual fruit or flowers. But many women believe that their own genitals are ugly, dirty, smelly and unattractive to men. These needless feelings of shame affect their pleasure in lovemaking, and can even make them too shy to have sex.

Sally, an attractive woman in her late twenties, shares these feelings with millions of other women. Disgust with her sexual organs makes her tense and unable to enjoy sex. Now she has fallen in love with a gentle, understanding man who finds her very desirable; but she is afraid that if they make love his passion will be destroyed by the sight and smell of her genitals. Fortunately, she can confide in a sympathetic woman doctor:

A problem of ignorance

'I am worried that I will never be able to enjoy normal sex because I can't bear a man to look at, or touch, my genitals. When I've made love before, I have felt that my partner is hiding his distaste for my body out of sympathy for my feelings.

Now I'm in love with a wonderful man, and we feel strongly attached to each other. Yet I can't bring myself to make love, and I'm ashamed to tell him the reason. How can I overcome my fears?'

In contrast with the penis, there is little open discussion about the female sex organs, and often no way of comparing them with those of other women because they are not obviously visible. So they are thought of as hidden and mysterious.

The problem often begins in early childhood, when girls are discouraged by their parents from pursuing natural curiosity about their genitals. If they're warned or punished for touching them, they grow up believing that there's something forbidden about the area between their legs.

Have you ever explored your genitals with your fingers or looked at them in a mirror?

'I've always avoided touching my genitals since my mother told me when I was young that it was wicked and would make them grow deformed. But I do occasionally look at them in the mirror. To me, they appear wrinkled, naked and ugly.'

Learning about your genitals

Perhaps it would help set your mind at rest if I explained what 'normal' sex organs look like. To begin with, your genitals are as unique to you as your fingerprints. No two women's are exactly alike: their size and shape vary enormously, and most of these variations are absolutely normal.

Looking in the mirror, the first thing you will see is the pubic hair. It is usually thicker in texture than the hair on your head, and it can range from very curly and wiry to relatively straight. Its colour can be anything from pitch-black to red — really blonde pubic hair is relatively rare. Some women have only a light sprinkling of pubic hair, while others have an abundance which spreads upwards towards their stomachs and grows across the top of their thighs.

'I feel embarrassed that I have too much pubic hair — it shows when I wear a bathing costume.'

Many men find the sight of pubic hair escaping from beneath panties or bikinis very arousing. But if you think it will help your confidence, there is no harm in carefully shaving off the excess with a small razor. Make sure you use unscented soap so as not to irritate the sensitive skin beneath. Don't use hair-removing creams or foams — the chemicals they contain may cause an allergic reaction.

'Would it be more hygienic for me to shave off all my pubic hair?'

Some women believe this, but it's not true. Others experiment by shaving the whole area to reveal their genitals as a turn-on for themselves and their lovers; though this can create problems — when the hair starts to grow back it can be a bit prickly and uncomfortable for both the woman and her partner when they make love!

Exploring the vulva

Below the pubic hair is the vulva — the outer genitals. This is often likened to a mouth, with its two sets of lips and its opening to the entrance to the vagina. The larger, outer folds are called *labia majora*, or large lips. These are pink or pinkish-brown, and protect the more delicate lips between them. These smaller, inner lips are the *labia minora*; they are generally a deep pink or coral shade.

The minor lips are very sensitive because the nerves coming into them are directly connected with the clitoris — the most responsive area of your body. During intercourse, the inner lips swell and become scarlet or wine-red.

You may worry that both sets of lips are wrinkled, or that your small lips appear too large and protruding, but this is perfectly normal. It is also common for one of either the large or small lips to be bigger than the other.

You will find your clitoris between the join at the top of the minor lips. Its exquisite sensitivity is protected by a little hood, and it feels hard, rather like a small pea. When stimulated, it swells, hardens and erects in a similar way to the penis. Even when erect, it is very tiny and, like the penis, there is no relation between its size and the amount of pleasure it gives. Nor can it be permanently enlarged or deformed by masturbation or by your partner's caresses.

Some sex education books sometimes confuse and worry women when they illustrate 'normal' female genitals, and so suggest that any variation is 'abnormal'. In reality, the exact location of the clitoris and the opening to the vagina depend on the size and shape of the vulva, and these naturally vary considerably from woman to woman.

Looking at yourself

'How can I tell whether my vulva is normal?'

Look at photographs of women's genitals in magazines or sex manuals; you'll see how many variations there are.

Then, using a large hand-mirror with good lighting, examine your own genitals, taking particular care to get acquainted with your clitoris. If you stroke it gently, you'll soon discover what sensations it is capable of giving, and you'll be able to pass this knowledge on to your lover when you are making love.

Most men find looking at and caressing a woman's sex organs one of the greatest pleasures of lovemaking. They are generally unaware of the fears women have, and that's why they don't take enough care in telling their partners how desirable they find their genitals. Better communication would go a long way towards reassuring many women about this frequent worry.

Is vaginal scent offensive?

'Even if my genitals look normal, I am still worried that my boyfriend will find their smell offensive. Sometimes I think that other people, too, are avoiding getting close to me because of the smell.'

This worry about genital odour is extremely common. Some women do have a rather strong odour, while others have almost none. This odour usually comes from various glands in your external genital tissues and not, as is commonly thought, from the tissues of the vagina.

The vagina itself secretes a natural fluid which is almost odourless. You can test this by washing there, inserting your finger and smelling the fluid.

The fresh genital scent is nature's way of signalling that you are sexually aroused. For this reason, most men find it very alluring. Each woman has a unique scent, which is why the same perfume smells different on different women. Smell is generally under-rated as a source of sexual excitement — your lover will come to know your body scents and to associate them positively both with his own and your sexual pleasure.

However, there is no doubt that a stale genital odour can be offensive, in the same way that stale sweat smells unpleasant.

Vaginal hygiene

'Many of my friends use vaginal deodorants or douches to hide their genital smell. Would you advise this?'

I think it's unnecessary, and can be harmful. First, a vaginal deodorant conceals the natural scent which men find so exciting. But it can also irritate the delicate tissues of the vulva and the vagina, causing allergic rashes.

Over-frequent douching or washing is inadvisable too, as it may dry out the natural vaginal juices which ensure the comfortable entry of the penis during lovemaking.

Daily washing with unscented soap and water should be sufficient for most women. If you think your personal scent is too strong, you can try the pre-moistened, unscented cleansers used for babies' bottoms. This will reassure you.

'Do I need to take extra precautions during my period?'

Menstrual blood is like any kind of blood — it has no odour when inside the body and smells only on contact with the air. Provided you change your tampons or sanitary towels frequently, remove stained panties immediately and wash regularly, there should be no unpleasant odour.

Self-examination

Sometimes I have a clear discharge from my vagina. It doesn't smell, but I worry there might be something wrong.

The vagina naturally secretes varying amounts of clear or milky white fluid, depending on the stage your monthly cycle has reached. There is no need to worry about this kind of discharge, though if it is heavy enough to stain your underwear, you might feel more comfortable wearing a light-weight sanitary towel. However, smelly, thick, yellowish or brownish discharges *are* abnormal and you should waste no time in going to your family doctor or local Special Clinic for an examination and, if necessary, treatment.

Many women worry needlessly about perfectly natural changes in their sex organs simply because they do not know how their own bodies work. Get to know yourself by examining your genitals regularly. Self-examination is not perverted or difficult — it is very sensible and extremely easy. All you need is a good mirror, a strong light and a speculum — the duckbill-shaped instrument doctors use for internal examinations. You can buy a plastic one from some chemists.

Lie propped against pillows with your knees apart, insert the speculum and look at your cervix and the walls of your vagina in the mirror. If you do this frequently, you'll learn how the cervix changes through your cycle and you'll be able to detect at an early stage anything unusual which might need expert attention.

Fear and ignorance of our own bodies is perhaps the greatest barrier to enjoying sex. I believe that such common problems as worry about the smell and appearance of the female genitals could be eliminated by more widespread knowledge. Once you have learnt to take pride in your own body — especially its most intimate parts — you'll find you are able to relax and enjoy your partner's caresses and develop a sexual relationship that both you and your partner will find fulfilling.

PREVENTING GENITAL INFECTIONS

Most women are troubled at some time in their lives by one of several genital infections. Most are not serious and can be easily dealt with by modern treatments. However, prevention is better than cure, and if you follow these simple rules you should greatly reduce the chances of infection.

● Wash your genitals and bottom at least once a day, using warm water and unscented soap (available from most chemists).

● After washing, pat, don't rub, dry. Make sure your towels are scrupulously clean and never borrow anyone else's.

● To prevent the transfer of bacteria to your vagina, always wipe your anus from front to back after visiting the lavatory.

● Wear stockings or crotchless tights and cotton panties. Avoid wearing synthetic underwear and too-tight trousers.

● Don't use vaginal deodorants. They are unnecessary and may irritate the delicate tissues of the vulva.

● If you must douche, do so only rarely, using plain warm water or a mild salt and water solution. *Never* use chemicals. Be very careful when douching — it is possible to introduce a dangerous amount of air into the uterus.

● Use non-deodorized, cotton tampons or sanitary towels. Remember to remove tampons — if forgotten they can cause infection.

● If you need to use a lubricant during love-making, buy a non-greasy, water-soluble jelly from chemists. Oily creams can upset the natural balance of secretions in the vagina.

● You may be allergic to your contraceptive jelly. If you suspect this is the case, ask your doctor or clinic to let you try different products until you find one that suits you.

● If you do have unusual symptoms, don't delay in seeking medical advice. Many infections occur spontaneously, but others can be spread by sexual intercourse, so make sure your partner also seeks treatment.

● Get to know the normal cycle of change in your own body. There are today numerous helpful books on women's health. Some women have formed women's health groups — why not join, or start, one in your area?

The male sex organs

Because a man's sex organs can be seen – unlike a woman's people often assume that they are easy to understand. But male organs and sexual responses are complex and often misunderstood.

At first sight, a man's sex organs seem very simple and straightforward. He has a *penis,* and hanging just below it a small sac of skin called the *scrotum,* containing a pair of *testes.*

The testes produce *sperm,* male seeds which can fertilize an egg inside the female. And the penis, by swelling and becoming firm and erect, is able to enter the woman's body and deposit the sperm close to the egg.

Because the external genitals, the penis and testes, are the only sexual parts which are deliberately stimulated during intercourse, it is natural to think of them as the only male sex organs. But in fact, the reproductive system is rather more complicated than this.

The testes do not instantly produce the millions of sperm needed to be sure of fertilizing an egg. Sperm are manufactured slowly and continuously, and are stored in the body at two separate points. The main storage area is in a long, thin tube coiled just above each of the testes called the *epididymus.* Here, young sperm are stored for up to 70 days as they mature. Leading from each epididymus is a duct called the *vas deferens,* which carries sperm upwards into the body and then loops behind the bladder to end just below it.

At this end, the vas goes into a small gland called the *prostate.* Inside the prostate, the vas feeds into a larger duct, the *urethra.* Here the vas is slightly larger, to form a second store for sperm.

The urethra comes from an opening in the bladder, and after passing through the prostate, it leads down to the penis, where it ends as the small slit in the penis tip.

The urethra has two jobs to do. Most often, its function is to carry urine from the bladder and pass it out of the body through the penis. But during sexual intercourse, the bladder opening closes up. The urethra can then carry *semen,* a mixture of sperm and two other fluids. The prostate gland produces one of the fluids which transports and protects the tiny, vulnerable sperm. It is a thin, milky fluid which gives semen its characteristic odour.

The second fluid is yellowish and fairly thick. It comes from the *seminal vesicles.* There are two of these, located just above the prostate. They empty into the two vas deferens just before the junction with the urethra.

Finally, there are two further glands, called *Cowper's* and *Littre's* glands, which feed directly into the urethra below the prostate. They produce the fluids which lubricate the tip of the penis. The fluids also neutralize any acidic urine left in the urethra which might harm the sperm.

Myths and misunderstandings

The male sex organs, and their relationship to one another, have already been described briefly. But it is worth looking at them in more detail, for there is a great deal of misunderstanding about many aspects of them.

The penis, as the most visible of the sex organs, has attracted the most attention. Many centuries of myth and folklore have built up some amazing misconceptions about what the penis is and does, and particularly about the size of the penis and how size affects potency.

In its normal flaccid state, the penis hangs down loosely between the legs. Its length will vary in the same person in different circumstances; the penis becomes temporarily shorter after vigorous exercise, after it has been in cold water, or after an unsuccessful attempt at sex.

Recent reliable surveys suggest that the average non-erect penis is about 9.5 cm long. When the penis is erect, surveys indicate that the average length is about 16 cm. The extremes in normal men seem to be 12 cm and 23 cm.

No relationship has been found between the size of the whole body and penis size. And needless to say, the old wives' tale about the size of the nose indicating penis size has been disproved.

Research has also shown that there is no link at all between penis size and a man's sexual prowess or potency.

Women are not any more or less satisfied sexually by a long or short penis. A woman's main sources of stimulation are generally the clitoris and the lips around the vagina. These areas are aroused equally by a long or short penis, and in fact the deeper parts of the vagina itself are less sensitive.

The penis is made up of spongy tissue which is capable of absorbing large quantities of blood. When the man is sexually excited, the tissues become swollen with blood. They press against the covering of loose skin round the penis, and this causes it to swell, increasing in length and girth. The erect penis juts out from the body at an angle which varies from horizontal, or just below horizontal, to almost vertical.

The small slit at the tip of the penis is the opening of the urethra. The tip, or *glans,* is the most sensitive part of the penis, especially where it joins the main shaft of the organ.

At birth, the tip is covered with a fold of loose skin called the *foreskin* or *prepuce.* In the Jewish and Moslem religions it is traditional to remove the foreskin in a minor operation called circumcision. Sometimes the foreskin becomes difficult to pull back off the glans, and circumcision solves the problem quite easily.

At one time, some countries, notably the US, circumcised all male babies for reasons of hygiene. A white secretion called *smegma* forms under the foreskin, and if it is not regularly removed this can become smelly and possibly cause irritation.

Occasionally, the opening of the urethra is not exactly at the end of the penis but slightly above or below the tip. This can cause difficulty or discomfort when a man urinates or has intercourse. The condition can be quite easily corrected by surgery, especially if the foreskin is still there.

The testes, although only 34mm long, contain about 480m of minute tubes! As well as sperm, the testes produce the male hormone testosterone, which regulates the growth and working of all the male sex organs. Testes will only produce sperm at a temperature of 2-3°C below normal body temperature. For this reason, they are suspended in the

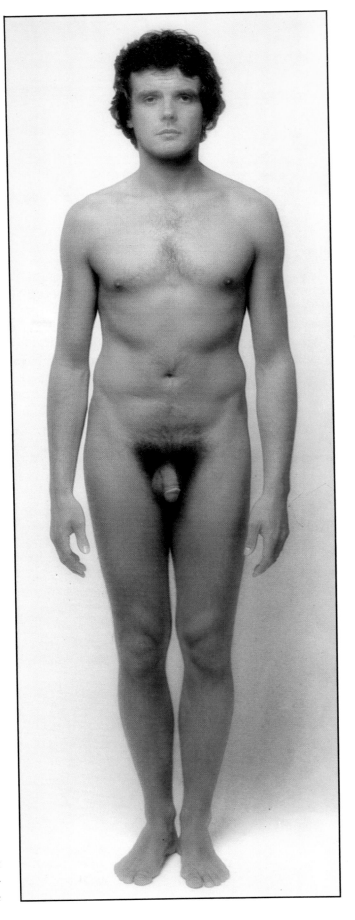

scrotum a little away from the body. The muscles in the scrotum can pull the testes towards or away from the body to control their temperature.

The developing male

At the start of life, and up to the eighth week of pregnancy, babies have both the male and female sex organs in a primitive form. Between the ninth and thirty-fourth weeks, if the baby is to be a boy the male organs develop. A little knob, which would have become the clitoris in a girl, develops into the penis. At the same time, the slit which would have been a girl's vagina closes up and descends to form the scrotum. Lastly, the glands called *gonads,* which become ovaries in a woman and testes in a man, move down into the scrotum.

Although the testes are the last to move, they are actually the first organs to show male characteristics. At about seven weeks, they start to produce a substance called *androgen.* It is this which changes the primitive organs to the male form. Without it, the organs would become female.

The key to whether a baby will be male or female is held in the nucleus of the cell from which the baby originally grows. From this cell, formed when a sperm unites with an egg to fertilize it, all the millions of other cells in the body grow.

Although it might be expected that the number of male and female babies conceived would be equal, in fact there are more male babies. This is balanced out by a higher rate of stillbirths among male babies, but in most developed countries there are still about 105 male babies to every 100 females born alive.

Changes during puberty

From birth until the onset of puberty, the sex organs grow more slowly than any of the other body organs. Thus at 10 years of age, when the body as a whole has reached on average 50 per cent of its eventual size, the sex organs are only 25 per cent of their full size. During this period, no real changes occur in the shape or nature of the sex organs. But with puberty, dramatic changes start to happen. The period of puberty varies quite widely between individuals. In general among males, it starts between the ages of 10 and 15 years and ends between 14 and 18 years. The average age for the start of puberty is 12.

It is during puberty that the testes first start to grow in size. At the same time, they begin to release

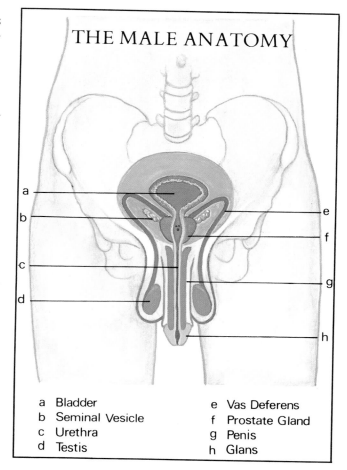

THE MALE ANATOMY

a	Bladder	e	Vas Deferens
b	Seminal Vesicle	f	Prostate Gland
c	Urethra	g	Penis
d	Testis	h	Glans

a hormone called *testosterone,* which induces other changes. Pubic hair starts growing round the penis, which itself begins to enlarge. The prostate gland also grows in size. As more testosterone is produced, the whole body suddenly grows taller, the shoulders broaden, and the larynx (the Adam's apple) grows, which causes the male voice to break and deepen.

As hair begins to appear on the face and under the arms, sperm production also increases to a level where nocturnal emissions of semen often occur while the boy is sleeping. A number of side effects caused by hormonal changes are quite common during puberty, such as skin troubles, increased body odour, a tendency to gain weight, and possibly enlargement of the thyroid gland in the neck.

Puberty, the period of greatest physical growth, has normally ended in full physical maturity in the male by the time he is 18 years old.

Physical ageing

Physical ageing, the decline of the human body, begins in the middle to late twenties. Fortunately, however, it is a *much* slower process than growth. And in contrast to puberty, ageing does not affect the male sex organs more than the other parts of the body.

Production of testosterone starts to drop from around the age of 20. At 60, less testosterone is made than at the age of eight or nine. But this does not mean that the working of the sex organs falls back to the level of a nine-year-old. As a man gets older, his need and desire for orgasm may decrease; less sperm is produced; it may take longer to get an erection and erections tend to last for less time.

All the same, provided deterioration of the muscles, joints and nervous system does not prevent it, a man should be able to enjoy sex at any age. The only restrictions are an increased tendency to illness, lack of a suitable partner or opportunity, or, most common of all, anxiety about ageing. Older men sometimes feel the physical exertion in sexual intercourse may cause a coronary, or that it is ridiculous for a man of such an age to be either sexually active or interested.

Infertility and impotence

The inability to make a woman pregnant is known as *infertility* and can be caused by insufficient sperm in the semen. In some cases, the reason may be temporary. Often the testes become too warm, which can be caused by nothing more than overtight underclothes or the effects of a hot bath. The testes may also become overheated because of obesity or accumulation of fluid in the scrotum, or because the dilated varicose veins in the scrotum carry too much warm blood round the testes. Simple surgery can usually help.

There can be more serious causes of infertility. Normally, the testes descend from the body of the foetus during the eighth month of pregnancy. But occasionally, a child is born with his testes still in the abdominal cavity. This condition, called *cryptorchidism,* is usually corrected surgically before puberty to avoid permanent sterility.

Some illnesses, particularly mumps, if contracted after puberty, can inflame the testes and leave them sterile (unable to produce any sperm). Sterility can also be caused by exposure to radiation, petrol fumes, carbon monoxide and some other chemicals and metals.

A man can also be infertile because of an excessive number of abnormally shaped sperm in his semen. Most men produce a certain number of abnormal sperm, but a high number reduces the chances of fertility.

A normal healthy man produces between 10

billion and 30 billion sperm each month. When he ejaculates (has an orgasm and produces semen) he will release from 150 to 400 million sperm. If the figure drops too much below 150 million in an average amount of semen, he is unlikely to fertilize the egg successfully.

Infertility should not be confused with *impotence.* Impotence is the inability to have an erection, or inability to reach orgasm. Over 90 per cent of such cases are thought to have psychological causes. Infertility may be combined with impotence, or even caused by it. But where infertility is caused simply by a low sperm count, for example, the man is still said to be fully potent — that is, able to have an erection and sustain it up to orgasm and ejaculation. Until tested clinically no man can know he has a low sperm count for sure, so if in doubt, he should visit his doctor.

Vasectomy

The vas deferens, which carries sperm to the prostate from the testes and epididymus, is probably best known in connection with *vasectomy.* This is an operation which prevents sperm from reaching the penis and is used as a means of contraception when the man is certain that he will not wish to have any children in the future. Generally, it cannot be reversed. A vasectomy can be performed in just a few minutes under local anaesthetic. The vas is cut where it passes through the scrotum and tied so that there is no chance of it reforming. Complete sterility is not guaranteed until about six weeks after the operation, as sperm is still stored in the upper parts of the vas and the seminal vesicles.

In addition to producing one of the components of semen, the prostate gland produces substances called *prostaglandins.* Their exact function is still unclear, but it is thought that, as they cause contractions of the muscles in the womb, they may aid fertility by helping the sperm in its passage to the egg inside the woman.

Even if you do not yet completely understand the entire process of reproduction in the male — and it is clear that the finer details are quite complex — it is not difficult to understand the basic principles involved. And although in the actual act of lovemaking you may be concerned only with the external sex organs, when problems arise it can be enlightening and reassuring to have some idea of the nature of the internal organs and how they work in the reproductive system and sex act.

'I think my penis is too small'

It is very common for a man to worry that his penis is too small. As a result, he may worry that he cannot satisfy a woman sexually, and this may make him afraid of sex. Such fears are, in the vast majority of cases, groundless, and are best resolved by the man himself in honest discussion with his partner or a sympathetic doctor.

The most widespread sexual fear shared by men is that of having a penis which is too small to satisfy their wives or lovers. Even a man with a happy and fulfilled sex life may believe, deep down, that his partner would prefer his penis to be bigger. And though such fears are generally groundless, anxiety about the size of his penis may cause a man to suffer from impotence and other problems of sexual inadequacy, which can cause problems with his partner.

Jim, a young man in his early twenties, has never made love with a woman, partly because he is afraid his penis will not satisfy her. But now he is engaged to be married, and his fiancée is obviously troubled by his reluctance to penetrate her, particularly as he is clearly aroused by their passionate petting. Unable to confide in her, he goes to see his doctor to find out if there is some way his penis can be enlarged:

'I've got a rather unusual problem. I think my penis is abnormally small, and I would like to know whether I can have an operation to lengthen it. I want to be able to satisfy my fiancée properly.'

Your belief that your *erect* penis is too small is probably unfounded. There are very few men who are totally content with their penis size. Most men do not have a chance to compare their erections with those of other men and may mistakenly believe their penises are undersized. It is extremely uncommon for a man's erect penis to be too small to satisfy a woman, and even without examining you I would judge that yours is perfectly normal. What makes you think it is too small?

'I have always thought so. When I was a child, my penis seemed tiny compared with my father's and big brother's. Now, when I play football with the local team, I can't help comparing my penis with those of my team-mates when we're in the showers together. Mine always seems smaller to me.'

You're making the same mistake as most men — believing that the size of your limp penis compared with another man's is a guide to its erect size. There are two reasons why it's misleading to compare limp penises. First, appearances are deceptive — when you look down at your own penis, you get a foreshortened view, which makes it seem smaller. Meanwhile, you're looking at another man's penis from the side, which gives a more accurate picture. So it's hardly surprising that yours comes off worse by comparison. Try looking at your penis in a mirror from the side: you will almost certainly be reassured to find that it appears larger than looking at it from above.

But second, and more important, the size of the limp penis is no guide to its sexual adequacy. During intercourse — when you are excited — it is transformed. Sexual excitement causes its blood vessels to expand and it can grow considerably as it stiffens into erection.

The facts of penis size

'Aren't some men's erections much larger than others?'

No; it is a remarkable fact of nature that, whatever variations exist between limp penises, they are all pretty much the same size when erect. A man whose penis is relatively small when limp will find

61

that its size may almost double when erect; while a man with a larger limp penis will probably only manage an increase of three-quarters — or less — of the original length. So somebody who appears 'well-equipped' in the changing room is unlikely to be at an advantage when his penis is erect.

'Is there any truth in the idea that tall, broadly built men have bigger penises?'

None at all. The size of the penis, just like the size of the mouth or nose, bears no relation to overall body size or build. Many slim, short men have

larger penises than tall, heavily built men.

Another common myth is that people of other races, especially black men, have larger penises. This also has no basis in fact.

'What is the normal size for a penis? And how can it be measured?'

Penis measurements are taken from the tip to the base, on the side nearest the stomach. Again, it is important to distinguish between the limp and erect states. A limp penis normally measures between 7-11 centimetres, the average length being approximately 9.5cm. Because the size depends on how much the blood vessels are open or shut, your penis can measure different lengths at different times. In cold weather or after swimming, for example, when the veins are contracted, you can expect it to be shorter.

The average length of the erect penis is about 16cm, but anything between 14 and 18 centimetres is quite usual. There are exceptional men with, say, 20cm members, but this is really quite out of the ordinary.

Satisfying the woman

'But how can I be sure that I'll be able to satisfy my fiancée when we are married?'

Compared to the penis, the vagina is actually rather small – only about 8 centimetres long in a woman who has not had a child. Even after childbirth, it is not very much longer. And unlike the penis, the vagina does not grow very much when the woman is aroused: it extends only about an inch. So the penises of all but the most exceptional men will fill the vagina completely.

If the penis is inserted gently and gradually, the vagina will grow slowly to accommodate it. This elastic construction of the vagina means that a woman will feel no difference whether the penis inside her measures 14cm or 18cm.

Occasionally a woman cannot feel her partner's penis inside her, but this is usually because either the woman is not sufficiently excited, or because the man's penis is not completely erect; while a partially erect penis may reach the full length of the vagina, it may not be thick or hard enough for the woman to get full pleasure from it.

Many men blame the size of their penises for any sexual difficulties, when the key lies rather in learning to understand their partner's responses.

A symbol of virility

'I still feel I would be a better lover if my penis were larger. Is it possible to have some sort of operation which will achieve this?'

There is no such operation; but even if there were I would advise against it. The penis is a sensitive and highly complex organ. The way it works depends on its elasticity — its ability to swell and become erect. It would be impossible to enlarge it without damaging this facility.

In any case, it is a fallacy that men with larger penises make better lovers. We have come to believe this because the large penis has been celebrated since ancient times as a virility symbol. Indeed, this 'cult of the penis' continues in modern films and literature: a man with a big penis is portrayed not only as the ideal lover but as having power over other men. This over-emphasis of the aggressive image of the penis has far more to do with men's sexual fears and their competitive feelings towards each other than with the penis's loving and pleasure-giving potential.

For instance in slang terms the penis is likened to a ram-rod and other hard, big, thrusting instruments. Its slang names, like 'prick' and 'cock' emphasize its aggressive potential, but ignore its other more pleasurable aspects.

The woman's attitude

'But surely women do get more excited by large penises?'

Concern with penis size is very much a male obsession. Indeed, homosexual men are far more obsessed than women with comparing penis sizes. There are some women who say that a very large penis makes them more aroused, but I think it's more the idea of it than the actual sensation it gives in lovemaking. And the majority of women don't distinguish between different penis sizes.

An interesting comparison is the way some women feel that large breasts are more attractive to men. Even her partner's reassurance that he loves her breasts as they are may fail to convince a woman that she's not physically inferior. Because of such fears, some women wear highly padded bras and a few go to the extremes of plastic surgery.

Mistaken views of female sexuality are mainly responsible for the idea that women care a great deal about penis size. Contrary to popular belief, most women do not secretly want to be violently

penetrated by an outsize penis. And the degree of passion in a sexual relationship has no connection with the dimensions of the penis or vagina. It depends on mutual communication between the partners and awareness of how to turn each other on in the most pleasurable ways.

'The reason I haven't been able to have sex with my fiancée is that I'm afraid she will laugh at my penis.'

I can't see this happening, because you seem to have a tender and sensitive relationship. Nevertheless, I feel that some women are not sufficiently aware of men's feeling of inadequacy about their penis size. Even a careless, teasing remark can cause great anxiety. Just as a woman needs reassurance that her partner finds her breasts and bottom desirable, a man needs to be reassured that his lover appreciates his penis.

'What can I do if my fiancée is unsatisfied but hides her feelings to protect me?'

The best course is always to bring the problem into the open. Encourage her to express her desires during lovemaking; explore your sensual potential together so that you can find the most satisfying ways for her to reach orgasm.

Confidence and lovemaking

The basic point to remember is that, for lovemaking, confidence and sensitivity count for more than physical equipment. You should never forget that there is much more to sex than the entry of the penis into the vagina. As you learn how to achieve erotic sensations in every part of your body, you will find that your fears about your penis come into perspective and eventually disappear.

Remember your problem is extremely common. Although the size of your penis seems so important to you, your fears are certainly exaggerated — your fiancée almost certainly does not realize that you are worried about your penis.

As you have discovered from petting with your fiancée, intense sexual arousal and orgasm can occur even without penetration. Indeed, over-emphasis on penetration can be unsatisfying for your partner, because, like many women, she may find it easier to achieve orgasm through stimulation of her clitoris, which happens only indirectly when the penis is inside the vagina.

Some partners are able to communicate sexually

simply by touching and sensing each other's response; others prefer to talk about their desires or read books on sexual technique together. Whatever pattern you establish, sensitive mutual communication is essential for building up confidence and technique.

If you do have sexual fears or problems, they will only be worsened by brooding about them alone. Share your worries with your partner or a counsellor. I am convinced that there are many men, who, like you, have secret fears about their penis size and ability to satisfy a woman. If the myths about sexuality were dispelled by more widespread knowledge of the real facts, these men would have a better chance of overcoming their fears and enjoying fulfilling sexual relationships.

Intimate examinations

The prospect of an internal examination makes a lot of men and
women feel nervous or embarrassed. But if they know what to
expect, they may welcome the opportunity to learn more about
their bodies.

When people talk about having an intimate examination they usually mean an examination of what are known as 'private parts' — that is, the internal and external genital organs of both men and women and also women's breasts. Some doctors believe that yearly genital check-ups should be routine from puberty onwards, reasoning that 'prevention is better than cure'.

There are many reasons for having an intimate examination. Boys and girls have been known to get objects stuck in the vagina, urethra and anus, and boys suffer from undescended testicles; both these conditions would necessitate a thorough check-up, as might an adolescent girl's painful, absent or irregular periods. However, for most men and women, the first intimate examination occurs when they become sexually active. Contraception, abortion and antenatal care are all reasons for women to be examined; whereas sexually transmitted diseases, infertility, and painful or unsatisfying sex are reasons which apply to both sexes.

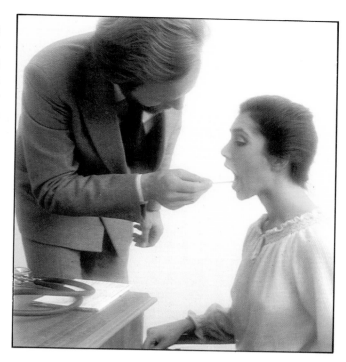

Getting prepared

Imagine that one of these problems applies to you, and you feel that you could do with some professional advice. The first step is to decide where to go. Many people forget that they have a choice and always go to their family doctor, even though he or she may not be the ideal person to help.

If you need contraception you could go to a family planning clinic, where doctors can also give initial advice on sterilization and abortion. If you have an unusual discharge or irritation in the genital area, or suspect that you may have caught a sexually transmitted disease (VD), you could go to a special clinic (genito-urinary or VD Clinic).

No more preparation is needed than the usual daily hygiene — washing the vaginal area or the penis (including behind the foreskin) and the anus using mild unscented soap, and wearing clean underwear. On no account should women douche (wash out) the inside of the vagina or use any sprays, spermicidal cream, pessaries or lubricating jelly for 24 hours before the examination, as these may prevent the doctor from diagnosing any infections. However, it does not matter if you have sexual intercourse before the examination.

Dress simply for the appointment, since you will have to remove at least some of your clothes. Find out beforehand if you will have to give a urine sample at the clinic. If not, empty your bladder before the examination — it will make it more comfortable for you and easier for the doctor. For women who still have periods, it is best to try to arrange your appointment for a time in the middle of your cycle. This is because the menstrual blood might make it harder to see the cervix (the neck of the womb which protrudes into the top of the vagina) or make certain tests less accurate. It is also easier for your breasts to be examined during the two weeks after your period, when they are less tender and lumpy. However, if your periods are irregular or you have constant bleeding or spotting — or an urgent problem — then make the appointment anyway.

For men and women who are likely to be nervous or forgetful when seeing their doctor, it is a good idea to jot down pieces of information such as approximate dates of pain or discomfort, as well as questions which they want to ask and names of any medications they are taking.

Men's examinations

Since the man's sexual organs are on the outside of his body and easily visible, a basic examination of the genitals does not require any special equipment. The doctor will examine the colour and texture of the shaft of the penis, including the underside, and will also look for any sores or spots. Then he or she will look at the urethra (the opening at the tip of the penis) to see if there is any discharge or soreness. If the man is uncircumcised, he will be asked to draw back his foreskin to reveal the glans (head of the penis), which in its healthy state should be pink. The doctor is also checking to see that the foreskin draws back easily and that there is no soreness.

The scrotum (the sac of skin containing the two testicles) will normally be examined while the man is standing. The doctor will look for extreme variations in the size of the testicles (it is normal for one to be slightly larger and hang lower than the other), will touch the testicles gently to test for extreme oversensitivity and will feel the entire scrotal sac to where it joins the rest of the body to find the two cords (vas deferens).

He will also look for varicose veins (*varioceles*), which may make the sperm count lower, and swelling around the testicles (*hydrocele*). Both conditions can be easily cured by minor surgery.

Finally, the doctor will check for hernias (a body organ protruding through the wall of the abdomen). This is done by asking the man to cough or strain and then looking for unusual bulges in the area just above the scrotum.

Ideally a check-up should include an anal examination. The doctor gently feels the mucus tissue inside the anus, looking for sores, bulges or unusual flaps of skin which might indicate infection, haemorroids or early signs of cancer of the colon.

In addition to this type of examination, the doctor may introduce a cotton swab, or thin wire with a loop at the end, half an inch inside the urethra, in order to take a sample for laboratory testing. This may sting for a while, especially if you have an infection. Swabs are also taken from the anus, behind the foreskin and from any sores. If you have had oral-genital sex with a partner and you suspect you have an infection, you should ask for a swab to be taken from your throat and tonsils. The pubic hair will also be examined for crabs and pubic lice.

Either before or after the examination, a small blood sample may be taken from a vein in your arm: this is necessary as some diseases can only be confirmed by a blood test.

Women's examinations

After undressing and lying down on an examining couch on your back, you will be asked to bend your knees and let your legs fall comfortably apart. Some couches have 'stirrups' for your feet on either side. You can also be examined lying on your side, with your legs bent.

To feel more comfortable, try to breathe deeply and slowly so that your whole body, including the muscles of your vagina, goes limp.

The doctor will first examine your external genitals (vulva). Oestrogen deficiencies as well as anaemia can be detected by the appearance, shape and colouring of the labia (lips) and clitoris. The colour and texture of the vulva indicate general healthiness (pinkish) or signs of infection (red, raw or swollen). The doctor will look for pimples, unusual swellings and sores.

The doctor will then insert one or two fingers inside the vagina to hold the cervix in place while examining the lower abdomen with the other hand, to check the position of the womb and ovaries and to check for any abnormal lumps which might indicate growths or a possible pregnancy.

The entrance to the womb itself is normally closed, and the doctor cannot feel inside. Unless there is some inflammation or a tubal (ectopic) pregnancy, the fallopian tubes cannot be felt. If you feel any pain say so — it may be that your doctor is handling you a bit roughly, or there may

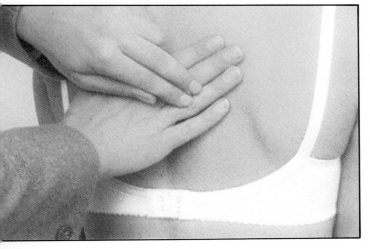
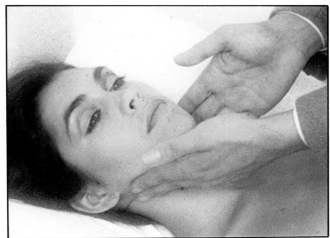
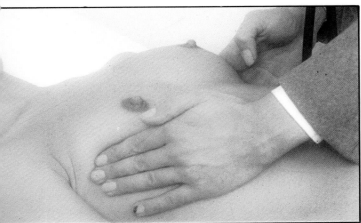
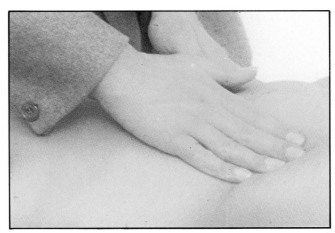

Before an internal examination, the doctor will often do a routine check-up. Among other things, he will check the lungs, the neck glands, the breasts and the abdomen.

be something wrong. Your doctor may need to do a recto-vaginal examination where one finger is inserted into the anus and one into the vagina: this may make the ovaries and the back wall of your womb easier to feel.

The doctor will then take a closer look at the vagina and cervix with the help of an instrument called a speculum and a strong light. The speculum separates the walls of the vagina, which normally do not leave a hollow opening. A speculum comes in different sizes and is shaped like a duck's bill, with two moveable parts and can be warmed and lubricated before insertion. The closed speculum is gradually inserted and then gently opened, just wide enough to reveal the cervix.

The colour and texture of the vaginal walls and cervix will be checked, plus the smell and appearance of vaginal secretions. A red patch (erosion) on the cervix commonly occurs in women, particularly when pregnant or on the Pill,

but very occasionally is a precancerous sign. The colour of the vagina and cervix changes slightly during the menstrual cycle and the consistency of secretions changes quite considerably.

Many doctors recommend that a cervical smear (cancer, Pap or Cyto test) be taken at least once a year. The doctor inserts the speculum and using a wooden spatula scrapes some tissue from the cervix and places it on a glass slide to be analysed. The speculum is then withdrawn from the vagina.

Breast examinations

Breast examination for women is also essential. First the doctor will look at your breasts as you sit with your arms at your sides: the nipples should not be turned in (inverted) unless they do normally. The doctor will note any dimples in the breast skin or unusual sagging. Although most women have one breast slightly bigger than the other, they should both be basically the same shape. Breasts increase in size and tenderness as you approach your period, but apart from this normal process, if you have noticed any changes in shape, lumps or bleeding from the nipple, say so.

Self-help health

Getting to know your own body can help you carry out your own preventative medicine. You are in a much better position than any doctor to be familiar with the usual appearance, feel, smell, texture and cyclical changes of your own body.

As well as examinations of the external genitals, women can also carry out a speculum examination themselves. Plastic speculums are inexpensive and can be obtained from surgical suppliers. You will also need a hand mirror, a light or strong torch, and some lubricating jelly (not vaseline as it is not water soluble). If you are going to examine yourself regularly, keep a chart on which to make notes and register changes.

Empty your bladder first, and practise opening and closing the speculum before inserting it. Sit or lie down comfortably and, after lubricating the speculum, insert it with blades closed, into the vagina. This may be easier with the handle pointing sideways. Then turn it so that the handle points upwards. Slowly open the blades, which will click into place. Using a light and a mirror, it should now be possible to see the cervix, which looks rather like the end of your nose, with a small dimple in the middle. You may have to re-insert the speculum a few times until you are practised enough to find the right position. *It is very important, however, not to close the speculum before removing it; it may pinch your cervix or walls of the vagina.* Pushing down with the stomach muscles will often bring the cervix into view.

Besides watching out for symptoms which warrant medical attention — sores inside and outside the vagina, an unusual discharge or a cervical erosion — certain minor infections can be detected early enough through self-examination to be treated by yourself. Whether it's self-examination or a doctor's examination, the importance of regular checks on these parts of the body cannot be stressed strongly enough.

Hormones: the body's messengers

Hormones play a vital role in keeping our bodies going. Without them the body's whole communications system would grind to a halt – there would be no sex drive and, ultimately, no reproduction.

Hormones are the body's messengers which race round the bloodstream and take instructions to the different parts of the body. If you step off the kerb into the path of a fast-moving car your hormones will send urgent signals to your legs to make you step back very quickly.

As well as sending messages, hormones have a powerful influence over everyday life. They affect a person's emotions and feelings and regulate blood pressure, keeping it at a relatively normal level.

What do they do?

There are many different hormones and each is specifically designed for one particular job — it is almost as if they are coded so that only the appropriate part of the body can decode a specific hormone and respond to the message it is carrying.

There are hormones that have a specific job to do in the digestive system, others which control the strength of bones and the colour of the blood, and still others that are released during times of stress and anxiety.

Where do hormones come from?

Hormones are made by special organs called glands. These glands automatically sense when hormones are needed and produce, or 'secrete', them accordingly. Glands are situated throughout the body. Some of the most important are those in the neck (the *thyroid*), just above the kidneys (the *adrenals*) and the sex glands in the ovaries and testes known as the *endocrine* glands.

Adrenaline is a hormone that is released from the adrenal glands when a person is under stress. It is known as the 'fight and flight' hormone because, under its influence, the body tones up for a great burst of physical activity. Blood pressure rises and muscles become tense while the digestive system slows up.

While other glands control the body there is a special gland that regulates all the other glands — the *pituitary*. It is about the size of a cherry and sits just under the brain at a central point midway between the ears. The pituitary has special receptors that tell it what all the other glands are doing and, in turn, sends out a series of its own hormones to control them.

The brain is the master controller. A small area of the brain, called the *hypothalamus*, sits on top of the pituitary and 'communicates' with it — this is why many glandular disorders seem to affect one's feelings and emotions and probably how emotions can alter the glands.

The sex hormones

One of the main functions of the hormone system is not just keeping the person alive, but keeping the species alive. There are sex hormones that are designed to make men and woman attractive to one another, and others that enable them to be fertile, but they work together so that their sex and fertility functions are sometimes difficult to separate.

In women, the most important family of sex hormones are the *oestrogens*. These are the vital substances that make women look female. They lead to growth of the breasts and the deposits of fat round the body to produce a curvaceous figure; they keep the skin fine and supple and suppress too much bodily hair. Oestrogens lead to the growth of the womb and regulate the secretions of the vaginal wall so that the vagina is kept smooth. They also interact with other hormones to produce strong bones.

Oestrogens are produced by the ovaries, which are a pair of almond-sized glands deep in the body, just above the womb. Doctors can rarely feel these glands — even with an internal vaginal examination — unless they are diseased and enlarged.

From puberty onwards the average level of oestrogens remains high, but varies according to the day of the menstrual cycle. When a woman's period starts, her oestrogen levels are very low. However, over the next two weeks they gradually rise as the ovaries are stimulated by a hormone from the pituitary called *follicle stimulating hormone* or FSH for short. The cells around one egg (*ovum*) pour out enormous quantities of oestrogen while the egg grows in size. At mid-cycle a second pituitary hormone called *luteinizing hormone,* or LH, is suddenly released in a quick burst, and this hormone releases the egg which rolls out of the ovary on the journey to the womb. The oestrogens continue at a lower level, and high levels of the hormone *progesterone* are now secreted by the ovary. Progesterone makes the womb receptive to the arriving egg, and if not enough is produced the egg cannot 'bed-down' and implant properly. It has very little effect on female appearance or behaviour, although some doctors think low levels of progesterone may be responsible for premenstrual tension.

In men, the same two hormones FSH and LH, are released from the pituitary, but their effects are totally different. Before puberty both are produced in small quantities and are difficult to detect. Then, gradually, increasing amounts of FSH are produced, which causes the testes to grow in size. The sperm within the testes increase tremendously in number, and this sudden rise in numbers may spill over at night — the 'wet dreams' of the adolescent boy. This is followed by a rise in LH, which stimulates specific cells in the testes to make the hormone *testosterone.*

Testosterone is the 'male' hormone which causes the muscles to grow in size and bulk, the voice to deepen, hair to grow on face, legs, chest and abdomen, and the penis to grow in size. It is testosterone that enables a man to show interest in sex, have erections and be potent. This sexual interest or drive is called libido — more precisely it means your general 'zip' or motivating force, but it has come to be associated with sexual drive.

Interestingly enough it seems that libido in women may also be due to testosterone which circulates in them at a very low concentration. It may be possible that the female brain is very sensitive to testosterone, so that very low levels are necessary for the female sex drive, but increasing testosterone level rarely increases it and may be dangerous.

Hormonal changes in adolescence

It is the rise in oestrogens in girls and testosterone in boys that causes them to change physically at puberty. This change usually takes place between 10 to 15 years of age for girls and a year or two later for boys. It can be a very difficult time for both the adolescent and the parents as the boy or girl tries to cope with the changes in physical make-up, awakening sexual urges, as well as exams, finding a job and striving for independence. Sexual drive may initially take a new focus, and homosexual interest, and even practice, is not uncommon in early puberty.

Many adolescent boys worry that their development is not as advanced as their friends. A boy notices that his penis and testes are smaller than those of his schoolmates and he gets laughed at in the showers. He remains small while other boys shoot up in height, and he may be the brunt of jokes. These boys are usually just a little late in entering puberty. Often there is a history of delayed puberty in the family.

Testosterone causes a short-lived growth spurt and causes the bones to fuse and stop growing, so it is possible that a boy enters puberty late because he has more room to grow before his bones fuse — he may go on growing long after other boys have stopped and in the end, be much taller than his friends. Very occasionally, when puberty is very delayed or causes great problems, a specialist will prescribe a short course of testosterone injections to speed up the process, but they will then limit the ultimate height that the boy would have reached naturally.

Pregnancy and the menopause

During pregnancy a woman goes through the greatest hormonal change since puberty. The fertilized egg nestles down in the womb and spins a cocoon around itself called the placenta. This process creates a great many hormones including oestrogen and progesterone, but particularly one called HCG, which stops menstruation. Measuring the amount of HCG in the blood is the most sensitive early indicator of pregnancy and HCG in the urine is the basis of common pregnancy tests.

Oestrogens may be responsible for much of the morning sickness many women get in the first three months of pregnancy, while progesterone acts on the brain to raise the body's temperature slightly.

Mood and emotions also change, with careers and other occupations taking second place in late pregnancy. These changes are probably hormonally conditioned, and orientate the mother to her future child. At term there is a sudden fall in oestrogens, which allows another pituitary hormone, *oxytocin,* to set the womb off on its rhythmic contractions that will eventually expel the baby. When a doctor induces labour, oxytocin is injected to start the womb contracting.

During pregnancy, the pituitary doubles in size as it produces increasing quantities of *prolactin,* the milk-producing hormone. The breasts are then ready to feed the baby. As the baby sucks the nipple, oxytocin is again released, this time to squeeze out the milk.

Each ovary has only a fixed number of eggs, which is determined at birth, and when women reach their forties and fifties the ovary gradually starts to fail. Periods become irregular, hot flushes may occur and many women become irritable and depressed. These emotional changes are partly due to an instability in the oestrogen level and partly to problems in adapting to changes in their lives. Children are leaving home and starting their own lives, personal career prospects may look limited, and loss of periods is often interpreted as a loss of 'womanliness'. Most women are able to get through this difficult year or two, but occasionally the physical changes become more prominent: the hot flushes may continue; excessive facial hair growth may become unsightly; and vaginal lubrication may fail and make intercourse painful.

Some experts think that in most women when the ovaries fail other glands are still able to produce enough oestrogens to prevent these symptoms. But for those women (especially slim women) whose oestrogen levels remain low, hormone replacement therapy (HRT) may be beneficial. This consists of oestrogen tablets much

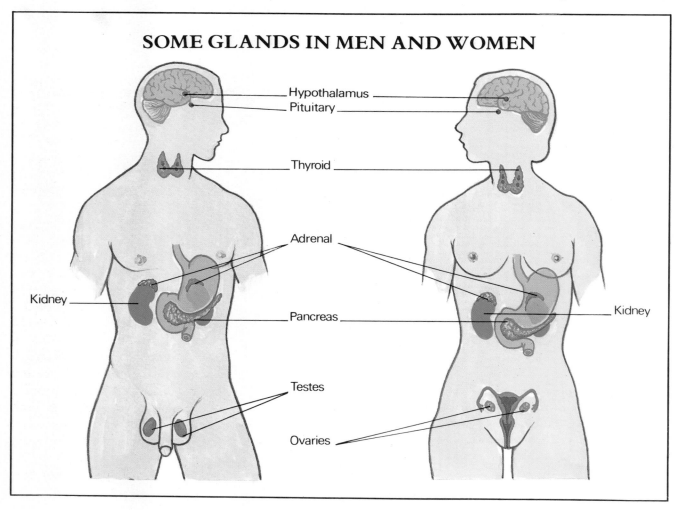

SOME GLANDS IN MEN AND WOMEN

Hypothalamus
Pituitary
Thyroid
Adrenal
Kidney
Pancreas
Kidney
Testes
Ovaries

like those used in the contraceptive pill, which prevent these changes and also the thinning of the bones which starts after the menopause.

Men do not seem to lose the function of their testes and some men reach their eighties remaining fully potent. However, there is a gradual failure of the testosterone production, and sexual activity and interest usually wane in men's sixties and seventies.

Sexual problems

Endocrinologists (doctors who specialize in glandular disorders) are often asked to see patients with sexual problems, but only a few are found to have hormone abnormalities. Although uncommon, these abnormalities are important to look into because they respond well to treatment.

Although impotence is usually due to psychological factors, there may occasionally be the case when an impotent man is found to have very low levels of testosterone in his blood. This indicates that either his testes cannot make testosterone or that his pituitary is not sending out the right instructions. The problem may be due to injury, a severe local infection, or the blood vessels which supply the testes having been damaged in some way. A condition, like a tumour, may have affected the pituitary gland and caused either decreased LH or increased prolactin production both of which may cause impotence and low libido.

There are also men who lack testosterone and never go into puberty. One reason may be that the testes fail to make testosterone because of an abnormality in the chromosomes (the genetic material) or the man may have been born with very little LH, and the amount he produces is not enough to stimulate his testes. Treating all these conditions is relatively simple, as testosterone can be given by injection. If impotence is due to an excess of prolactin, drugs can lower the prolactin level and restore potency. If a man's hormone levels are proved to be normal a doctor will then recommend that he see a specialist to find out why he is impotent.

Hormone abnormalities usually show themselves in women as changes in menstrual bleeding rather than in sex function. A decrease in oestrogen or an increase in prolactin may dry the walls of the vagina and cause painful intercourse, and some type of hormone treatment — usually tablets — relieves the problem. In all cases of hormone abnormality you should see your doctor who may refer you to a specialist.

Although one person in twenty may be homosexual, there is no simple answer as to what makes a person homosexual. It seems very unlikely that it has anything to do with hormones since the hormone levels in homosexuals do not seem to differ from heterosexuals, but research is being done in this field.

Sex drive (libido) is dependent in both men and women on testosterone, but the drive does not seem to affect a person's hetero- or homosexual relationship. There are some women who, because of an inherited defect, produce vast quantities of testosterone as well as their other sex hormones. Although this produces problems at birth — for example, the clitoris so large it resembles a penis — girls suffering from this condition seem to develop heterosexual relationships. Men who are treated with oestrogens, or agents that block the production of testosterone, become less interested in sex but do not become homosexual. Early childhood experiences or other psychological reasons may be more likely to determine homosexuality than hormones.

Can sex determination go wrong?

The sex organs in men and women start developing shortly after conception. The sex is determined by genetic materials called chromosomes. If an embryo has a chromosome known as the 'Y' chromosome, it produces testosterone, which causes male organs to develop. If the embryo does not have the 'Y' chromosome, female organs develop.

A rare case when this mechanism can go dramatically wrong is if a male embryo has tissues that are unable to respond to testosterone. Despite high levels of testosterone in the blood the growing foetus cannot react to it, so the genitals remain female. The baby looks female at birth, and only when the girl fails to start her periods does the problem come to the attention of a doctor. Although female externally, the internal organs are male. There is no womb and the testes may be found sitting inside the abdomen. The girl, who is genetically designed to be a boy, cannot menstruate, but will notably become a woman in both appearance and behaviour. Plastic surgery can usually correct appearance problems, although the person will never be able to function biologically as a woman.

Hygiene and sex

Sex itself certainly isn't dirty, but infections can sometimes be passed on during the close contact of lovemaking. However, any risk can be considerably reduced if both partners follow a few simple rules of hygiene.

People are at their closest, both physically and emotionally, when they are making love, and both partners normally want to be at their most attractive so that their lovemaking is as beautiful an experience as possible. But lovemaking can be spoiled because one of the partners has neglected his or her personal hygiene.

Why hygiene is important

Love and desire can survive most things, but dirtiness is one of the greatest turn-offs in any relationship. Together with the unpleasantness of such things as bad breath or smelly feet inevitably go the disappointment and sadness that your partner hasn't made the effort to be fresh and clean for you. Some people — probably most of us at one time or another — find natural body smells exciting, but this rarely extends to finding dirt and overpowering odour attractive.

As well as being distasteful and unromantic, lack of hygiene can be positively dangerous — it may lead to infection or disease, some of it serious. Bacteria of all sorts thrive on stale sweat and body secretions as well as on dirt itself, and because of the specially close contact of two bodies during sex,

these bacteria can very easily pass from one person to the other, putting a clean partner just as much at risk as the dirty one.

Cleanliness for lovemaking

There are a number of simple hygiene precautions you can take which will considerably reduce the risk of infections and at the same time make lovemaking more pleasurable for you both.

First have a thorough all-over wash, preferably a full bath or shower. At the very least, make sure the genital area is scrupulously clean; many of the conditions that are frequently passed on during lovemaking cannot survive even simple soap and water. Give your teeth a thorough cleaning too and, if you like, use a mouthwash — nobody likes smelly, sour-tasting kisses. Smokers need to pay special attention to this; you are already at a considerable disadvantage if your intended lover doesn't like smoking, so the least you can do is freshen your breath.

Clean clothes are a good idea too. There's not much point in taking the trouble to get your body clean and then putting it back into the same old dirty clothes you've been wearing all day. Besides, a change from your daytime working clothes into something special is good for the morale.

It may be argued that all this preparation is too premeditated and that it takes the spontaneity out of lovemaking. But this need not be so. You can make these preparations *in case* a situation leads to making love. If it doesn't, the extra bath or wash certainly won't have done you any harm. The alternative — finding that you both want to make love but that you aren't as clean as you would like to be — is much worse.

The importance of timing

No matter how careful or thorough you are with personal hygiene, you can't stay clean all the time nor can you remain perfectly clean and fresh hours and hours before making love. So the timing of your preparations is almost as important as the hygiene itself. Even the most patient and long-suffering lover's desire is likely to cool to freezing point if you have to disappear into the bathroom just when things are getting passionate. Similarly, nobody will appreciate you jumping up to clean your teeth when your partner is on the point of orgasm just because you suddenly remember you didn't do it before. If you and your partner are

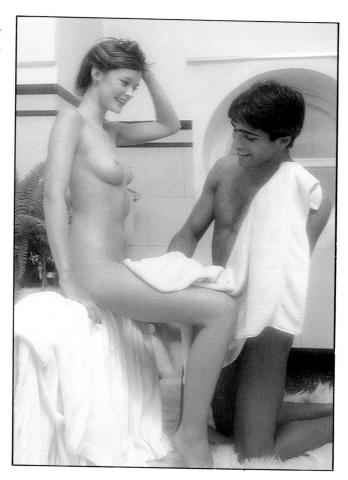

planning to spend a long time together before making love, find a moment to freshen up when it won't interfere with your pleasure in each other.

Can sex be dirty?

People sometimes worry that some kinds of sex are in themselves unhygienic or that making love at certain times carries more risk of infection.

To some people oral sex may seem unnatural and dirty, but such feelings are really a reflection of personal views on sex in general, and there is no evidence — as long as both partners are particularly careful about hygiene — that oral sex is any more risky than conventional ways of making love. Remember, though, that the mouth as well as the genitals can be affected by venereal disease and that you can catch VD just as easily when making love in this way as in any other.

There are all kinds of taboos about making love when the woman is menstruating, but there is no evidence that it is dangerous or unhygienic. Similarly, lovemaking during pregnancy does not carry any special risk to the couple, though the doctor may advise temporary abstention in the interests of the baby if the woman has had several miscarriages, or has a uterus which is tilted backwards (retroverted). Many doctors also advise that sex should not be resumed after childbirth until the post-natal examination — usually done about six weeks after the baby is born — has confirmed that the pelvic organs have settled back to normal, otherwise there may be some danger of any unhealed areas being infected by ordinary bacteria introduced during intercourse.

However or whenever you make love, simple hygiene measures will go a long way towards reducing the risk of developing a wide range of disorders of the genital area, including lice in the pubic hair, scabies, pubic warts, small, tender ulcers called herpes genitales, and fungal infections such as ringworm (tinea) and thrush (monilla).

Hygiene for men

Circumcision — surgical removal of part of the foreskin (prepuce) of the penis — was until recently performed on many, if not most, boys in the interests of hygiene, quite apart from any religious reasons, because it was believed that it made diseases of the penis less likely.

Nowadays most doctors think that circumcision is not essential to cleanliness of the penis and it is therefore carried out far less frequently. Nevertheless, men, especially those who haven't been circumcized, do need to pay special attention to keeping the penis clean with regular soap and water washing, since lack of cleanliness can lead to several diseases of the penis.

Secretions (smegma) collect underneath the foreskin and, unless removed every day by pulling the foreskin right back and washing the area, can give rise to inflammation (balanitis). Bacteria and fungi, such as thrush, also thrive on smegma, which can also lead to an increased risk of cancer of the penis. Furthermore, the man's partner can be put at risk if he does not clean under his foreskin properly before they have intercourse. Smegma, which is exposed during erection, can cause inflammation and irritation of the vagina and cervix, and some doctors believe it can sometimes lead to cervical cancer.

Hygiene for women

Women also need to pay special attention to sexual hygiene and they too can prevent many infections by careful washing with mild soap and water. Care must be taken, though, if your skin is sensitive, not to use a strongly scented soap, as this can irritate the delicate tissues of the vulva. Pure, mild, unscented soap is the most suitable kind to use, and this can be bought at most chemists.

Tampons can sometimes cause soreness and discharge. This is particularly likely to happen — not surprisingly — if the tampon is forgotten or is left in a long time for some other reason. In a few women, the vagina always reacts badly to tampons, even if they are left in only for a short time. If this applies to you, change to sanitary towels and use tampons only for special occasions.

An increasingly common reason for soreness and vaginal discharge is the wearing of tight

trousers and nylon tights or underwear. There is no 'cure' for this kind of personal sensitivity, but such complaints may be controlled by wearing trousers only rarely and changing to cotton underwear and stockings or open-crotch tights.

Similarly, vaginal deodorants and other products designed to improve the appearance, taste or smell of the female genitals can frequently give rise to rashes, soreness or discharge. If you must use them, do so very occasionally and even then sparingly, and stop at the first sign of irritation — anyway, vaginal smells are not nearly so unpleasant as some women think, in fact men often find them arousing. Above all, never spray on a deodorant to cover up a bad-smelling discharge. If it's that bad

it needs proper investigation and treatment — so see a doctor about it. Any vaginal discharge should be taken seriously, and may well need tests and treatment, but a great many turn out to be quite normal and only a few are due to anything serious.

Preventing VD

What you do in the interests of hygiene after you have made love largely depends on how well you know each other. If you are married or regular lovers who are sure of each other, you can safely leave anything further until morning, unless you feel the need of a wash later on to freshen up. The secretions you have both produced are in no way harmful and there's no need to wash them off straight away.

If you don't know each other very well, however, you may be worried about catching VD, and may wonder whether there is anything you can do after intercourse to prevent it. Ideally, of course, you should have thought of this before you started making love and taken precautions then, preferably by saying 'no' if you had the slightest suspicion that your partner was infected. But even an infected person may have been honest in saying he or she had not got VD — the disease could have been in an early stage without any symptoms. Using a sheath will give both of you quite a lot of protection against all forms of venereal disease although it should not be relied on. Nevertheless, there are things that are worth doing after you've made love with a new partner.

For both men and women, a thorough washing of the genitals with soap and water a civilized time after you've finished making love — there's no need to leap out of each other's arms the moment your orgasms have subsided — will kill a large proportion of the bacteria with which you may have been infected. Passing urine has the additional benefit for men in that it is quite likely to flush out of the urethra any microbes that may have got in there during intercourse. Urinating will of course have the same effect in women, but in them VD usually develops in the vagina and cervix rather than in the urethra; in men the urethra is nearly always involved.

Women often wonder whether douching (squirting water or other liquid inside the vagina) will prevent venereal disease. Although it is a very old practice, its disadvantages outweigh any advantages: there is no evidence of any positive benefits and there is the extra risk that any infected material is as likely to be flushed upwards into the womb as to be washed out — definitely an undesirable result. It is much better for a woman to soak herself thoroughly in a hot bath, allowing the water to flow freely into her vagina. If you feel you must douche, use only water or a mild salt and water solution. Never use chemical douches; they are quite likely to cause inflammation and damage to the lining of the vagina.

Applying antiseptic lotions or ointments to the outside of the genitals is extremely risky for both men and women. Occasionally, people who think they may have caught venereal disease try to 'cure'

themselves by pouring a strong antiseptic or household disinfectant into the urethra or vagina. This is extremely foolish and dangerous and could well lead to serious and permanent internal damage.

If, for whatever reason, you are worried that you might have caught VD, it is essential that you consult a doctor immediately. If the idea of discussing your love life with your family doctor is embarrassing, most hospitals nowadays run VD clinics (usually called Special Clinics or Departments of Genito-Urinary Medicine) where you will get effective treatment in complete confidence, and where you can go without being referred by your doctor.

The Nature of Sexual Response

The range of human sexual response is astonishingly wide and varied. Though there are elements which are common to most people the nuances are immensely subtle. What makes up the precise nature of an individual's response is a unique combination of emotional and physical factors to which a good lover is highly sensitive. Understanding the ways in which your bodies respond when you are making love is the first step to a happy sexual relationship.

The sex drive

Expecting your partner always to want to make love when you do can be unfair. Individual libido – or sex drive – differs, and understanding why can help to make your sex life happier.

Every couple knows the frustration of times when one feels like sex and the other would rather turn over and go to sleep. The most common experience of this sort seems to be early in the morning when the man wakes up with an erection and feelings to match — and his partner is asleep or determined to look as if she is! At other times of the day or night they both want to make love with just as much desire, so why does it sometimes happen that one partner is 'turned on' and the other 'switched off' at certain times of the day?

Sex drive — otherwise known as *libido* — differs from person to person and between men and women, although studies have shown that there does seem to be a pattern within the sexes; men often feel sexiest early in the morning and women in the afternoon. It seems that sex drive, like sleeping and waking, and appetite, is governed by our 'biological clock'; an internal in-built mechanism which we know very little about as yet.

But knowing that feeling in the mood for sex at different times from your partner is 'just one of those things' is little help to your love life. Perhaps it does help to know that it is a common problem and not just cussedness on your partner's part, but the only practical answer is to make love when you both really want to, no matter what the time is.

How libido develops

In Victorian times sex drive was widely believed to be something that 'afflicted' men. And it was only *immoral* women who ever felt stirrings of this nature. It is hardly surprising, then, that there was such an outcry at the turn of the century, when the Austrian psychiatrist Sigmund Freud introduced the idea that children were sexual beings. By this he meant that they gain intense pleasure from parts of their bodies — first from sucking at the breast, then from touching their anus, and then their genitals.

Freud believed that girls centred their sexual pleasure in their clitoris during puberty, switching to their vagina as they matured. Recent research by sexologists Kinsey, Masters and Johnson, and Shere Hite, suggests that no such change takes place and that the clitoris remains the focus of the female libido.

Recent surveys show conclusively that men are more sexually active at all ages than women, even today — but the difference between the sexual appetites of the sexes has lessened. This suggests that the more permissive sexual attitudes of our society have had some effect on 'liberating' the female libido. The availability of reliable contraceptives and the relative ease of obtaining legal abortion has meant that most of the more traditional restraints on women's sexuality have been lifted.

But even in the most permissive countries there still appears to be much less female sexual activity than male. However, women are thought to suffer less from sexual frustration than men, perhaps because they tend to find an outlet for their sexuality in diversions like sentimentality, romance and love.

The male sex drive

There is little doubt that men have a stronger overt sex drive and are more open in their desire for sexual contact than women. Recent research has shown that there are both physical and social reasons for this stronger sex drive.

For men, orgasm and intercourse are inevitably linked. It is very rare that a man fails to experience

● The higher your sex drive, the more frequent and varied are your erotic fantasies. The low-drive person is likely to only fantasize about intercourse with one person; the high-drive person is more likely to fantasize about having sex with more than one partner, about oral lovemaking, or about being 'forced' to have sex.

● The intensity of your sex drive is about one-third due to your upbringing and environment but is two-thirds inherited: in fact, sexy parents tend to produce sexy children.

● Going without sex for a long time is likely to *decrease* your sex drive, however unexpected this may seem. The evidence suggests that people who stop making love for some reason and have no sexual outlets whatever, have gradually less urge to seek sexual satisfaction.

● The sex drive of people who enjoy sado-masochistic fantasies (for example, about whipping or bondage) is usually higher than average; the sex drive of transvestites (men who enjoy dressing as women) is generally below average, and that of people who actually change sex is even lower.

orgasm through intercourse, so for him, the sexual act is something that is sure to provide a pleasure so intense that it is well worth seeking.

It is socially acceptable for men to enjoy and want sex. Men with great sexual prowess, such as the legendary Casanova, have become great heroes. Needless to say, a woman who exhibited the same desire for sex as the great lover would almost certainly be condemned, or be thought of as 'loose' by society.

Men are *expected* to be lustful — in fact, men who fail to show an interest in sex are treated with suspicion. It is normal for a man openly to admire girls in the street or on television, be interested in titillating literature and to actively seek sexual contact. Sex is also associated with dominance and power and is often regarded, by men and women alike, as simply one more sphere in which a man can prove his virility. With such encouragement from society, it is not surprising that most men are more interested in sex than the majority of women.

Upbringing also plays its part in teaching males to be interested in sex. From about the age of 14, boys are encouraged to seek sexual experience — in fact many parents worry about sons who are reluctant to go out with girls. In times gone by, fathers ensured that their sons were sexually experienced before marriage by either taking them to a prostitute or providing a willing older woman. This kind of initiation rite is still practised in some primitive societies. Fathers do not go so far today but many will raise no objection if their son buys 'girlie' magazines, goes to see sexy films or is 'a bit of a lad' with the girls.

The female sex drive

There are a number of reasons why women have a less intense sex drive than men. One important factor is that many women find it difficult to achieve orgasm. *This is perfectly normal* and is nothing

to feel inadequate about. Achieving orgasm does not come through intercourse alone but is achieved by skilled lovemaking and the stimulation of sensitive areas such as the clitoris. Unless a woman has a partner who understands this, she may find orgasm impossible to achieve. Even with the right man, many women do not always experience orgasm through intercourse. This does not mean that these women do not enjoy sex at all. Many experience great pleasure and comfort from intercourse without reaching the heights of orgasm.

Intercourse, therefore, does not automatically mean such intense pleasure to a woman as to a man, so many do not seek it as eagerly. A lower sex drive is the result.

Just as boys are encouraged to be interested in the

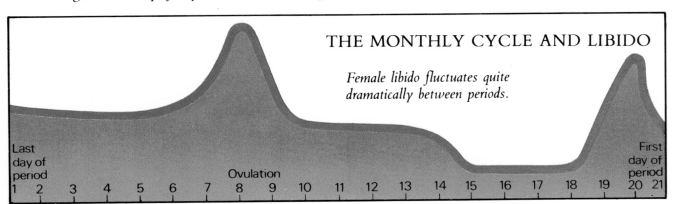

THE MONTHLY CYCLE AND LIBIDO

Female libido fluctuates quite dramatically between periods.

Last day of period
1 2 3 4 5 6 7 8 9 10 11 12 13 14 15 16 17 18 19 20 21
Ovulation
First day of period

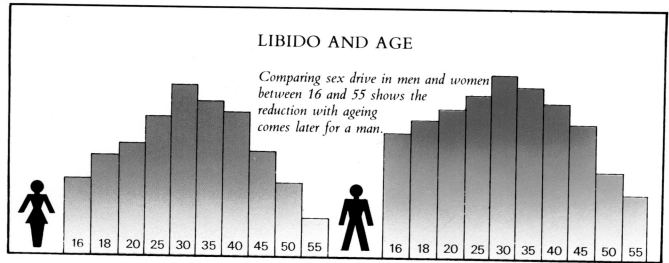

LIBIDO AND AGE

Comparing sex drive in men and women between 16 and 55 shows the reduction with ageing comes later for a man.

16 18 20 25 30 35 40 45 50 55

16 18 20 25 30 35 40 45 50 55

opposite sex, many girls are actively discouraged. Mothers fear their daughters will get a 'reputation' and may ban boyfriends until the girl reaches 16 or older or put strict limits on the number of times a week a girl goes out with a boy (and the time she comes home). It is accepted for boys to have intercourse before marriage but even in these permissive times the double standard prevails and many mothers are shocked to find their daughter is sleeping with someone.

Very few parents point out to daughters that sex is a joyous, pleasurable thing. There is still a tendency for some mothers to make it out to be a 'duty' — something that men need and women have to tolerate. Very few girls are taught to regard sex as something to look forward to, something to enjoy, or even to take the initiative or an equal part in.

For the sensual woman, times are almost always hard. Attitudes to sex today are freer than ever before but a woman who actively seeks sex or is known to enjoy it outside a stable partnership is condemned by many women or is known as 'fair game' by men. Not surprisingly with all this discouragement they receive from family, friends and society, relatively few women discover the joys of sex without much trial and error.

If your sex drive is down

If you find that you lack sex drive, or have lost interest you once had, it could be because something — be it physical or buried deep in your subconscious — is suppressing your desire. For example, painful intercourse is one very good reason why some men and women cannot enjoy sex. For the women, pain on penetration caused by tense vaginal muscles is sometimes the problem. This condition is known as *vaginismus* and can be

treated. Women who suffer from cystitis (the condition sometimes called 'honeymoon disease', that makes you want to rush to the toilet every few minutes), find intercourse very painful. If cystitis is a problem, you must consult your doctor as this condition can eventually cause kidney damage. For men, a tight foreskin which makes erection painful is occasionally a problem. This can also be treated.

However, even when someone has received successful treatment for a physical problem of this kind, it can still leave a sense of inadequacy behind and somehow make the person feel he or she is still out of the running sexually. A sympathetic counsellor will help you to see your problem in perspective, once the basic medical factors have been improved. For exactly the same reasons, worry will always suppress libido. If home or work worries are affecting your sex life try and share them with someone. Whether you talk to your partner, a friend, relative or a professional counsellor it is important to find an outlet to help relieve the mental pressure.

If you and your partner have had had a tense or worrying time that has affected your sex life, make the effort to go away so that you can forget your problems and relax. The disturbing thing about sex is the longer you do without it, the less inclined either of you will be to start again, so do try to remedy the situation as soon as posible.

Claustrophobic conditions that inhibit sexual activity can also have a damaging long term effect on the love life. A young couple who have to live with in-laws for a long time or parents who have very little privacy from their children, may suffer from the fear of being disturbed or overheard — which can easily suppress the most enthusiastic lovers.

There are also a number of natural factors which affect the sex drive. Just before menstruation, many women experience a loss of libido. This can usually be ascribed to pre-menstrual tension and the feeling of apathy and listlessness caused by fluid retention.

Ageing inevitably causes some loss of libido, although it is quite normal for elderly couples to have a reasonably active sex life. The charts on page 85 show how libido fluctuates with age. For men, libido is high between the ages of 16 and 38. Women experience their peak years between similar ages but, after this point, the decline in sex drive is slightly greater than in men.

Effects of drink and drugs

Alcohol taken regularly and in large quantities affects the drinker's general health and capabilities, and is likely to have a strongly depressant effect on the sex drive. An excess of alcohol on an occasional basis will probably cause temporary loss of sex drive, although in small quantities alcohol may act as a sexual stimulant. This is especially true in the case of people who are extremely shy and tense — they often find that alcohol loosens their inhibitions so that they can relax and enjoy sex.

It is thought that the contraceptive pill can in some cases cause loss of libido. If your doctor thinks this is causing a problem for you, a solution may be to change to a lower dosage pill or to a mechanical method of contraception.

In fact loss of sex drive related to the Pill is usually for psychological rather than physical reasons, but if you are worried about it you should ask your doctor's advice. Tranquillizers and some antibiotics can also cause temporary loss of libido.

Aphrodisiacs

Whatever the problem that is causing a loss of sex drive, there is no miraculous potion which will solve it. Aphrodisiacs are substances which are supposed to increase sexual desire — oysters, stout and powdered rhinocerous horn are a few of the strange traditional notions. At best these are harmless but useless, at worst they can be dangerous; one aphrodisiac known as Spanish Fly is a serious irritant which can be very damaging to sensitive tissues.

The idea that special foods or concoctions will arouse the libido is pure fantasy, but there certainly are human factors which increase the sex drive. Being in love is the greatest stimulant any couple could ever hope to find.

Most couples find that they are much more sexually active in the early days of marriage, while their love is still new, than when they are more accustomed to one another. By the same token, many partners find that after a brief separation their sex drive is very strong. In the end, there are no aphrodisiacs as powerful as love, caring and consideration.

DIFFERENCES IN MALE AND FEMALE SEX DRIVE				
AGE	FEMALE		MALE	
	Per cent sexually active	Monthly sexual activity (approx.)*	Per cent sexually active	Monthly sexual activity (approx.)*
Under 16	22	1	95	11
16–20	50	2	99.3	11
21–25	72	5	99.6	11
26–30	84	7	99.5	12
31–35	88	7	99.7	11
36–40	89	7	99.5	11
41–45	87	6	99.1	8
46–50	84	4	97.5	7
51–55	77	3	96.0	6
56–60	66	2	95.3	5
61–65	47	1	81.0	3
66–70	37	1	73.3	1

Includes masturbation and intercourse.

Balancing your sex drives

Adjusting to a partner's sexual needs is an important part of any loving relationship, and by recognizing that sex drives do differ, a couple will be able to work out the best way to fulfill each other's sexual desires.

The importance of sexual adjustment in a relationship is often overlooked. And, although most couples would agree that it takes time to get to know and understand a partner, many confine their knowledge to the ordinary, day to day, social side of a relationship, leaving the success of their sex lives to chance.

Working at the sexual side of a relationship may seem unromantic, but, in reality, the opposite is true. However similar, no two people's sex drives are exactly the same, and there will always be times when one partner feels in the mood for sex and the other doesn't. But, with a little patience and understanding, a happy balance can usually be found, allowing lovemaking to develop into a satisfying rhythm of approaches and responses. It is only when couples, through a lack of sexual communication, allow these imbalances to become sexual barriers, that problems can occur, leaving them both feeling angry or rejected.

A question of timing

Timing may often be a problem. A man who responds rapidly to sexual stimuli may not realize that his partner's apparent slowness may be due to the fact that he is not stimulating her enough. His approach to lovemaking may be too hurried, when all she needs to bring her to the necessary stage of arousal for intercourse is a period of foreplay.

In some cases, a woman may be unconsciously resisting stimulation. Here the reasons for her holding back have to be discovered. She may be afraid of pain on penetration. Her inability to relax which has caused her pain in the past is very likely psychological, and a patient, understanding partner may be able to help her (see page 130 for details). But he will not be in a position to do this if he is totally preoccupied with his own performance, and blames her for spoiling things.

Sexual reassurance

Likewise, a woman who complains that her partner takes too long to reach orgasm, should realize that he probably needs more stimulation than she is giving him. Her partner might welcome the idea of her taking the sexual lead, because it makes him feel desirable and boosts his ego. Some men, too, need the added stimulation of seeing their partners wearing specific articles, such as black stockings or leather boots. Bizarre as some of these requests may seem to a woman, a balanced sexual rhythm may be reached, provided that she can understand and accept her partner's needs.

There may be disagreement over lovemaking positions or oral sex. One partner may feel that sexual experimentation is wrong. For instance, a woman brought up believing that women are not supposed to enjoy sex, might be afraid to give rein to the sexuality within herself. If her partner is much more self-confident, he may try to force his ideas upon her, possibly with disastrous consequences for the relationship. If, however, he has a powerful sex drive combined with gentleness and understanding, he may gradually convince her that the enjoyment of sex is something to be shared.

Finding the 'right' time

Sticking rigidly to the idea that there is a 'right' time and place for sex — for instance, in bed every Saturday night — can make lovemaking stale and mechanical. If one partner seems to be losing interest in sex, it may only take a few sessions on the living room couch to reawaken sexual desire.

For some people, however, tensions can arise simply from not being able to find the 'right' time. It is a physical fact that some people wake up fresh in the morning, but find themselves exhausted in the evening, while others are quite the reverse. If the sleep cycles of both partners are very different, they may have difficulty in finding a time when they are both physically in tune. Rather than making demands on a sleepy partner who is not in the mood for sex, it is better for the couple to come to terms with this imbalance and to take the trouble to find a time for sex that suits them both.

Airing the problems

The effect of menstruation on sex drive should also be taken into consideration. Some women feel noticeably sexier around the time of their periods, whereas others — particularly women who suffer from pre-menstrual tension — may temporarily lose all sexual interest. A man who is unaware of the symptoms of pre-menstrual tension — for example, depression and irritability — may feel rejected and think that his partner is no longer interested in him. Equally, the woman who does try to make love to please her partner may be further depressed because she is unable to have an orgasm. She may wonder what is wrong with her, not realizing that it is her tension holding her back, and that once the physical effects pass off she will revert to her normal pattern of response. Casting blame on each other is only likely to increase tension on future occasions. A situation like this can be avoided if the couple get into the habit of being open with one another, and discuss each other's problems in an understanding way.

Keeping the balance

At the beginning of a relationship, when a couple's sex life seems to be taking good care of itself, it may seem like an invitation to failure if they start to air their sexual differences. And, indeed, the relationship may be harmed if the couple take too serious and critical an approach. Although it may not always be easy, they should remember that the ability to keep things in perspective is essential to a happy life, and that being aware of each other's sexual needs and appetites will lessen the possibility of sexual problems developing.

However well-adjusted a couple may become, they should bear in mind that, even in the years of maximum sexual activity, their rhythm will fluctuate from time to time. The effects of over-work, childbirth, as well as illness, may temporarily lessen potency and sexual desire. And unless the real cause is recognized and accepted, considerable distress can be suffered by one or both partners.

A couple who can talk openly and honestly about their own and each other's sexual needs, stand a good chance of bridging any arousal gaps that may occur, and of preventing feelings of frustration from building up.

Stages of arousal

Being aroused is more than just feeling excited and sexy – it involves physical changes in your body and your partner's. Knowing what these are can help you both to make the best of more exciting lovemaking.

Sexual arousal starts with the urge to have sex with a particular person in a particular situation, and builds up through the various stages of sexual intercourse, until it ends in orgasm. The pattern of the body's reactions during arousal is always the same, whether the lovers are a man and a woman or a homosexual couple. It is also the same for someone who becomes aroused and reaches orgasm by masturbating alone.

The American sex researchers Masters and Johnson, after observing many people going through the various stages of arousal, have been able to divide the process into four stages: *excitement, plateau, orgasm* and *resolution*. These stages overlap and vary in length from person to person, and even time to time, but the sequence or pattern remains the same.

Excitement – the first stage

Arousal begins in the mind. People can sometimes reach orgasm while dreaming, or through fantasies. Reading about sex, looking at erotic pictures, or even hearing other people making love can be physically arousing. So can seeing your partner naked, or wearing clothes that emphasize a particular aspect of his or her body — the breasts, buttocks or genitals.

This basic desire for sex depends to some extent on the production of hormones — chemical messengers in the bloodstream which stimulate body organs to work. As hormone levels change, emotional responses may change as well: a woman may find that her desire for sex increases just after menstruation begins, and about halfway through her menstrual cycle. A man, too, may notice that his sex drive — libido — varies over a four to six week cycle.

Mood also plays a part in how much a person can be aroused; tiredness, worry or embarrassment can make lovemaking impossible. When a couple are particularly relaxed — on holiday or after a special celebration — they are more likely to want to make love. In some cases, a couple may want to *deliberately* set the mood by, say, going out to dinner at their favourite restaurant. Perfect lovemaking is not guaranteed, but some of the stress and tension of everyday life will be removed so that the couple can enjoy their lovemaking more. Memories, particularly of smells, can be very potent. A hint of perfume can bring back a sexually satisfying, happy event and trigger off an intense desire to have intercourse.

Unfortunately, memories of a bad time — a period of impotence in the man or of tension in the female — can be set off in much the same way, making the problem repeat itself. Gentle, patient, sympathetic lovemaking can usually overcome this, as it can many other sexual difficulties.

A couple who are aware of each other's wish to make love show signs of desire before they even touch each other. They become totally absorbed in each other — ignoring everyone and everything — their hearts beat faster, the pupils of their eyes widen and, as they caress each other, their excitement grows. Recognizing a partner's sexual excitement and desire is in itself arousing. At every stage of sexual intercourse, each partner can be aware of the other's responses, even subconsciously. As their hearts race, they gasp for breath and clutch each other; they share their excitement and heighten it in each other.

Your sense of smell may also play a part in the arousal process. Recent studies have involved pheromones, the smells one person's body gives off which affect another person's behaviour. These pheromones are not consciously recognized by the brain but do play a part in whether you attract or repel another person. Smell can also play a part directly, as during arousal the odour of a woman's vaginal secretion may heighten her partner's excitement.

Women particularly need a period of love-making or foreplay before they are ready for intercourse. This begins with touching — stroking and kissing. Skin is sensitive over most parts of the body and a touch or a squeeze may be very stimulating, although some areas — the cheeks, ears, neck and shoulders, waist, hands, buttocks and the inside of the thighs — tend to be more sensitive than other parts of the body.

The most sensitive areas of the whole body, sometimes called the *primary erogenous zones,* are the mouth, lips, nipples and genitals themselves. A couple who make love regularly learn from each other which caresses are particularly exciting, and this can vary from instant to instant. During the times when a woman's breasts and nipples are particularly tender — during her period, for example — a touch can be painful rather than stimulating. Movement and changes are important too: a caress or stimulus that stays the same soon loses its effect.

Changes in the body

Arousal brings about physical changes in the body. At the beginning of the first stage the glands which cap the kidneys, the adrenal glands, secrete the hormone adrenalin — as they do in response to any kind of excitement. The adrenalin tenses up the muscles, speeds up breathing and makes the heart beat faster and stronger.

The blood flow increases, the skin may develop a flush on the top part of the body and sweating may increase. Blood is forced into the pelvic region, filling the tissues by a process called *vascongestion.* This produces sensations of fullness, warmth and excitement. In a man, the arteries of the penis pump blood into its spongy structure, so that it stiffens into an erection, and muscles at its base limit the amount of blood that can flow away from it. Eventually, the skin around the scrotum — the pouch containing the testicles — thickens and the testicles are drawn up against the body.

In a woman, the breasts enlarge slightly, and the nipples become erect. The increased blood supply to the pelvis makes the tissues of the vagina secrete a lubricating fluid. The outer lips of the vulva draw back and the inner ones swell and darken. Later in the excitement phase, the diameter and length of the clitoris increases, the vagina begins to relax and expand to accept the penis, and the cervix and body of the uterus (womb) changes its position and lifts higher into the pelvic cavity, providing more room in the upper part of the vagina.

Genital reactions in men and women depend on body processes that are very similar. Although the penis and the clitoris are very different in size they are alike in structure. Both are well supplied with nerve endings and both are a focus for sexual responsiveness.

The developing responses of a woman's clitoris and the full readiness of the vagina to accept the penis happen at a later stage of excitement than the

first erection of the penis. The penis may enlarge and stiffen with the first stirrings of sexual interest, and though the woman's vagina may very quickly become lubricated, it may not yet be ready for the penis. If the man tries to push his penis into his partner's vagina too early, she may not be ready for him and may feel pain because her vagina is not sufficiently lubricated. A couple who enjoy lovemaking will probably want to extend foreplay and spend more time stimulating each other so that this does not happen.

Sometimes, a man's penis will need to be directly physically stimulated by his partner to bring it to a full erection, and it may harden and soften during lovemaking as this stimulation varies. A woman may need direct friction against her clitoris or more pressure around the genital area so she can be fully aroused and have orgasm.

What happens in later lovemaking?

The process of sexual arousal found in the *excitement* phase continue into the next one — the *plateau*. With experience, partners can learn to control the speed at which this phase develops, and relax into lovemaking that is satisfying and fulfulling for them both.

The man's penis fills with even more blood, so that its smooth cap, or glans, increases slightly in size and may darken to a deep purplish colour. In a woman, the breasts may continue to swell and the inner part of the vagina continues to expand, while the outer third becomes even more suffused with blood and narrows, allowing it to grip the shaft of the penis. The congestion of blood may make the skin darken, and the clitoris withdraws beneath its protective hood of skin and decreases in length. Further stimulation comes from general pressure around the pubic area, moving the hood against the clitoris glans.

The movement of the penis within the vagina increases the pressure and acts as strong, effective and continuous stimulation. The pupils of the eyes dilate, breathing rapidly accelerates, the nostrils flare and veins on the neck stand out.

As the couple shift from the plateau phase to *orgasm,* the caresses and reactions become more vigorous and they focus even more narrowly on their sexual feelings. Their heart and breathing rates increase still further and their muscles grow tense as sensations flood the genital area and rapidly spread all across the body.

At orgasm, sexual tension rapidly increases to a

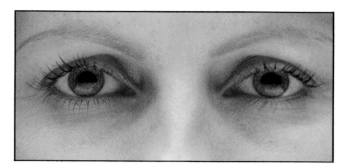

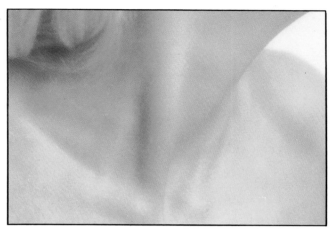

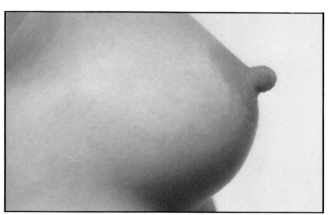

further peak. The experience of orgasm can vary widely: on one occasion all sensation may appear to be in the genitals themselves, on another, it may spread and produce an intensity of feeling throughout the entire body. Whatever the feeling, the sensation of orgasm depends on a series of reflex muscular contractions in the genital area. The heart races even faster, heavy breathing may become deep and rapid gasping which in turn can, very rarely, produce a brief loss of consciousness. Many of the body muscles contract strongly and almost involuntarily — the jaw muscles in particular can clamp into a bite, which is why anyone nearing orgasm should avoid nibbling a sensitive part of

SIGNS OF AROUSAL IN MEN

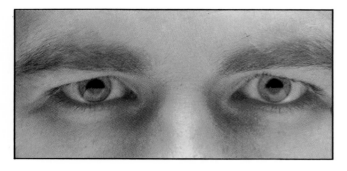

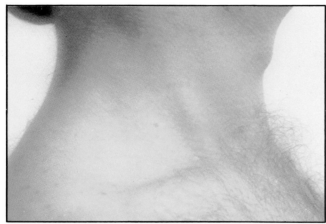

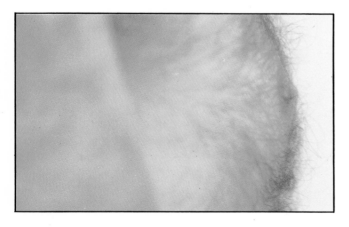

In a woman, the muscles around the uterus and, in particular, around the outer third of the vagina begin a series of rhythmic contractions, similar to those of the man. Sometimes orgasm begins with a single contraction lasting two to four seconds. If the woman continues to be stimulated effectively, she can go on to experience a number of 'mini-climaxes' after the first orgasm. In this, she is unlike the man, who may not be able to have a second orgasm for many hours, though a young man may be able to have several in one night.

Afterwards

Immediately after orgasm, both men and women may break into a sweat as they pass into the *resolution* phase. Blood drains away from the congested pelvic regions and the genital swelling decreases.

A man's erection may collapse rapidly and the penis returns to its normal size. This happens very quickly if he wants to urinate but can take several minutes if he is relaxed.

In a woman, the vagina slowly goes back to its usual state and the clitoris and uterus return to their usual positions — the clitoris within 20 seconds and the uterus within 20 minutes.

A period of sexual arousal without a climax leaves the congestion of the pelvic and genital areas unrelieved and can cause a dull pain, which may last for some hours.

Like most human relationships, lovemaking depends very much on how the two people concerned feel, and how much they understand what arouses one another. Having some idea of how the body changes as it goes through the process of sexual arousal, and how the body moves effectively from one stage to the next, can help a couple get more fulfilment from their lovemaking.

Enjoyment of sex together can grow over the months and years, as couples share experiences and learn how to please each other, guiding each other to the stimuli they like best and pacing their lovemaking so that their excitement grows at about the same rate. Unfortunately, many men and women may still grow up with the feeling that the whole process of sexual arousal is something that should just happen satisfactorily, rather than being something to discuss and explore.

However, with a little knowledge, and some commitment, a couple can learn from each other how best to pace their lovemaking and give each other more pleasure and satisfaction.

the body as an accidental bite could be painful. Muscular tightness shows up in the tense expression on the face of the man or woman.

In a man, the sensations of orgasm develops from recurring contractions of the muscles linked with the penis and urethra, the passage running through the penis. It begins with the feeling that ejaculation is inevitable and cannot be delayed. The muscles around the urethra contract strongly, driving seminal fluid along its length and out in a spurt at the tip, while the bladder is closed off. A series of contractions follows less than a second apart — driving out more seminal fluid and then dying away after a few seconds.

The female orgasm

Having an orgasm is the climax of making love, but some women do find it difficult to achieve. Understanding what orgasm is, and how it happens, is a helpful first step in making sexual intercourse more enjoyable and fulfilling for a woman.

There is no other area of sex that is argued about by the experts and laymen as much as the female orgasm. Theories about it have changed as frequently as fashion and all too often, the real experts — women themselves — are not asked about their experiences. As a result, many women worry that the way they enjoy sex is the wrong way, or they get so confused about what is supposed to happen that they do not enjoy intercourse.

Put simply, the female orgasm is a reflex to sexual stimulation. But in reality, it is much more complicated because it is an individual experience. Different women need different kinds and amounts of sexual stimulation to achieve orgasm, but worry and uncertainty about sex can stop the natural progression towards a climax.

A different intensity of orgasm may be achieved by experimenting with various lovemaking positions, by extending foreplay and delaying orgasm — which can increase its intensity and pleasure. Even changing the time of day or the place where you usually make love can affect how much enjoyment both you and your partner get from having intercourse and orgasm. Whatever you do to vary lovemaking, the final result — the orgasm — remains the culmination of the sexual experience and the pattern that it takes depends on the individual.

One of the most important aspects of sexual enjoyment is relaxation, and if a woman is tense about sex she will not enjoy it. Understanding what happens during your own sexual arousal can help you enjoy it more, and you will find that you have your own pattern of needs. You may find that you do not fit exactly to the ideas of every sex manual, or enjoy it in the same way as your friend or next-door neighbour, but that is no reason to feel sexually inadequate.

The experience of orgasm

A woman's mood affects how intense her orgasm will be. Love, tenderness and a partner who is responsive to her needs will act positively to increase her pleasure. Women who have loving, long-standing relationships will usually get much more enjoyment from intercourse than those who have casual sexual encounters.

Some studies show that a woman's monthly cycle may have something to do with the intensity of her orgasm. For example, she may feel much more sexually responsive during ovulation — 14 days before her period starts — than at other times or she may feel more responsive at night because she finds that lovemaking and orgasm takes away her tension and tiredness. The time of day or the time of the month depends on the individual — it is a purely personal matter.

The orgasmic cycle

There are four phases of the female orgasm: sexologists describe them as excitement, plateau, orgasm and resolution and each woman has her own individual way of going through these stages. If a woman does not reach orgasm it means her sexual response was stopped in some way at either the excitement or plateau phase.

Every woman is different and therefore the sensory awareness and sexual response depends upon her age, health (both physical and mental), hormone level and kind of stimulation she is getting from either her partner, or in the case of masturbation, herself.

During the *excitement phase,* the sexual organs become filled with blood, in much the same way as a man's penis fills with blood to give him an erection, except it is not so noticeable. The inner lips of the vulva (external female organs) will swell a little as a result, and so will the clitoris and its hood. The vagina begins to expand in length and width, and the vaginal walls begin to lubricate themselves by means of a kind of sweating action. The whole body becomes sensitive and a woman may develop a fine rash or flush on her chest, back and abdomen.

The second stage of arousal, the *plateau phase,* is essentially a continuation of the first phase. The inside two-thirds of the vagina expand so that it is about two inches longer than normal and the outside third narrows so it can grip the man's penis more easily. The breasts may swell, and the nipples become erect, particularly if the man strokes and caresses them. All the muscles around the sexual organs will tense up. A woman's breathing becomes deeper and faster, and her whole body can feel tingly and warm. Though men and women often think that they should begin intercourse at the first signs of sexual arousal, a woman may not really be ready for it. The walls of the vagina may not be sufficiently lubricated, and if this is the case, extending foreplay may help. For extra lubrication you and your partner may want to use a lubricating jelly or saliva to moisten the vagina.

The most sensitive part of a woman's sexual organs is the clitoris, which plays the most important part in the female orgasm. During the excitement phase it becomes erect, just like its male counterpart, the penis. During the plateau phase the clitoris pulls itself back into its hood, and if stimulation continues, the third stage of the cycle — *orgasm* — will probably occur. Orgasm during intercourse may be brought on by rubbing the inner lips with the penis as it moves backwards and forwards inside the vagina, which in turn causes friction on the clitoris. This action is called *indirect* stimulation of the clitoris. You may, however, want *direct* stimulation for orgasm, and your partner can do this by using a lovemaking position where his body rubs on your clitoris, or he can stimulate it with his fingers or tongue.

The orgasm phase itself starts as a rush of pleasure, usually concentrated on the clitoris, but quickly spreading all over the body. The muscles around the vagina, vulva and anus then go into a series of rhythmic contractions, which are very pleasurable. It is this strong sensation around the vagina which has caused confusion between vaginal and clitoral orgasms, with some people saying a vaginal orgasm is the 'best' one to have; in fact, all orgasms start from the clitoris. Recent studies have shown that there is no difference in the orgasm achieved by stimulating the vagina from the one achieved by stimulating the clitoris — both orgasms go through the same pattern and give the same amount of pleasure.

During the orgasm, the pleasure you get from these contractions will spread deep into the vagina and pelvic area. You may want to move your hips back and forth, or you may prefer to stay still.

Some women, particularly those who have not had orgasm before, are surprised and worried by the strength of sensation they are experiencing. You may find that you cannot think of anything except the erotic pleasure you are having, but you will not faint or lose consciousness. You may have a series of smaller contractions, which end in a final burst of pleasure — this is what is often described as a *multiple orgasm*.

After orgasm, the *resolution phase* occurs. This begins when the last vaginal contraction subsides and it continues until all the pelvic organs have returned to their normal state — this usually takes about 30 minutes although the clitoris usually returns to its normal size and position within 20 seconds after orgasm.

If you don't reach orgasm

But often arousal does not go through all these stages quite so easily, particularly if you are worried about whether or not you will have an orgasm. Your partner may have had his orgasm, and want to stop lovemaking, leaving you unsatisfied. Sometimes the muscular tension that happened during arousal continues, only now it can make you feel keyed-up and uncomfortable.

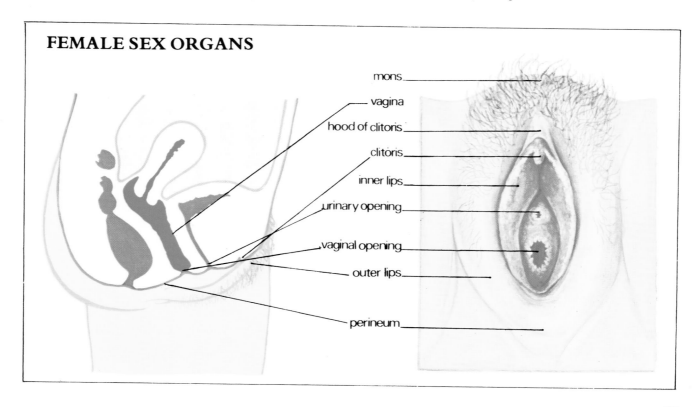

FEMALE SEX ORGANS

mons

vagina

hood of clitoris

clitoris

inner lips

urinary opening

vaginal opening

outer lips

perineum

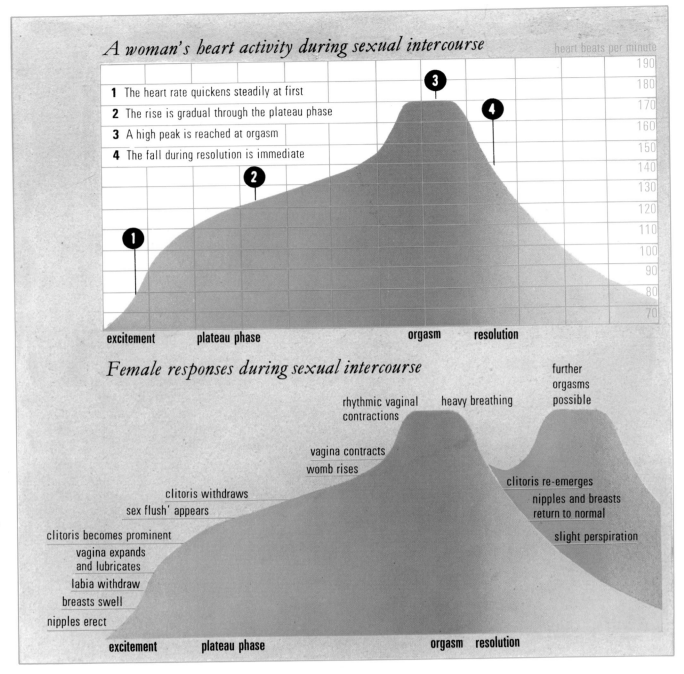

A woman's heart activity during sexual intercourse

heart beats per minute

1 The heart rate quickens steadily at first
2 The rise is gradual through the plateau phase
3 A high peak is reached at orgasm
4 The fall during resolution is immediate

190
180
170
160
150
140
130
120
110
100
90
80
70

excitement   plateau phase   orgasm   resolution

Female responses during sexual intercourse

further orgasms possible

rhythmic vaginal contractions   heavy breathing

vagina contracts
womb rises

clitoris re-emerges
nipples and breasts return to normal

clitoris withdraws
sex flush' appears

slight perspiration

clitoris becomes prominent
vagina expands and lubricates
labia withdraw
breasts swell
nipples erect

excitement   plateau phase   orgasm   resolution

Orgasm acts as a way of releasing the blood that has filled the sexual organs, and you may feel heavy inside if you do not get that release. This kind of experience can make a woman feel as if she is the only woman in the world who does not find sex satisfying. Perhaps you worry that your partner will think that you do not find him sexually attractive, or really love him if you do not respond to him fully. Some women may feel tense and irritable for hours afterwards.

There are women who feel so ashamed of not reaching orgasms that they get into the situation where they pretend they have them. These women hide what they feel is their own inadequacy and attempt to bolster their partner's confidence by pretending to achieve a 'climax'.

Simultaneous orgasm

Some women feel they are supposed to climax at precisely the same time as their partner — *simultaneous orgasm* — so they pretend to 'come' as soon as they think their man is about to have an orgasm. And the more often they do it, the more difficult it becomes to tell their partner that they have been faking. Telling him that you have been doing this is a difficult step, but it is a problem that millions of women have had to cope with at some time in their lives. Simultaneous orgasm increases the pleasure of both the man and the woman, but it should not be considered the ultimate goal when you make love.

Or perhaps you do not pretend to have an orgasm, but never discuss your dissatisfaction with your partner. You know that he probably knows this, and he knows that you know that he knows, but never a word is spoken about the problem. Because

a great many women grow up believing that the only right way to experience sexual pleasure and orgasm is from intercourse, they feel that they have something wrong with them and cannot bring themselves to ask their partners for anything else.

The majority of women need clitoral stimulation to bring them to orgasm, while others can achieve orgasm just as a result of nipple stimulation. The important thing to remember is that any of these widely differing needs are normal — each woman has a different sexual threshold she has to cross before she reaches an orgasm. If you can learn what your own personal threshold is, and tell your partner what you need to get there, you are far more likely to enjoy sex. Honesty is the best policy in the long run.

Masturbation

Masturbation — or self-stimulation — is the best way to start learning about your own sexual feelings, so that you know what to ask for when you

are with your partner. It can also be very exciting to give yourself the kind of pleasure you may have thought you would never experience. The most important obstacle to cross is embarrassment.

Children are often told that it is wrong to touch their sexual organs, and therefore a woman can feel guilty if she gives herself pleasure in this way. But masturbation is not bad or 'dirty', and it will not harm either your health or sex life — in fact, quite the opposite.

It is important to try to masturbate at a time when you will not be disturbed and do not have to worry about time. Look at your body, and stroke it gently. Appreciate each curve and line, and which parts are the most sensitive and enjoyable to touch.

Move your hand down to the area around your clitoris, and gently stroke or rub it. You may want to moisten your fingers with saliva or some of the lubricant from the vagina. (Many women have sexual daydreams while masturbating which increase their pleasure, but it is impossible to generalize about what the subjects include.) Try different ways of stroking your clitoris. Some women do not like to touch it directly, as the sensations are too strong, others may want to exert quite a lot of pressure with their fingers on the clitoral area.

Once you are relaxed about achieving orgasm by yourself, you should concentrate on achieving orgasm by having intercourse with your partner. Try to show him what gives you the most pleasure and when you are ready for intercourse. It is important that your lover realizes that you may take a long time before you are ready, so do not be afraid to say 'not yet'. He will learn that hurrying you is not going to please you any more in the long run, as well as realizing it may be difficult for you to ask for certain kinds of lovemaking. Both of you must build up the confidence to accept pleasure from each other, as well as learning how to give it.

A woman may find that she cannot achieve orgasm during intercourse unless the clitoris is caressed at the same time. She may want to do this herself, or have her partner do it. Experiment with different positions, and see which ones give you the most pleasure. You both may want to concentrate on your own pleasure first, and have an orgasm before you actually have intercourse. You may find that you start worrying that your lover is getting bored or frustrated if he concentrates on you for too long. Most men are pleased and excited when they see their partners sexually aroused, and this adds to their sexual enjoyment.

When a woman can't 'come'

*Many women find that they are unable to have an orgasm
with their partner. If this problem is tackled early
it can be easily resolved, but if not, it can
have a disastrous effect on a relationship.*

A generation ago a woman who went to see her doctor about difficulty in achieving an orgasm would have been called 'frigid'. Today, this term is no longer commonly used, because it covers a very wide range of problems — low sex drive, pain or vaginal spasm during intercourse, difficulties in reaching an orgasm or morbid fears of having sex. Some men even say that a woman is frigid when she simply refuses to have sex when he wants it — it is easy to see why the term has outlived its use.

Orgasmic dysfunction

The 1953 Kinsey report showed that about 80 per cent of women had at least one orgasm of some sort by the end of their first year of marriage. Unfortunately, they gave no details of how the women achieved it. A recent magazine survey showed that only one out of five of the women who returned their questionnaires could have an orgasm without the help of manual stimulation.

This is not surprising in view of the complicated stimulation women need to get an orgasm during sexual intercourse. In fact, it is surprising that so many women have climaxes without the help of manual stimulation. The position of the clitoris varies from one woman to another as does its sensitivity. Similarly, everyone's body make up is different so the angle at which the penis touches and stimulates the clitoris will vary.

Almost every woman is capable of having an orgasm by masturbating and most women will be able to climax following manual stimulation by their partners, but far fewer women will have orgasms during full sexual intercourse.

Many couples will evolve a technique which puts sufficient pressure on the clitoris during penetration for the woman to reach a climax, or they

are perfectly happy for the woman to achieve orgasm only through manual or oral stimulation. But, for other couples, serious difficulties can arise. In some instances it is a case of 'unfulfilled expectations' — in other words, because both partners *expect* the woman to have an orgasm during penetration, if she has difficulty achieving it both partners worry that this is abnormal and the problem becomes even worse. Both partners are disappointed and the man may feel inadequate and unmanly because he has failed to satisfy his partner sexually. In other cases, the woman may have a severe problem which inhibits her sexual responses to all kinds of stimulation. Because the couple cannot talk to each other about their difficulty, the situation worsens, and, unless a couple try to get help, the marriage may crumble.

Why don't women have orgasm during sex?

Although many women feel that there must be something physically wrong with them if they don't have an orgasm, this is very rarely the case. Generally, apart from poor arousal technique (foreplay), the reasons for not having orgasm are largely psychological. Almost all of them are associated with anxiety about sex or orgasm.

Strong religious attitudes and beliefs can affect a woman's chances of climax. Women brought up in a home where parents believe that enjoying sex is 'sinful' will often have difficulties in achieving an orgasm under any conditions. Even when they do achieve it, they feel guilty and most of the pleasure is lost. As one woman recalls: 'Every time I have sex, I can imagine my mother pointing a finger at me, saying that it's a sin and I'll be punished for it'.

Related to this is the belief that sex is aimed at producing babies and so if contraception is used sex is wrong. Many women do not enjoy sex when they are using any form of contraception for this reason. It is also far from rare to come across women who report having an orgasm only on days of the month when conception is likely.

Parental attitudes, especially the mother's, can also have an adverse affect. Women whose mothers had sexual difficulties will often recall that their mothers told them sex was an unpleasant duty that they would have to undergo for their husband's sake. These women learn at an early age that sex is something to be feared and find it very difficult to learn to relax during intercourse.

Unpleasant sexual experiences during childhood or in later life may produce fears that are difficult to remove. Sexual assault, interference or even seeing a man exhibit himself can often leave a young girl with scars that make sexual enjoyment difficult. If a woman is to enjoy sex again she will often need patience and a great deal of understanding from her partner.

Some women fear that if they climax they will lose control, become 'animal-like' and disgust their lovers. Fear of losing bladder control will often contribute to inhibition. Usually all that is required is reassurance that even if the woman does urinate, it will only be a few drops and there is nothing to worry about.

Worries such as the fear of pregnancy, attempting to get pregnant and the possibility of contracting venereal disease will also affect a woman's ability to relax enough during sex: but other more general problems such as money, job and domestic worries can also prevent a woman from relaxing.

Often, ability to achieve an orgasm is markedly reduced following the birth of a child, especially the first. Childbirth is a physically exhausting experience and often the mother becomes depressed for a while after the birth. A new baby in the house will change both the couple's relationship with each other and their daily routine. If the wife has intercourse before *she* feels she is ready for it sexual difficulties can arise.

The conditions under which the couple have sex are also important. Whether the light is on or off may be crucial for the female partner as well as the male. A man who has poor personal hygiene may turn a woman off sex altogether and can interfere with her ability to have an orgasm. The fear of being interrupted, so often a problem when a woman has her first sexual experience, may continually affect her chances of orgasm.

Whatever the initial reason for a woman's

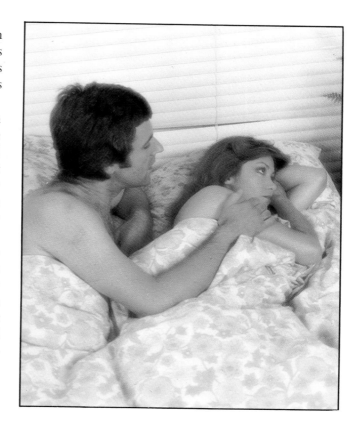

orgasm problems, they can get worse as she becomes anxious about her ability to reach orgasm itself, and anxiety about having an orgasm will make it more difficult to achieve. Some women try so hard to have an orgasm, because it worries both them and their partners, that they suffer from what is called 'performance anxiety'. In fact, their very strenuous attempts to reach climax stop them relaxing enough to actually achieve it.

Does a partner make problems?

However, it is not only the woman's present and past situation that will affect attaining a climax, her partner is also involved. An inconsiderate partner, who is interested only in his own pleasure will not stimulate a woman carefully or long enough so that she can achieve orgasm. She may even be repelled by his efforts.

Many men do not know what is likely to 'turn a woman on' and since they do not like to ask they often carry on doing the wrong thing or do nothing at all.

What 'feels nice' for a woman varies from occasion to occasion so it is very difficult for a man to guess how best to stimulate his partner. Simple instructions from the woman or, better still, guiding the man by placing his hand over or under her hand, provides a simple and straightforward

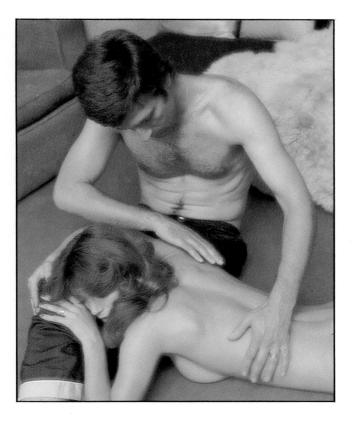

way of telling him what you want him to do.

If a man has a sexual problem his partner will often develop an orgasm problem. If a couple are not using manual or other stimulation in their lovemaking then a man who 'comes too quickly' (premature ejaculation) will have a great deal of difficulty in giving his partner sufficient stimulation to allow her to 'climax'. The man who has difficulty getting an erection presents obvious problems.

In this situation the woman will often 'switch off' — refusing to get sexually excited — so she will not feel 'let down' if she doesn't reach orgasm. In this way she loses not only her ability to climax but also her sex drive.

Choosing the right partner can be crucial to a woman's ability to orgasm. Research has shown that most women require tenderness, trust and security to get the most out of lovemaking. But there are exceptions to this.

Lisa, for example, only has an orgasm with aggressive dominating men, whom she feels are totally unsuitable as marriage partners. Usually they are married or obviously not interested in having an emotional relationship with her. 'I feel it's all right to enjoy sex with them and I do. But for marriage I want someone who is less aggressive.'

Lisa's mother had always told her that she

should not enjoy sex and that any woman who did was no better than a prostitute. By separating the men she enjoyed sex with from the men she might marry, she felt that she was making sure that her future husband would not think she was a prostitute. Also, if her lovers treated her like a prostitute this allowed her to enjoy sex.

Not 'climaxing' – the effects

Caroline and Simon had been married for seven years. After the birth of their first child, Caroline suddenly found she was losing interest in sex and was no longer capable of having an orgasm. She and Simon were becoming increasingly irritable towards each other and were constantly rowing about the infrequency of sex.

Simon said that on the last few occasions that they did have sex he had been having erection problems. He now felt that the problem was partly his fault because: 'Even if Caroline wants to have sex, I don't have a strong enough erection to satisfy her'.

It may appear a little drastic for a couple to consider separation due to what is, at first glance, Caroline's loss of ability to have an orgasm — but it does happen. This is not usually because of the difficulty itself, but because of the pressures that result from it if the couple do not discuss the problem or seek some outside help.

Caroline's temporary inability to orgasm could include any of the factors already mentioned. But once the process had begun the effects on the relationship are typical.

After Caroline's return from hospital, Simon began asking her to resume their sexual relations. Although she agreed, not surprisingly, she felt tired and somewhat resentful and she did not have an orgasm.

At first Simon did not notice her resentment but still kept insisting on intercourse. Eventually however, he realized that she was no longer having an orgasm, and although he was satisfied, he felt that ' . . . my performance has become inadequate. After all, I'm supposed to be able to give her pleasure — that's part of being a man. But besides, I love her and want to give her pleasure'.

One of the most common consequences of a woman's lack of an orgasm is that the man feels less 'masculine'. Men, like women, are often taught that performance is what counts in sex and Simon having failed to 'perform' (by not giving Caroline her orgasm) now feels that he is less of a man because of this. In the meantime, Caroline gradually began to dread having sex. She was also beginning to worry that the problem would become a permanent one. The more she worried about orgasm the more she dreaded sex — in case her worst fears were proved right. She was beginning to dislike Simon even touching her.

At first it is just frustrating not to have an orgasm, but later the woman realizes that the problem is having an effect on her partner. Often the simplest way to cope with all this seems to be to 'switch off' and avoid sex altogether.

In many long-term relationships, the couple only touch each other before they have sex. Since sex has become so distressing, and touching leads to sex, any touching is automatically discouraged. Often for these couples even cuddling and affection disappear from the relationship.

The man may begin to worry that she no longer has any interest in him as a sexual partner and has found someone else, or alternatively that she soon will start searching for another man. This further undermines his self-esteem and confidence. The woman, on the other hand, worries that, if she is not having an orgasm (in this way undermining his pride) and is gradually becoming less interested in sex *he* will look elsewhere for sexual pleasure.

The relationship can come under a great deal of pressure and if the couple neither understand nor discuss what is happening, a great deal of damage can occur. Many couples just need to be reassured that the problem is temporary and will work itself out, provided that neither partner pressures the other. If Simon had been more patient and Caroline had told him of her difficulties, instead of simply pretending everything was the same as before, the problems might have been resolved. Instead, Caroline, in an effort to reassure Simon that the new baby did not in any way change her attitude towards him, felt she had to have sex with her husband.

Very often a man tries to avoid rejection. Instead of asking outright or giving clear messages through *touch* that he wants to have sex, he makes more timid approaches. He hopes that if his partner does not want sex, she will think he has just touched her accidentally and so he will not feel rejected and his pride will not be hurt. If his partner does want sex, he hopes she will respond to his caresses.

Unfortunately, the woman is not quite sure whether the touching is accidental or not, so she often takes the easiest way out and ignores her partner's advances instead of encouraging him.

In the case of Simon and Caroline, the couple avoided having sex for over a year. By the time they resumed sexual relations, Simon developed anxieties about his own sexual abilities — which made his problem worse. By now both partners had difficulties and the marriage was in a very poor state.

What could Caroline have done? Should she have pretended to have an orgasm or should she have confronted Simon with the problem and discussed a solution?

What can help?

Many women think that they ought to try and fake an orgasm. However, this is no solution as it then becomes impossible to talk about sex at all, without the woman admitting that she has been misleading her partner all this time. Besides, it will not help her enjoy sex any more or resent it any less.

Discussing the problem will always help. Although it will probably not resolve the woman's orgasm problems, communication can help alleviate some of the strains placed on the marriage.

Education about their bodies and a change of approach, by the man making more realistic goals for intercourse, will help. However, generally therapy would have usually involved both partners starting their sexual relationship from the beginning as if they were new lovers.

Starting with a ban on intercourse, the couple would be instructed to massage each other to start to enjoy each other's touch once again (what Masters and Johnson call *senate focusing*). The woman would be encouraged to touch herself all over her body and from there have her partner touch her and gradually build up to full intercourse when she is ready.

Removing performance anxiety from both partners is necessary for resolving the problem. This applies not only to long standing relationships but to casual ones as well. It is simply a case of the woman telling her partner what she wants.

Certainly some women may never have an orgasm during sex. However, if the relationship is open enough, and the couple are prepared to use other methods of gaining sexual satisfaction, then there is no reason to go through the difficulties that are caused by the woman failing to have orgasm.

The male orgasm

Orgasm is a crucial part of a man's sexual performance. Every individual knows what his climax feels like but, how is his body working to produce this sensation, and does orgasm follow a specific pattern?

For both a man and a woman, orgasm — the climax of sexual intercourse — is a process which involves not only the sex organs, but also other parts of the body. Orgasm is basically the same for both sexes because, apart from sexual differences, their bodies are similar. Orgasms are very hard, if not impossible, to describe but they are an intensely pleasurable experience.

Most men can reach orgasm by themselves, by masturbating, and most achieve it easily through sexual intercourse. One reason for this is that the male orgasm is an involuntary physical response as compared with the orgasm that a woman experiences, which is a voluntary physical response.

What is the male orgasm?

Generally speaking, a man reaches orgasm when he is able to ejaculate semen from the penis. Some sexologists argue that ejaculation does not always mean orgasm, but most people think that ejaculation and orgasm are the same thing. It is actually possible to have an orgasm without ejaculating semen. This happens most often in pre-pubescent (teenage) boys because their prostate glands and seminal vesicles — their sexual 'apparatus' — are not fully developed, so they are unable to ejaculate.

There are also times when a man gets an erection, but can't reach orgasm during sexual intercourse. This condition is known as 'retarded ejaculation'. It is a common occurrence for which there is treatment, but it is rarely reported to doctors or therapists because most men feel embarrassed about it. The condition is usually caused by some kind of anxiety or an unconscious feeling of guilt, which may inhibit his pleasure in lovemaking, and may turn him off altogether.

Lovemaking is also helped if you forget about trying for a fixed number of orgasms. The pleasures of intercourse can't be measured by how many times you come. (The idea 'quality not quantity' holds true.) If a man only manages to come once or twice during an evening it doesn't mean he is a failure in bed. If he and his partner feel good after intercourse, that is what matters.

One of the main causes of impotence is worry over how a man's performance compares with those of his friends, or rather the performances they brag about. The 'superstud' of legend is rare; once a man realizes that his modest success is perfectly normal he can relax and get on with his own lovelife and forget about his performance.

The orgasmic cycle

Masters and Johnson, the American sexologists, spent 11 years studying the physical changes that take place during lovemaking and found that there is a clear pattern of responses in men which leads them to orgasm. Each orgasm is the end of a separate 'cycle' even though there may be only a few minutes between each ejaculation. According to Masters and Johnson this cycle consists of four stages: *arousal*, *plateau*, *orgasm* and *resolution*.

Arousal

Love is the biggest 'turn on'. It sets the mood and prepares the body for expressing that love through sexual intercourse. Partners who relax, take their time and stimulate each other by mixing manual and oral techniques during foreplay tend to have more orgasms than the couple who use the quick 'in and out' approach.

During this period of growing excitement, the penis becomes larger and more erect. This is because the blood supply is increased by the action of hormones. At the same time the heartbeat and blood pressure increase, breathing becomes heavier and the nipples can harden and grow erect, lasting throughout the cycle.

In a long-lasting relationship there will be times when love alone is simply not enough and you need some other kind of stimulation. Your partner can do this by either *direct* or *indirect* means. Kissing, touching and caressing the genitals and other erogenous zones — lips, earlobes and buttocks — are direct methods of arousal.

Indirect arousal depends on the experiences we unconsciously connect with a smell, sight or sound — and the sexual fantasies associated with them. Almost anything in the right circumstances can act as a stimulus. For example, the smell of a particular perfume can trigger off a memory of a beautiful, long-forgotten experience, which can cause a surprising erection.

Some 'turn ons' are more common. Photographs of naked women or a sexy striptease can arouse a man — even though he knows that intercourse with the particular woman is unlikely. But conversely, *clothes* can also be a stimulant. Seeing your partner in leather trousers, thigh-length boots or a see-through nightie can work wonders when sexual excitement is flagging. On the other hand, some people regard these things as distasteful. If your partner feels self-conscious about this kind of stimulus the whole thing is likely to be a disaster and may prematurely end the evening.

Arousing each other should be relaxed and natural. But if you use indirect methods, such as sexy clothes or magazines, you are not abnormal. They do not reflect badly on either you, your partner or your relationship — something new keeps love fresh.

Intensifying excitement

During the *plateau* stage of the cycle, the penis reaches its maximum size, the testicles increase by 50 per cent and elevate to give a more forceful thrust in ejaculation. The body becomes tense and a measles-like rash called the 'sex flush' often develops over the top half of the body.

If the man has been sexually excited for a long time, the penis may secrete a few drops of seminal fluid before actual ejaculation. This is one reason why a sheath will not always effectively prevent sperm from leaking into the vagina. Even if the sheath and a spermicide are used at the final stage of the cycle, unforeseen pregnancies can still occur.

There is a birth control method used by some couples at this stage called 'withdrawal' or *coitus interruptus,* where the penis is withdrawn from the vagina just before ejaculation. This is an unsatisfactory contraceptive method for several reasons, mainly because the man cannot always 'pull out' in time. Even if he does manage it, there is a high risk that some sperm has leaked out and neither partner feels particularly satisfied or relaxed when the session of lovemaking has finished.

The moment of orgasm

Just before ejaculation, and at the height of his excitement, a man has the feeling of being about to come, which is caused by the build-up of sperm and seminal fluid in the urethra entrance (the canal through the penis which leads to the opening at the tip of the penis). The feeling lasts about four seconds and once a man feels it he can't hold back orgasm any longer. It is at this stage that men may utter short, sharp sounds — almost bark-like — or cry out short aggressive words. On the whole, men tend to verbalize more than women during intercourse.

The penis ejaculates sperm and seminal fluid (anywhere from 2-6 ml) by rhythmic contractions of the urethra's penis muscles. The more fluid ejaculated, the more pleasure a man will get, which is one reason why the first orgasm gives the most pleasure — because the most fluid is ejaculated. Repeated orgasms temporarily reduce the amount of seminal fluid that is ejaculated and it may take a few days or even a week for the level to return to normal.

If a couple are trying to have a baby they should build up a reserve of fluid by not having intercourse for a few days. They can then concentrate all their efforts on the time around ovulation when conception is most likely.

THE MALE ORGANS

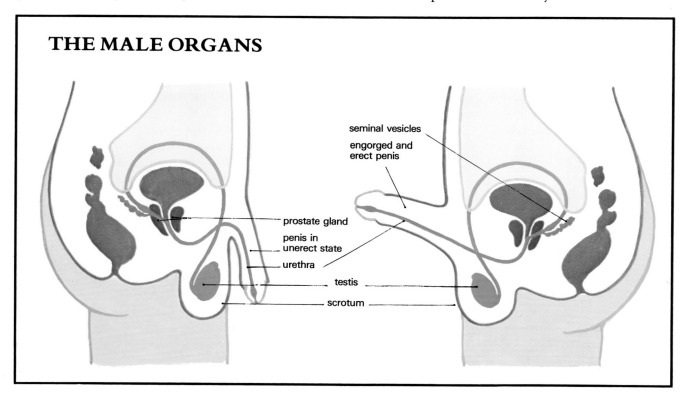

seminal vesicles

engorged and erect penis

prostate gland

penis in unerect state

urethra

testis

scrotum

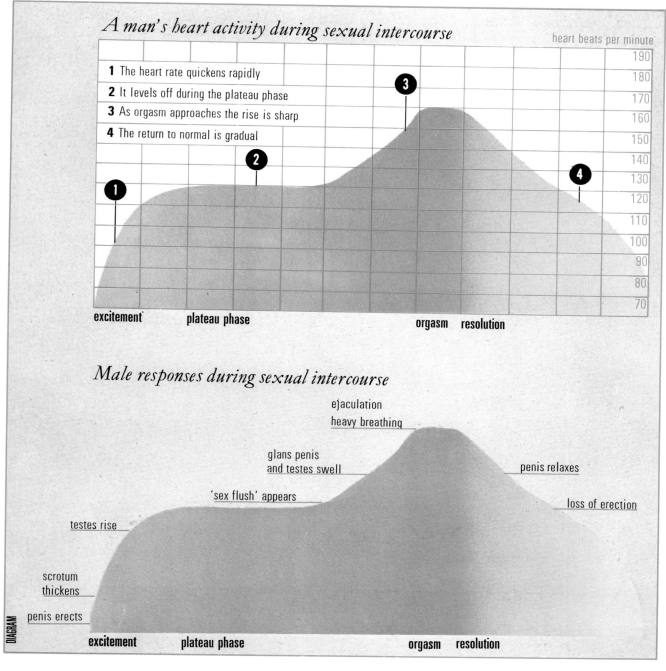

A man's heart activity during sexual intercourse

heart beats per minute

1 The heart rate quickens rapidly
2 It levels off during the plateau phase
3 As orgasm approaches the rise is sharp
4 The return to normal is gradual

190
180
170
160
150
140
130
120
110
100
90
80
70

excitement   plateau phase   orgasm   resolution

Male responses during sexual intercourse

ejaculation
heavy breathing

glans penis
and testes swell   penis relaxes

'sex flush' appears   loss of erection

testes rise

scrotum
thickens

penis erects

excitement   plateau phase   orgasm   resolution

'Coming' together

For many years the mutual orgasm was stressed in sex manuals and inevitably many people became upset when they found it difficult, if not impossible, to come together. The idea of trying to achieve this may place such a burden on both parties, especially the man, that he can never truly relax and have fun. While really skilled lovers can sometimes achieve simultaneous orgasm, inexperienced partners rarely manage it. Lovemaking can be satisfactory and fulfilling if one partner reaches a climax some time before the other as long as neither one feels he or she has 'failed' because they have not had a simultaneous orgasm.

Returning to normal

In this last stage of the orgasmic cycle, the penis gradually loses its erection and returns to normal size. Quite a few men feel tenderness in the penis and cannot bear to be touched there for a while. The testicles return to their normal size and position and the 'sex flush' disappears.

After intercourse, some men feel so drowsy that all they want to do is fall asleep. Another common reaction for some is to break out in a heavy sweat.

Masturbation

One of the most common ways to have an orgasm is by masturbation — using your hands to stimulate the genitals.

Masturbation is practised by practically all men at some time in their lives (and, recent surveys have shown, by most women). But despite its prevalence it is still disapproved of and myths linger on. It does not harm you either physically, mentally or sexually and does not leave any tell-tale marks, so people cannot tell you do it simply by looking at you. Sometimes men feel tiredness in their legs

After orgasm a man usually feels very calm and relaxed, and he may even fall asleep.

after masturbation which they don't feel after intercourse, but studies show that in some cases this might be due to the effect of deep-seated guilt feelings. Biologically there is no difference between an orgasm resulting from intercourse and one resulting from masturbation, and it is a perfectly normal and common way for a man to experience the pleasure of orgasm when sexual activity with his partner is not possible or available for some reason.

'I can't come inside my wife'

Many men, at some time, have difficulty in ejaculating inside their partners. Often, though, the problem is temporary and rights itself, but some men feel inadequate and this can affect the relationship. However, simple but effective therapy can quickly restore a man's sexual self-confidence.

One of the most common sexual problems that men share is that they are sometimes unable to achieve orgasm inside their partners — while a man can sustain erections and enter his partner's vagina, he cannot ejaculate inside her. This condition, known as retarded ejaculation, is usually temporary and clears up of its own accord, but occasionally a man will suffer for long periods.

If the problem continues without treatment, the couple's relationship can be seriously damaged, as a vicious circle is set up whereby the more the man worries about his condition, the less able he is to overcome it, and the more he sees it as a threat to their mutual happiness.

Fortunately, sexual therapy can help cure this condition and a man and his partner need not suffer any long-lasting ill effects. It was just such a situation that led John, a married man in his mid-thirties, to overcome his shyness and seek help from a therapist:

I understand you have come to see me, John, because since you were married two years ago, you have never been able to reach orgasm during normal sex. You feel aroused, have an erection and enter your wife, but after literally hours of love-making — during which she may have several orgasms — you still do not come. You tell me that though your wife caresses you with her hands and mouth, you can only have an orgasm' when you masturbate, and that your problem is damaging your relationship.

'Although she has been very understanding, my wife worries that it is her fault and that I don't find her desirable — which certainly isn't the case. Now she is

beginning to worry that we will never be able to have children. Will I always be impotent?'

You are not impotent — impotence means that a man cannot have an erection. Like yourself, a man suffering from the problem of retarded ejaculation is able to have erections, and can often sustain them for some time. Many sufferers can come when they masturbate; some can also ejaculate when caressed by a woman's hands or mouth, and some find that the problem is connected with one particular woman — with other partners they can reach orgasm without difficulty.

The causes of retarded ejaculation

'I had only one sexual relationship before I was married and I did manage to have orgasms inside my partner then. Why do you think I can't succeed with my wife?'

The commonest reason is fear of repeated failure. After it has happened once, the memory of that experience is revived every time you penetrate a woman and so you become tense. Since ejaculation requires relaxation and confidence, you find you can't manage it and a vicious circle is set up.

We should also consider carefully your relationship with your wife. Do you communicate well enough? Are you in tune with each other's sexual and emotional needs? Perhaps, without recognizing it, you resent some aspect of her behaviour or personality. You may be unconsciously punishing her for this when you have sex.

For a minority of men, there are more deep-rooted reasons, mostly psychological. For example, in common with many other sexual problems, retarded ejaculation can occur because of depression or anxiety about problems at work or with money or following bereavement.

Sexual fears

Another underlying reason for retarded ejaculation is fear of sex. Many men with this problem tell me that they have never felt sexually confident. This can date back to early childhood if their parents punished them for masturbation, or to adolescence if they were made to feel ashamed of wet dreams.

Some men never recover from an early sexual experience with a woman which left them feeling humiliated or inadequate, and they show the mental scars in the form of retarded ejaculation. And it can also be a response to the widespread male

fears about the size of the penis. Or it can be unconscious fear of the vagina itself.

Finally, there is the fear of pregnancy, even though the couple may use contraception. In the past the man may have been forced to practise withdrawal, and it may have become a habit he cannot break very easily.

Physical and chemical causes

'Could there be some physical reason for my problem?'

In your case, I doubt it — most sufferers are physically normal, though there are a few physical conditions which cause retarded ejaculation. Some

diabetic patients, or men with high blood pressure, may be slightly at risk, and the problem can occur temporarily after certain operations, but normally a doctor will warn patients about this. And a tiny group of men may be affected because the foreskin doesn't retract properly during sex — but a simple operation can remedy this.

However, as with other sexual problems, there can be chemical causes. Most men know how bad too much alcohol can be for their sexual performance. The man who drinks too much on one occasion and can't manage an orgasm that night may end up with retarded ejaculation if he loses his self-confidence. Drugs can have a similar effect. Those prescribed tranquillizers or anti-depressants sometimes find themselves affected. The simple remedy is ask your doctor for a different pill.

The only other physical conditions which can trigger retarded ejaculation are fatigue and generally poor health, but as long as the man recognizes the cause, he should not worry that the problem will persist once his health improves.

The effects on a relationship

'Does retarded ejaculation often lead to the break-up of a relationship?'

It does place a severe strain on both partners. If you cannot ejaculate you are bound to feel inadequate. Guilt that you are denying your wife the full pleasures of sex, and fear that your problem is permanent, will only add to the stress.

Most women don't worry about the occasional time when their partners cannot ejaculate inside them. And sometimes a woman will discover her potential for multiple orgasms in this way.

However, if the problem continues, the woman is likely, first of all, to blame herself — she may feel that there is something either physically or sexually wrong with her. Later, she may be afraid to initiate sex, or feel unable to mention the subject to avoid hurting her partner's feelings, but deep down she may feel resentment or a lack of respect for him. Tensions will mount if, like your partner, the wife wants to have children.

'My wife says she wants to help in order to save our marriage. What can we do?'

That's very positive, because the success of the therapy depends on the woman's sympathetic co-operation and readiness to experiment sexually.

The best way to overcome any reluctance or embarrassment she may feel is for us to have a first session altogether, where we discuss the possible reasons for your problem and I can explain to her what the therapy involves.

Your wife may feel she is 'owed' something because she has lived so long with the problem. She may find it difficult to accept that treatment must focus on your satisfaction rather than on hers. However, once I have explained that only by learning to 'give' can she help you and thereby build a fulfilling sexual relationship, I think she will be reassured.

I should emphasize that throughout the treatment you should remain sensitive to her reactions. On the sexual level, you should help her to reach orgasm by methods other than penetration whenever she wants, because she is likely to feel aroused even when you are not. On the emotional level, keep reassuring her about how desirable she is. Don't forget the gestures which make a partner feel appreciated — from flowers to surprise outings.

Sensate focussing therapy

'How does the treatment work?'

The particular treatment, which I believe will help you, is called 'sensate focussing' and was pioneered by the famous sexologists, Masters and Johnson. It is based on learning sensuality through touch, with emphasis on tender, loving communication between the partners. After the first session with you and your wife, I will ask the two of you to set aside a specific time to begin when you feel especially close to one another and can be undisturbed.

With both of you naked, your wife should massage, fondle and caress all parts of your body except for your genitals. The aim is to discover what sensations give you most pleasure. You are under no obligation to do anything except to enjoy it and communicate that enjoyment to your wife in any way you wish.

At the same time you should caress your wife; if you want to swap over to become the 'giving' rather than the 'receiving' partner you should do so. I won't give you precise instructions because, as a couple, you should discover and develop your own ways of achieving mutual pleasure.

Each day continue this exploration, extending it eventually to touching the genitals. Meanwhile we'll continue meeting to discuss how things are going and to work out your emotional problems.

Gradually you will find the sexual tension building up between you until by about the fifth day, when you are sufficiently aroused by the caressing, your wife will concentrate on your penis, stimulating it in the way you find most arousing. At this stage, many men find they are able to ejaculate while their penises are being caressed.

'Even that would be an improvement on our present state — but it's not the same as coming in my wife. When will I be able to do that?'

By this stage of the treatment — your wife caressing your penis — you will begin to identify your wife with the pleasures of ejaculation, rather than viewing her as a threat. And it shouldn't be too long before she is able to excite you to the point where you can enter her and come to orgasm. The best position for this is usually with the woman sitting over the man and moving her body to increase his excitement.

The first experience of reaching orgasm inside your wife will probably be enough to break the vicious circle. After that we will continue the therapy until you can prolong your erection so that your wife can also reach orgasm.

The beauty of this therapy is that its effects extend far beyond curing the particular problem of retarded ejaculation. Its emphasis on full and open communication of sexual needs and desires means that partners learn an entirely new and deeper approach to lovemaking.

The mutual pleasure of giving and receiving — together with the knowledge that your wife has been patient and understanding — will undoubtedly enhance your emotional relationship and produce a greater sense of security. You will be able to go on to discover together the full scope of your sexual and sensual potential.

'But will I be fully cured?'

There is no guarantee that the problem will not recur. It is possible that you may have future difficulties with your wife because of some change in your circumstances.

However, the most important thing to remember is that almost every man occasionally has problems with retarded ejaculation, and that you should not worry about it. If it does happen to you, think of it as an isolated incident, and the strong likelihood is that the problem will right itself within a short time.

Is orgasm necessary?

Some people believe they should have an orgasm every time they make love and are worried if they cannot climax, but many couples have occasional problems and these are not usually serious. However, long-term difficulties can cause unhappiness and partners may need expert help.

Is orgasm necessary?' seems a straightforward question, but there are in fact a number of possible replies. Most men would find it difficult to imagine making love without orgasm and so would be certain that orgasm was necessary. Although women are becoming increasingly aware of their sexual needs, some don't have orgasms and so might not think they were necessary. Medical experts would probably also disagree. A psychologist might say that orgasm was necessary for psychological health, while a biologist could point out that orgasm isn't necessary for a physically healthy life, and that pregnancy is possible without orgasm.

Orgasm and pregnancy

It is well known that women don't need to climax to become pregnant, though some doctors have suggested that the contractions of the womb during orgasm may create a vacuum which sucks sperm more quickly towards the egg. But some people mistakenly believe that sperm only escape from a man's penis during orgasm.

In fact, when a man is excited he produces secretions from his penis, which very often contain a small number of sperm. If his penis comes into contact at this stage with the opening of the vagina —for instance, during 'heavy petting'—sperm can reach the egg and the woman can become pregnant without even having intercourse.

Living without sex

Human beings don't need orgasm in the same way that they need food and water to survive. As far as is known, no one has ever died from a lack of orgasm—and some people lead quite

satisfactory lives without any sex at all.

Although there are few truly asexual people, there are those with such a low sex drive that they rarely, if ever, feel any desire for sex, and so don't need to make love or to masturbate to orgasm. Sometimes people who enjoy an active sex life choose to become celibate, usually for religious reasons, and live quite happily.

The need for orgasm

Although there are people who can live without any sex, the need for orgasm can't be so easily dismissed. Lack of orgasm may not result in

long-term physical problems, but some people who have an active sex life may experience discomfort if they cannot reach a climax—and, in addition, they may develop emotional and psychological problems.

How lack of orgasm affects women

When a woman is sexually excited, a number of changes take place in her body. The clitoris becomes erect. The vaginal lips (labia) enlarge and secrete various fluids. The muscles round the sex organs contract—the vagina gets longer and wider and the womb changes position, ready to receive sperm. The nipples become erect—although as arousal continues the dark areas (areola) round them swell and the nipple erection may seem to disappear—and the breasts can also change shape.

If all this physical tension is not released through orgasm, the woman can be left feeling intensely frustrated. She may have back and abdominal pains, probably due to the movement of her womb (which would have adjusted quickly after orgasm), and she may experience headache, breast pain and other discomfort. This is because her blood pressure will have risen during intercourse and will return to normal more slowly than it would have done after a climax.

Some women appear not to need orgasms, but sometimes they are in fact frustrated and this may show itself in, for example, migraines, excema and stomach ulcers or upsets. However, masturbation can relieve some of these tensions, although it is no substitute for the emotional satisfaction of having an orgasm during shared sex.

How lack of orgasm affects men

As a man becomes more sexually excited, his heart beats faster and pumps harder. Blood flows into his penis, giving him an erection. A valve closes to prevent the blood from leaving the penis before he has ejaculated. When a man has an orgasm the valve opens and the blood flows easily out of the penis. If he doesn't have an orgasm, however, the return blood flow is much slower and pressure can build up, causing a pain which affects the whole area around the genitals.

This very often happens in young men, who are probably without a partner and who become turned on very easily. If it happens in public, they can't masturbate and so have to control or retard ejaculation. One young man described seeing an attractive young woman on his way home from college and having to rush back to the privacy of his own room in 'absolute agony' to masturbate. But—as with women—masturbation may relieve physical tension yet lack the fulfillment of shared sex.

It is totally untrue that if a man doesn't have an orgasm his penis will suffer long-term damage which can only be repaired by surgery. This myth is probably based on a misunderstanding of priapism, a painful permanent erection which is treated by a simple operation. Priapism is not caused by sexual excitement—it is a symptom of an illness which can be treated.

Being a good lover

The man who can't 'come' (because he suffers from retarded ejaculation) might believe that this makes him a better lover because he can concentrate all his energies on giving his partner multiple orgasms. But, in reality, this is a sign of emotional inadequacy. A woman generally welcomes a man who can delay his orgasm until she's had hers, but with retarded ejaculation a man *never* comes, no matter how many orgasms his partner has and how much she excites him. So the woman may feel that it is somehow her fault and wonder what's wrong with her, especially as many men with this problem have little difficulty in climaxing during masturbation. Also, she may want children and her partner's virility is no compensation for a much wanted child. (For more information on retarded ejaculation, see pages 109-113.)

Sometimes lack of communication between partners can cause long-term difficulties in a relationship, especially if the man always 'comes' too soon (premature ejaculation). In this case, a woman may not be excited enough to have an orgasm, and she is left feeling very frustrated and also perhaps anxious to avoid the same experience in future. A sensitive man who wants to satisfy his partner will feel that he, too, has failed, but because some men believe that a quick orgasm is a proof of potency, they may not realize that this is a problem. Unless the woman tells her partner of her frustration, he may go on believing he is a satisfactory lover and will be mystified if she tries to avoid sex. Both partners can become increasingly resentful in this situation and their relationship may be in danger.

Outdated ideas about orgasm

Until comparatively recently, lack of orgasm in woman was not regarded as a problem. 'Decent' women were not really supposed to enjoy sex, never mind have orgasms. There is still a hangover from this view in that some men ignore foreplay, believing penetration to be the only important aspect of lovemaking. This can cause much unhappiness, especially if their partners find it difficult to discuss their sexual needs.

Women can perhaps be forgiven for thinking that today attitudes to female sexuality have swung too far the other way. If a woman doesn't have an earth-shattering climax every time she makes love, she can be made to feel she is not a 'real woman'. The truth is that the normal female orgasm can vary in the same woman from gentle ripples of pleasure to an exhausting climax.

Solving the problems

Although orgasm isn't essential for survival, it does seem to be necessary for many people's physical and mental well-being.

However, it is important to keep things in perspective. Trouble starts only when lack of orgasm constantly recurs and a person feels rejected and a sexual failure. Even then, such problems can often be solved quite quickly by an understanding partner or, in more difficult situations, by therapy at a psycho-sexual clinic.

Understanding masturbation

Although it is a subject still shrouded in guilt and 'shame', masturbation is being increasingly accepted for what it is — a harmless and, often, beneficial part of sexual activity in men and women.

Masturbation is a way of becoming sexually aroused and achieving orgasm by stimulating the genitals — or some other sensitive area of the body — without sexual intercourse. If a person masturbates alone it is known as *self-stimulation* or *auto-eroticism*. Mutual masturbation, commonly called 'heavy petting', occurs when a couple stimulate each other's genitals, either as a preliminary to intercourse, or as an alternative way of reaching orgasm.

Masturbation is a perfectly natural activity and one that is practised by men and women every-

where. Yet in the nineteenth century particularly it was denounced with almost hysterical fervour. Medical books stated that masturbation caused weakness, blindness, impotency and insanity — among other illnesses — and doctors claimed to be able to tell if a person masturbated from his or her appearance.

Although the extreme attitudes about masturbation have disappeared, there is still a tremendous burden of guilt and shame attached to the subject. In most households it is not discussed and remains a source of shame and anxiety to men and women of all ages — afraid perhaps of discovery by parents or partners. Probably most husbands and wives would not admit to masturbating privately, or would find it very difficult to talk about it with each other.

Who masturbates?

The growing awareness that masturbation is a natural and healthy urge is supported by recent American research, which shows that in spite of social stigmas and taboos, masturbation is practised by about 93 per cent of the male population and 82 per cent of the female population.

Children

Men and women vary greatly in their response to masturbation, however. Generally women begin to masturbate at a later stage than men, largely because of their physiological make-up. Whereas a girl's first experiences of masturbation may be at adolescence or after, most boys discover masturbation much earlier. Boys can have erections within a short time of birth, and although it is not certain when they are first capable of orgasm, research indicates that it coincides with the ability to have erections.

In male babies and young children an erection may be caused by an irritation of the genitals, which leads the child to rub his penis, or by the chance discovery of pleasurable sensations while playing with the penis; erections due to sexual tension or desire occur only after puberty. Although baby boys are able to reach orgasm, conscious masturbation does not begin until after the age of five and ejaculation cannot take place until after puberty. The fact that boys have their sexual organs visible, and are made aware of this source of pleasure by spontaneous erections, makes masturbation common among boys under 10 years old.

Girls, whose genitals are more hidden, and lack the unavoidable 'signal' of an erection, are on the whole less curious about their genitals. Even though almost half of all girls have had 'exploring' games with boys or other girls before the age of 10, deliberate masturbation is much less common than it is among boys. Often girls discover masturbation by rubbing the vaginal lips because of genital irritation and find that pleasurable sensations result. Frequently, girls experience their first orgasm quite accidently — while riding a bicycle, for instance, or while involved in sport — and then afterwards try to reproduce the sensations by themselves.

For children, the repetition of any pleasurable experience is natural and, unless they have been discovered and reprimanded by angry adults, they will continue to masturbate quite instinctively. All too often, however, the idea that masturbation is a 'dirty' habit and that it is wicked to do it or enjoy it is planted in the child's mind early on by his parents and tends to colour the child's whole future view of sexual activity. Even the most liberal parents would probably experience a sense of shock on coming upon their 'innocent' seven or eight year old, red-faced from the effort of masturbation.

But even if the adults are careful not to give the child the impression that masturbation is wrong, they are still left with the problem of explaining it is not a thing to do in public. The attitude most likely to encourage a guilt-free and healthy outlook in the child is to avoid extreme reactions of any kind and give the matter as little emphasis as possible.

Puberty and after

With puberty, the difference between male and female responses continues. For men, masturbation is no longer merely a pleasant sensation, but a necessary relief of sexual tension; sexual arousal brings with it an intense urge to reach climax and ejaculation. Even after adolescence, the link between a girl's sexual arousal and the desire to reach orgasm is far less direct and urgent, and so the temptation to masturbate is less. The difference is reflected in the speed with which men and women respond to sexual arousal — the average man takes between two and five minutes to reach a climax, whereas the average woman takes from 10 to 15 minutes. Masturbation accounts for the first experience of orgasm and ejaculation for two-thirds of all boys, but only just over one-third of women experience their first orgasm in this way.

Throughout adolescence, masturbation continues to be the main sexual outlet for 99 per cent of all boys. As experience of sexual intercourse increases towards the late teens, masturbation is practised less frequently, although it still accounts for between five and ten per cent of a married man's sexual outlet. However, as masturbation in men declines with age, it increases in women until a peak is reached between the ages of 40 and 50.

The techniques of masturbation

The ways which men and women use to stimulate themselves vary, as individuals usually discover for themselves the best, quickest and most pleasurable means of achieving orgasm. Most ways, however, are variations of a few basic methods. The essential requirements for satisfying — rather than frustrating — masturbation are privacy and time. Without these, any benefits that masturbation can bring — in terms of relaxation and greater knowledge of one's own sexual responses — will probably be lost.

The usual method for a man is to take hold of his penis with one, or both hands and rub it up and down vigorously with a stroking movement until orgasm is reached. The most common alternative is to grasp the penis between two fingers and a thumb. And of course there are variations in the part of the penis concentrated on, the speed of hand movement and degree of pressure exerted. Sometimes, men masturbate lying on their stomachs and, by thrusting with their buttocks, rub the penis against the bed or pillow.

When a woman masturbates, she does so in most cases by rubbing one or more fingers around and over her clitoris, while lying on her back or stomach. As too much direct pressure on the clitoris can be painful, the woman might prefer to rub the vaginal lips or press them together. Some women find that by squeezing their thighs together, crossing their legs and tensing their muscles, orgasm can be achieved.

Quite a number of women rub the area surrounding the clitoris up and down on a smooth hard area such as the edge of a door or the rim of a bath, or an object such as a candle or vase. A few women reach orgasm by placing a pillow, a rolled towel or scarf between the legs, pulling it up tightly between the vaginal lips and buttocks and rocking to and fro.

Mutual masturbation

Mutual masturbation between a man and a woman leading up to sexual intercourse is probably the most common method of foreplay, arousing excitement and tension in both partners. Even men and women who might draw back from stimulating their own genitals find 'heavy petting' a fairly natural preliminary to intercourse. Usually the masturbation is carried out simultaneously, with the couple stroking or rubbing each other's genitals, but sometimes it is carried out orally, with the genitals being aroused by the partner's mouth and tongue. For some couples, oral and manual masturbation to the point of orgasm is also enjoyed at times. If both partners are willing to do this, and enjoy it, it can certainly be helpful to the relationship, especially when intercourse is impractical.

The uses of masturbation

Far from causing physical and moral decay, masturbation can be an important means of maintaining physical and mental health and well-being. For couples masturbation can be helpful in solving difficulties where one partner is ill, or disabled, or when there is a temporary separation for some reason. It is also helpful at times when the couple are together but intercourse is impractical — during the woman's menstruation, during later months of pregnancy or during the period after childbirth.

Masturbation can be useful as a learning experience, particularly for adolescent boys and girls, teaching them to recognize and control their sexual responses which will make for better relationships later. For women, especially those who find it difficult to reach orgasm through intercourse, learning to masturbate and reach orgasm successfully can bring them sexual satisfaction for the first time.

Orgasm can be a learned response to lovemaking and so those women who already know what is needed for them to reach orgasm can help and guide their partners to bring them the same pleasure.

Solitary masturbation can, for men and women, be the most simple, certain and undemanding sexual outlet. But for most normal men and women it would never be more than a substitute for sexual intercourse because of the huge emotional dimension which makes sex within a relationship fuller and more satisfying.

Seen in its proper place, as a way of providing relief from tension, as a means of satisfaction for those unable to have intercourse within a relationship, or as an enjoyable part of a sexual relationship, masturbation is a normal and healthy part of human sexuality which should be accepted and enjoyed.

'I only get orgasms from masturbation, not from sex.'

Many women are unable to reach orgasm with their partners, and this can cause much anxiety, but a thorough understanding of female sexual needs can help solve the problem.

The woman who only has orgasms from masturbation, not from shared sex, often fears that she is frigid and a sexual failure. In fact, she suffers from a very common problem affecting between half and three-quarters of all women at some time in their lives. Only a tiny minority are truly frigid — incapable of any sexual feelings at all. The vast majority of women enjoy sex; but they do not always experience the release of orgasm as their partners do — and the pleasure of their orgasms from masturbation makes them all the more aware of what they are missing in failing to climax during sexual intercourse.

Being sexually stimulated without having orgasm is physically and emotionally frustrating, and both partners may feel cheated of the mutual enjoyment which should come from sex. But with a proper understanding of both partners' sexual responses, ways can be found to overcome the problem, as 25-year-old Jane discovered when she talked to a sexual therapist:

In my experience, your problem is by no means uncommon. More than half of my patients have similar histories. Many can't admit the problem to their partners and pretend they have orgasms.

Your case is fairly typical in that you have had intercourse since you were 19, but now you are

finding sex increasingly frustrating because you never have orgasms. Although you resort to secret masturbation — especially after unsatisfactory sex — you nevertheless feel you are missing something. Your guilt feelings that you are not a 'proper woman' only make the problem worse, especially if your partners feel they are bad lovers because they cannot give you orgasms.

'Do you think that the reason I can't have orgasms during sex is that I masturbate?'

It is possible that you feel guilty about masturbating, and this sets up a psychological barrier to your fulfillment with a partner. Unfortunately, some people still believe that masturbation is harmful and 'dirty' — even though most doctors consider it harmless, even beneficial in relieving tension. Your guilt about sex may stem from your parents' attitude towards it when you were a child. In fact, masturbation is the natural way we learn about our own sexuality. Indeed, for people without regular sexual partners it is a necessary form of release; even those with perfectly satisfactory sex lives may masturbate for the different sensations it gives them from time to time.

Far from feeling guilty, you should take encouragement from your ability to reach orgasm through masturbation. This shows that there is no physical barrier to your sexual fulfillment, and it means that you have learnt to understand your own sexual needs and responses. The woman who can masturbate successfully has a better chance of enjoying shared sex.

Fear of sharing

'Does this mean that, even if I manage to have orgasms during sex, I might still prefer masturbating?'

Some women feel more relaxed and more in control when masturbating, so they say they prefer it to sex. But it is important to separate various forms of sexual enjoyment. Masturbation is essentially a solitary act, and cannot be a substitute for sex with a partner. When you make love with someone else, you are sharing pleasure. Part of that pleasure is to enjoy his climax and for him to enjoy yours. But there are also other pleasures, which masturbation cannot give you, such as caressing each other's bodies, oral sex, and the intimacy of penetration. Above all, there is the emotional bond created by shared sex.

Fear of this emotional bond is very often the reason why a woman can't have orgasms during sex. Orgasm requires complete relaxation and a feeling of trust in your partner. Many women unconsciously fear that if they 'let go' they will become vulnerable and lose their partners' respect. They do not realize that surrendering themselves to the sensations of the moment allows them to respond, releasing their potential for orgasm.

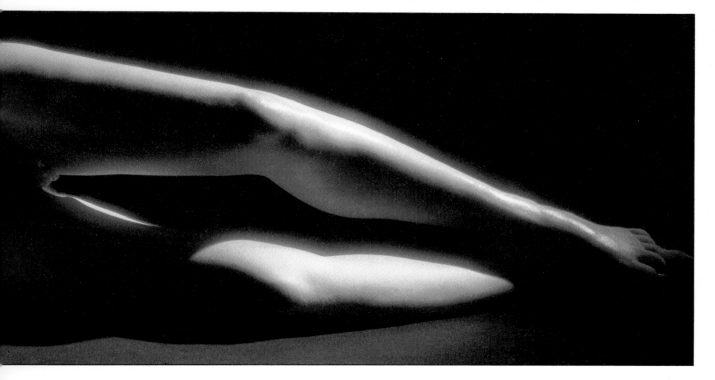

Fear of penetration

'*You have mentioned some of the psychological barriers to orgasm during sex. Are there also physical barriers?*'

A woman's sexual response is so complex that it's very difficult to separate physical and psychological causes. There are some women, for example, who have a psychological fear of penetration. They can have a physical reaction known as 'vaginismus' — where the muscles of the vagina tighten up and make penetration very painful. These women need expert therapy, preferably together with their partners' understanding and support.

A woman who fears penetration will find it very hard to have orgasms during sex. Her vagina will be unable to produce the lubrication necessary for the penis to enter easily, so penetration may result in soreness. Using a lubricating jelly will help to prevent the soreness, but it won't overcome the tension which causes the problem.

Fear of penetration should be considered in two ways. Firstly, you should try to understand what causes the fear: guilt feelings about sex, unhappy experiences, worry about pregnancy and so on. Secondly, you must think carefully about what actually happens when you have sex and try to pinpoint the problem areas. Try and decide whether your difficulties are rooted in physical or emotional problems and how you can overcome them.

'*Since I can have orgasms through masturbation, is it possible that I am one of those women who has sexual feelings only in my clitoris rather than in my vagina?*'

This could be the key to the problem. Even the experts can't agree whether there is such a thing as a pure 'vaginal orgasm', or whether the female orgasm is mainly dependent on stimulation of the clitoris. However, there is no doubt that clitoral stimulation is essential, and that the vaginal sensations women experience during sex are directly connected with the degree of clitoral excitement.

Nevertheless, the vagina is far from insensitive. A woman can feel powerful sensations when her partner's penis or fingers stroke the walls of her vagina, or when the penis pushes high up into the vagina against the cervix, the opening to the womb. But this depends on her being sufficiently aroused beforehand. Most of the women I have treated find that some form of clitoral stimulation is necessary before they are able to achieve orgasm with their partners.

'*But isn't that just the same as asking your partner to masturbate you?*'

Some women do have this embarrassed response. But think carefully: when you make love, you almost certainly spend some time caressing your partner's penis with your hands or perhaps your mouth. I'm sure that, far from objecting, he finds it very exciting. Yet the clitoris is every bit as important to a woman's sexual fulfillment as the penis is to a man's.

The first step towards helping yourself have orgasms in sex is to concentrate on foreplay. Bear in mind that men and women have different patterns of sexual response. Men become aroused and reach orgasm far more quickly than women. Indeed, it is not surprising that so many women fail to achieve orgasm when some men neglect foreplay, and climax too quickly, leaving their partners feeling sexually frustrated.

'*How can this be avoided?*'

A couple should work towards harmonizing the pace of their sexual reactions. Don't rush into lovemaking, take time to explore each other's bodies and find out what excites you. Encourage your partner to explore your sexual organs, and use the knowledge of your own body gained through masturbation. Many men know the clitoris is important, but they don't know exactly how to stimulate it correctly. If your clitoris responds best to gentle stroking, you may lose all sensation if your man rubs it roughly; or you may prefer him instead to stroke the lips of your genitals or your pubic mound. Confide what you want to your partner; he will find it exciting to be shown how you masturbate.

Oral sex is a highly enjoyable form of clitoral stimulation, particularly if you take your partner's penis in your mouth at the same time as he licks and sucks you. Some couples regularly achieve orgasm together like this; and some women find they can have orgasms during oral sex or other foreplay — which relax them sufficiently to go on to have more when they are penetrated.

Finding the right position

When you are ready for penetration, you will feel your vagina moistening. It can be made more sensitive if your partner feels inside it with his fingers, and spreads lubrication on to your clitoris.

When he enters you, you may want him to continue touching your clitoris until you reach orgasm. But some women find that, with sufficient foreplay, the movement of the pelvis alone will continue to stimulate them.

You may find that certain lovemaking positions intensify your enjoyment, and you should experiment to find those which suit you. Try sitting astride your partner, as in that position you can control the movements to suit your own needs, with the hood of the clitoris rubbing against the base of the penis, or with your partner caressing it.

Your partner should try not to move too quickly so that he matches his rhythm to yours, but if he has an orgasm and you don't, there's no reason to give up. After he has relaxed from climax, he can help you achieve yours either through masturbation or oral sex.

You can also train your vaginal muscles to increase your own and your partner's pleasure, by contracting them gently when his penis is inside you. This will heighten the stimulation and sexual

pleasure you get from penetration.

Although you need your partner's help and understanding, you must not allow yourself to become passive. While he is stimulating you, you can be caressing him and suggesting positions and techniques. Some partners occasionally leave out penetration altogether and simply masturbate each other to orgasm using hands, showers, vibrators and whatever else excites them.

'*Sometimes, when I've despaired of ever having an orgasm in sex, I've felt, what do orgasms during sex matter anyway?*'

There is perhaps too much social pressure to achieve orgasm. But there are very few people who don't find it hard to have orgasms at some time. We should recognize that sex can be enjoyable without them, because of the emotional aspects. There is so much more to sex than the orgasm itself.

Nevertheless, a normal healthy adult does need the release from sexual tension that orgasm brings.

The knowledge that they can give each other orgasms generally enhances a couple's sexual and emotional relationship.

There is also a physical reason why sexual stimulation should not always end in frustration. Once a man is sexually aroused, he usually finds it easy to have an orgasm; but an unsatisfied woman can remain aroused for some time. What happens physically is that her sexual organs become congested with blood, and without the release of orgasm she may experience discomfort or pain.

But, of course, what is most at stake is the psychological relationship between the couple. If the man achieves orgasm and sees his partner left unsatisfied, it is hard for him not to feel inadequate and for his pleasure not to be undermined. However much a woman may enjoy her partner's climax, she must inevitably feel resentful if she never experiences similar fulfillment. Both partners will end up blaming themselves and each other. Fortunately this problem can be easily solved if you adopt the methods I have suggested.

Sexual dysfunction

Sexual dysfunction — the name for serious, long-term sexual problems — can cause much unhappiness. Today we are beginning to understand how a wide variety of personal anxieties can affect an individual's sex life.

All men and women experience dissatisfaction with their sex life at some time. This is quite normal. But when a sexual problem is persistent and a cause of great concern, they are said to be suffering from sexual dysfunction.

What causes it?

Sexual dysfunction will usually occur for psychological reasons, but in a few cases the cause is physical. Any disease which limits movement will obviously affect the ability to make love, an essentially physical activity. People suffering from paralysis from birth or because of an accident or stroke may need special help to achieve sexual satisfaction.

Although impotence is usually caused by anxiety, it can also result from damage to certain nerves caused by severe diabetes or from taking certain drugs.

The fear of hereditary disease being passed on to a child may also inhibit sexual intercourse. Genetic counselling — advice about the amount of risk there is of a certain disease being passed on — is now available to couples who are worried in this way, and a doctor can arrange it.

However, anxiety about personal sexuality is by far the greatest cause of sexual dysfunction. It is important to understand what a great influence attitudes, prejudices and fears about ourselves have on the ability to enjoy sex, and to some extent we are all burdened with this kind of psychological 'excess baggage' which we've picked up during the course of our lives. While there is no real way to erase the experiences that give rise to debilitating anxieties over sex, trying to face up to' and understand what has caused them — and how groundless these fears are — is the best way back to a healthy and enjoyable sexual relationship.

The variety of anxiety-producing situations is as wide as the variety of human experience. The following case histories, briefly related by a doctor involved in psychosexual counselling, illustrate the many causes of this anxiety and the ways in which it is manifested in sexual problems.

If you recognize yourself, you will know you are not alone — one of the greatest fears of those who have sexual problems. Many people with sexual problems feel they are 'freaks' in some way and feel the problem is too private to talk about.

Inability to 'let go'

Stella complained to her doctor that her marriage was not going well, that she and her husband were tetchy with each other, that he always wanted sex but she couldn't be bothered.

She had been married a year and worked as a secretary. Before she was married she lived at home where her mother did all the housework and even washed her clothes for her. She had had a good social life and when she met her husband Brian, they went on holiday together where she had enjoyed making love, although she never reached a climax.

After marriage, she kept her job but did all the cooking and housework — cleaning almost became an obsession. Her husband had also lived at home before he was married, and although Stella worked, Brian expected her to do all the household chores.

Stella's sex life rapidly deteriorated: at first she was simply unhappy that she couldn't have a climax but later didn't want to make love at all.

When she came to his surgery, the doctor allowed her time to discuss her feelings: her resentment at the drudgery of marriage and at her husband's ability to enjoy lovemaking much more than she. She learned, through the discussion, that her obsession with efficiency — her strong desire to keep the house spotless and her standard of perfection in her job — was because she felt she had to prove herself to her parents. She was not allowing herself to have fun, to lose control and experience orgasm.

Once she had come to terms with this, she was, in time, able to climax. Her husband became less aggressively demanding — now he felt he could make his wife happy he was content to make love when they *both* felt like it.

Anxiety over performance

Johnny was impotent and, as he and his wife, Jenny, wanted a child, they went to see their doctor. Both had had a strict religious upbringing. His parents pushed him hard to succeed academically but he failed his exams to get into college. He married and came to live in London.

As a teenager, Johnny had had erections and masturbated but always felt very guilty. Sex before marriage was out of the question, although he had experienced erections when he and Jenny kissed and cuddled.

On his honeymoon, he had a partial erection and failed to penetrate Jenny. When they were settled in their flat, his erections returned and they were pleased to find they could make love successfully. However, when Jenny did not conceive she went to see a doctor who suggested tests, some of

which involved having intercourse on certain nights — and Johnny became impotent again.

Again, Johnny was encouraged to discuss his feelings with the doctor. He realized there were two causes of the anxiety which had led to his impotence. First was his fear of failure, which was brought about by his strict upbringing: he had lost his confidence when he failed his exams and later when he had an 'unsuccessful' honeymoon — and this had returned when Jenny failed to conceive. Secondly, he felt guilty about masturbating in his youth and feared this had damaged his sexual ability.

When Johnny understood these feelings he realized his anxiety was unnecessary — that failing exams was not the worst thing in the world, that masturbation was perfectly natural and that his manhood was not in doubt because he had temporarily suffered from impotence.

As his anxiety waned, his potency returned; Jenny became pregnant and his self-confidence grew, helping him to make good progress in both his career and his marriage.

Sexuality and motherhood

Eleanor complained to her doctor that the Pill was making her 'frigid' that she was 'as cold as a fish'. She had been on the Pill for three years and had hoped to stop taking it and have a baby but found that she and her husband could not afford it.

Her lack of interest in sex was improved by talking with the doctor; Eleanor came to understand that her 'frigidity' was not due to the Pill but because of her sadness at not being able to have a baby. Subconsciously, she was associating making love so strongly with the desire to have a

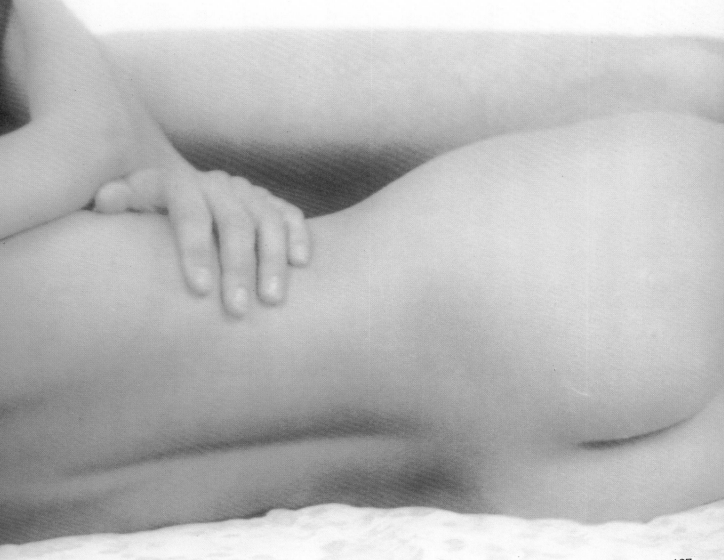

child that she had been rejecting the idea of having sex when she was using a safe contraceptive.

In the opposite situation, another patient, Emily, was referred to a special psychosexual problem clinic after she had complained to her doctor of pain during intercourse, nine months after her baby was born. But her post-natal examination had been normal, her stitches were well healed and there was no tenderness around her vagina.

Before she gave birth, Emily enjoyed working; she and her husband had plenty of money and a good social life; she spent money on fashionable clothes. Before the baby, the couple had made love whenever they felt like it but when Emily became pregnant she believed — quite wrongly — that

intercourse would harm the baby so they stopped. And since the birth they had only made love twice because she said it was painful.

With the presence of the baby, Emily's life had radically changed — her whole day and parts of the night were taken up caring for it. She no longer went out with her husband and she felt drab because she could not afford new clothes. She felt her vagina had been damaged and needed to be protected.

During a long chat with her doctor, she began to understand that subconsciously she believed her femininity had been spoilt by childbirth; that making love was not 'right' for a mother. Her feelings about sex were improved when she came to realize that her vagina had completely healed

and that it was perfectly possible to be a fully sexual woman *and* mother.

Feelings of inadequacy

Joe told his doctor that he 'came too quickly', what doctors call premature ejaculation.

His background history revealed that he had lived with his parents until he was 35 and had been too shy to ask out any young woman and form a sexual relationship. He had always been frightened of women but also felt a need to please and make himself useful to them.

When a close male friend of his died, leaving a widow, Sally, and several children, her need for support overcame his shyness and he asked her to marry him, which she did.

After he moved into her house, she was always busy with the children and they had little time on their own. He enjoyed making love to her but always 'came' too quickly. Sally became disappointed that they never made love long enough for her to experience a climax and she became irritable, occasionally comparing Joe with her former husband.

Through expressing his thoughts to the doctor, Joe realized that it was his own feeling of inadequacy, hidden by his urge to be 'the strong supportive one', that was causing his premature ejaculation. Just recognizing these anxieties made him see how silly they were and that Sally didn't love him simply because he supported the children but as a person in his own right who was allowed to have weaknesses and needs of his own. In time, as he developed confidence and learned to regard himself as someone loveable, he was able to maintain an erection for longer periods.

Fear of penetration

Susan, who had been on the Pill for years, and who had always avoided having an internal examination, finally burst into tears when her doctor began to insist that she have one to safeguard her health.

As her doctor waited quietly, she began to tell her story. She had been married for almost a year and although she enjoyed being kissed and caressed, and both she and her husband had been able to reach a climax through mutual masturbation, when he tried to have intercourse with her she froze up and pushed him away saying she was too small. Her husband, a quiet, gentle person, had since become afraid of upsetting her and now kept his distance from her in bed.

Over the next few weeks, she had regular discussion sessions with the doctor. She gradually overcame her shyness and described what had led up to this fear of penetration.

Her mother had been a prim person, never allowing her daughter to get herself untidy or dirty. She learned about the 'facts of life' through friends and magazines and believed sexual intercourse to be unpleasant. As a teenager, visiting her doctor for a vaginal discharge, his insensitive remark, 'Relax, you'll have difficulty when you're married' confirmed her suspicions that she was too small for intercourse, as did the inability to insert a sanitary tampon later on.

Relating these experiences and describing her fears helped her relax enough to accept an internal examination and finally, to her delight, to have full sexual intercourse.

The tightening of the vagina which Susan experienced is called vaginismus and sufferers almost always believe they are alone in experiencing it, although it is quite common. In the past it was thought to be due to a rigid hymen — a crescent-shaped piece of skin across the vagina entrance — but this is extremely rare and the usual reason for a woman's vagina being too tight is a basic fear of sexual intercourse.

Treatment

The treatment described in these cases is called psychosomatic therapy, which simply means that the doctor talks to patients at length and helps them to understand their anxieties and thus eventually solve the sexual problem. Other treatment includes behavioural techniques, in which the doctor not only discusses the sexual problem with the couple but suggests ways in which they can 'relearn' their sexual behaviour. For example, the doctor may suggest the couple kiss and caress each other at set times without actually having sexual intercourse — so that they can learn more about each other's bodies without the anxieties caused by penetration.

This treatment does not provide a quick, magical cure, however. Some deep-rooted anxieties require every bit of patience, honesty, determination and understanding an individual or couple can bring to bear. But the rewards speak for themselves, and the techniques of open communication, once learned, go a long way towards sweeping away groundless fears and ensuring they will never regain their grip.

Gay Relationships

There are many myths associated with homosexual and lesbian lovemaking, but gay sexuality is very similar to that of heterosexuals, though there are also important differences. A problem unique to gay relationships is the weight of social disapproval which they may encounter, even in today's more liberal climate of opinion. This can make it difficult for gays to accept their own sexuality, or to admit to family and friends that they are gay.

Homosexual love

Many people do not know what two men do when they make love together. The subject is so often treated with distaste and disapproval that people do not realize that homosexuals can have sincere and lasting relationships.

Attitudes to homosexuality, and the feelings that homosexuals have about themselves, depend largely on the social and historical circumstances of the times they live in. The development of their sexuality will vary according to the degree of toleration or rejection they experience, and although the initial sexual impulse will probably be the same in all cases, there will be a marked difference in how the person feels about himself, how others react to him and what kind of life he can lead.

Homosexuality and the law

The legal position of homosexuals differs from country to country. In England, for example, homosexual relationships involving anal intercourse (inserting the penis into the partner's anus) are not illegal between consenting adults as long as they are 21 or over, conduct themselves in private, and are not members of the armed services or merchant navy. In Scotland, Northern Ireland and Eire, however, such active sexual relationships between men are still illegal. The age of consent

varies, too, according to the country — being as young as 10 in Hungary and as old as 23 in Spain. Although homosexuality is illegal in most Australian states, the relatively liberal social climate of that country tends to foster a tolerant attitude to homosexuals.

Changing social attitudes

As social attitudes change, homosexuality is less likely to be considered a perversion, but even in the most tolerant societies there can still be problems of 'coming out' or admitting to it in the heterosexual or 'straight' world. Many young people feel confused when they hear things about 'queers' or 'gays' and what they do in bed. In countries where sexual relations between men are legal most schools still do not counsel sixth-formers about homosexuality, and sex education is invariably slanted towards heterosexual needs.

Many gays begin their sexual development without any knowledge about how to enjoy their sexual experiences to the full or how to avoid venereal diseases.

A commonly held misconception is that gays indulge in dangerous and perverted sexual practices, but of course gays cannot do anything in bed that cannot also be done between a man and a woman. Some homosexual lovemaking practices may seem offensive to heterosexuals and even to gays at first, but lovemaking can take place in just as intense an atmosphere of personal involvement as with heterosexual partners and the exploration of each others' bodies is as exciting to gays as it is to straights.

Homosexual lovemaking techniques

Homosexuals spend as much time enjoying foreplay — kissing, cuddling and touching each other's bodies — as do heterosexuals. Since both partners are of the same sex, communication is often closer than in heterosexual lovemaking as each partner knows from personal experience which areas best respond to special caresses.

Personal hygiene is as vitally important in male gay sex as it is in sexual activity between men and

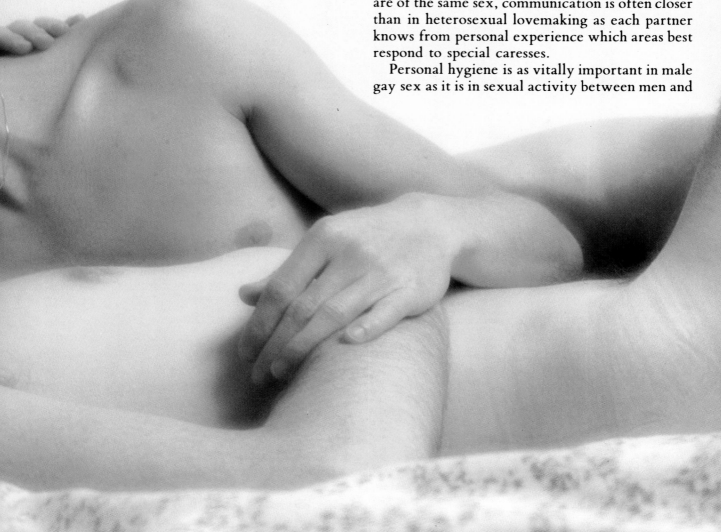

women. A thorough wash and a douche with warm water helps, and many gays prefer to empty the bowels if anal intercourse is going to be part of lovemaking.

Male homosexuals use manual stimulation, oral contact and anal penetration to bring each other to orgasm. Mutual masturbation between men can be very intense and is the simplest and easiest technique. First-time sexual encounters between gays usually consist of mutual masturbation while kissing, cuddling and exploring each other's body.

Oral sex

Most men have a very sensitive glans — the head of the penis which is covered by the foreskin — and sucking and licking it is usually all that is required to reach orgasm. Deeper penetration of the penis into the mouth must be undertaken carefully to make sure that the receiving partner does not gag if the tip of the penis should touch the back of his throat. With practice, many gay men are able to relax the throat muscles sufficiently to let their partner's penis into the back of the throat, and of course many women can do this as well.

The position called 'soixante-neuf' or '69' — when both partners suck and lick each other's genitals — is popular among homosexuals and of course with heterosexuals, too. It can be performed with one partner lying down and with the other on top of him, or with both men lying on their sides. Many men prefer this position as equal emphasis is given to both partners, unlike anal intercourse where there is usually an element of role playing — one partner is passive and the other takes the active role.

One partner may enjoy having his testicles gently fondled while his penis is being sucked; another may enjoy having his anus stimulated by his partner's fingers. Much depends on their personal desires, and as two men get to know each other they will develop mutually pleasurable techniques. Quite a lot of men, whether they are gay or not, have sensitive nipples and like them to be stimulated, either with the tongue or fingers.

Passive and active partners

It is difficult to know what percentage of gay men have anal intercourse, but it is rare to find a gay who is exclusively passive or active. Quite often he may be both in the same session, or vary between one and the other over a period of time and in different relationships.

Two rings of muscles, called sphincters are sited

at the opening to and just inside the anus. They are normally closed to prevent waste products being released involuntarily. The outer sphincter can be relaxed or tensed at will, but the inner one is less under conscious control. However, homosexual men learn to relax both these muscles, to avoid pain during anal intercourse, and most men find that the muscles relax if they are at ease with their partners. When the penis has passed through the two sphincters it reaches the rectum, which is wide and does not register pain.

Applying jelly to the penis of the active partner and the anus of the passive partner can be an extremely pleasurable part of foreplay, and stimulation of the anal sphincter will help to relax the muscle so that entry is made more easily.

The passive partner in anal intercourse usually experiences intense pleasure which is partly due to the erotic sensitivity of the anus (which is familiar to many heterosexuals also) and partly because his partner's penis tends to rub against his prostate gland, which is near the rectum. Stimulation of the prostate seems to produce an especially prolonged and intense orgasm. During orgasm the anus automatically tightens and puts pressure on the penis inside it, so intensifying the pleasure of the active partner.

The right position is important for anal intercourse, especially if the passive man is inexperienced. Gay men use as many different positions as heterosexuals — these depend on the skill and imagination of the partners and the best ones are those that occur spontaneously.

The easiest and most comfortable position is for the passive partner to be on his hands and knees and to be entered from behind. This enables the active man to stimulate his partner's penis with his hands, in time with his thrusts, and helps the anus to relax while maintaining a high level of excitement.

Dangers to health

Many homosexuals have lots of partners over the years and venereal disease is always a danger if

people are sexually active, especially in a small social group. Most homosexuals go to a VD clinic for a check-up at least every six months. This is essential as VD is prevalent in the gay scene.

If a gay man has an infection in his penis this is usually immediately noticeable as any discharge is painful. However, inflammation or infection of the anus can often go unnoticed and an examination with a *proctoscope* — an instrument used to examine the inside of the rectum — can reveal the presence of infection. These checks should only be carried out by qualified medical staff who will probably make a VD test as well.

Secondary stage syphilis can develop in gay men who have been infected without noticing any symptoms. There is also the possibility of developing haemorrhoids or 'piles' if anal sex is undertaken without due care and the passive partner finds it difficult to relax — the veins

supplying blood to the sphincter become inflamed and protrude from the muscle tissue of the anus. Often haemorrhoids are only mildly uncomfortable, but severe cases can be very painful. However, doctors can provide treatment.

A loving sexual relationship

There are many out-of-date myths associated with male homosexuality, but nowadays most people tolerate gays. It is generally accepted that what takes place in a loving sexual relationship between two people — whether they are gay or heterosexual — is for the couple alone to decide.

Lesbian love

Lesbian sex is so often used as a 'turn-on' in some men's magazines that many people have very mistaken ideas of what gay women do when they make love. In fact, lesbian lovemaking is not very different to heterosexual lovemaking and the object is the same — mutual pleasure for both partners.

The popular picture of a lesbian relationship is that of the 'butch dyke' who has set up house with a more feminine lesbian in a parody of the traditional heterosexual marriage. There may be couples like this — in the same way that stereotyped heterosexual marriages exist — but lesbian relationships are, generally, very varied. Some are purely physical affairs lasting for a comparatively short time while others are long-term relationships in which the partners share their lives.

Whatever the depth or permanence of their relationships, the aim of many gay women is a partnership of complete physical and emotional equality. They want to relate to and support each other without role playing and become free to develop and define themselves as people and not as stereotypes.

Techniques of lesbian lovemaking

Some lesbians have argued — correctly in some cases — that penetration is overemphasized in heterosexual and male homosexual lovemaking, and that it is unnecessary for one gay woman to be active and her partner passive when they make love. In lesbian sex, therefore, foreplay and oral sex are usually more important than any form of penetration.

It has also been suggested that the pleasures of lesbian sex can be greater than those experienced by heterosexuals. It can be very difficult for a man and woman to understand each other's sexual needs and responses — for instance, a man may ignore his partner's clitoris because he believes she feels her orgasm in her vagina. Unless they can discuss their lovemaking — and some couples are too embarrassed ever to do this — they may never truly realize each other's needs. On the other hand, partners of the same sex can more easily understand each other's desires. If a woman has masturbated or made love before, she will know what excites her and will realize that, in general, the same things are likely to turn on her partner. Of course, a particular caress may not necessarily be similarly exciting for both women, and lesbians, like any other couple, need time to get to know each other, but their lovemaking is based on shared experience of the female body.

The importance of foreplay

Foreplay is the most important and exciting part of lovemaking for many gay — and heterosexual — women. It includes not only hugging, kissing, touching and caressing each other, but also the creation of a warm, secure environment for love, perhaps by sharing a meal or a drink, listening to music or talking quietly together, dancing, bathing or giving each other body massage. Like some straight couples, gay women can find that reading erotic books or looking at some kinds of pornographic pictures with their partners can also help to create the right atmosphere for sex.

By holding and hugging each other, gay women can create a feeling of intimacy and closeness. Pressing their bodies together can be arousing for both partners, and some women can be turned on if one brushes against the thighs and breasts of the other while dancing.

Most women find that their breasts and nipples are very sensitive and can give them a great deal of pleasure if they are caressed during lovemaking. Sucking, kissing or stroking the nipples will make them harder and more responsive, while cupping the whole breast in the hand, gently pressing and rotating, can be very exciting. One partner using her nipples to caress the other's breasts and genitals can be arousing for both.

Being able to use the breasts in this way does not mean that lesbian women ignore the rest of the body — the whole body is capable of giving and receiving pleasure. Kissing, stroking, nibbling and lightly pinching the body all over is exciting, as are light caresses down the spine, on the inside of the arms and thighs, and across the stomach. Some women also find that the nape of the neck, behind the ears, across the palms and behind the knees are also very sensitive and responsive to light stroking, nibbling and kissing.

Reaching orgasm

Once aroused, the women can stroke each other to orgasm. Gently stroking round the outside of the vulva or playing with the pubic hair and using it to lift the lips of the vulva up and down will usually stimulate the entire area. The partners can then go on to caress the inside of the vulva and round the clitoris to bring each other to orgasm.

Gay women use several methods for this, depending on their own and their partners' preferences. Gently pulling and shaking the clitoris, tap-

ping it with the fingers, or squeezing it between the lips of the vulva can all result in orgasm. If the partners lie side by side, one can put her first finger and thumb into her lover's vagina in such a way that she touches the clitoris. Regular in-out movements in this position will bring her lover to orgasm.

With practice, gay women find that one or both partners can have an orgasm when one lies on top of the other so that either their vulvas rub each other's thighs, or so that their genitals are in direct contact. If the lovers move together rhythmically, both can reach orgasm.

Orgasm can occur at any time during lovemaking, depending on the responsiveness of both partners, and several orgasms are by no means uncommon.

Oral sex

Many lesbian couples use oral sex in foreplay to achieve orgasm and positions such as 'sixty-nine' in which both partners can enjoy oral sex are as popular as they are with heterosexuals.

A woman can begin by lightly kissing her part-

Even in countries where lesbianism is legal it is still very difficult to admit to being a gay woman. With the gay rights movement, however, more and more women are taking pride in their sexuality and are no longer willing to be regarded as 'unnatural' or somehow second class.

Another problem that lesbian women experience is that they cannot assume that all other women are potential partners, and so many have found that going to lesbian groups and gay bars and clubs has been useful in helping them over any feelings of emotional or sexual isolation.

Coming out can take many forms. Some women are concerned only to be honest with their friends and families; others feel they should become

ner's stomach and thighs, gradually working towards her partner's genitals. She can then open the lips of her lover's vulva, kissing and stroking inside round the lips and clitoris, occasionally putting her tongue deep into her lover's vagina. Most women find that a regular movement, either tonguing round the clitoris or to and from it to the vagina, will over a time result in orgasm.

Sex aids

Contrary to one popular belief, not all gay women use dildos — some would deny they need a 'substitute penis' — and some dislike vibrators. However, some lesbian (and heterosexual) women find them helpful, especially if they have difficulty in reaching orgasm by any other means. Sex aids like these can be bought in sex shops or by mail order through advertisements in magazines, and can be used at any time during lovemaking.

If a couple do decide to experiment, it is very important first to make sure that the dildo or vibrator is perfectly clean to prevent any infection, and secondly to remember that too hard or prolonged pressure can cause discomfort.

involved in the gay movement, working to improve conditions for all homosexuals.

By coming out, gay women hope to challenge assumptions about lesbians and hope in this way to banish prejudice. The main reason for openness, however, is that once a woman has recognized her feelings and has not been intimidated into thinking she is abnormal, she is more able to be spontaneous and free in forming sexual and emotional relationships with other women.

Coming out

Many people find it difficult to accept their sexuality and worry about their sexual performance or normality. For the homosexual these problems are often greater — feeling able to say to friends and family that you are gay can take a great deal of soul-searching. Dealing with their reactions requires confidence and courage.

'Coming out' — recognizing and declaring the strength of their sexual feelings — is probably the most important personal decision homosexuals will ever take. People who come out are rejecting all the prejudices about homosexuality and indicating a willingness to say to other people, in a variety of ways, that they are confident — even proud — of their sexuality.

Coming to terms with one's sexuality, whether heterosexual or gay, is never easy. Both young heterosexuals and homosexuals often have feelings of guilt about such things as masturbation. But young gay people have the added difficulty of coming to terms with their sexuality in an environment which is largely hostile to them.

This is not to say that all young people who have inclinations towards their own sex should immediately stand up and say that they are gay. Most adolescents go through a stage of apparent homosexuality, but many of them find that they become more interested in the opposite sex as they mature. However, if society were less prejudiced against homosexuality, perhaps young boys and girls would be less afraid about the possibility of being gay.

Many young homosexuals feel that the forces against them are too great, so they reject their sexual feelings as 'just a passing phase'. When homosexual feelings do get translated into sexual activity it is often excused as an 'accident' or a 'drunken error'. Even when gay people recognize the strength and importance of their sexual inclinations, the social unacceptability of these feelings often inhibits them from coming out.

Widespread prejudice against homosexuality can produce anxiety and fear in a gay person. The law still treats homosexuals (especially men) as unequal, medicine still has a tendency to treat homosexuality as a disease and popular prejudice rejects most things that are not average. All can contribute to a homosexual's feelings of insecurity.

These attitudes are deeply ingrained in everyone, homosexual as well as heterosexual, so much so that sometimes homosexuals feel guilty for being gay and inhibit themselves from coming out. This is called self-oppression.

Faced with these potential problems, many gay people never come out and the result is often either guilt-ridden, furtive sex or unhappiness as gay men or women try to live hidden or heterosexual lives.

The coming out process

The process of coming out consists of at least three stages. In the case of a young man, for example, the first stage would be his recognition of the importance of his homosexual feelings and the realization that they cannot be denied or suppressed. Second, he would admit to himself that he is gay. At this stage he may tell his close friends although he may still feel worried and isolated. The third stage arrives when he is prepared to be known as a homosexual. He will be ready to go to gay bars, discos and meeting places without being afraid of being seen. He will come out not only to close friends, but also with family, people at work and casual acquaintances.

Generally, gay people who have come out will feel happier about their sexuality than those who have not. But there is no necessity to come out as gay, and if a person chooses not to no one will know the truth — most homosexuals blend in with a crowd of people just like almost everyone else.

Homosexuality covers the whole range of possible appearances, personalities and jobs. There are lesbian models and lesbian factory workers, male homosexual hairdressers and male homosexual coal miners. So it is perfectly possible for a homosexual to live an ostensibly heterosexual life.

Many gay people wonder why it is important to be open about their sexuality. After all, they say, 'My sex life is a private matter.' Or is it? Until recently male homosexuality was illegal in many Western countries and, in some, the very existence of lesbianism was denied. (When asked what she intended to do about the legal status of lesbians, Queen Victoria of England refused to believe women did such things so no law was passed.) But even where homosexuality has been legalized gays are still discriminated against in various ways. The age of consent, for example, is often higher than it is for heterosexuals.

The Gay Movement

In the early 1970s the Gay Movement developed to challenge attitudes and laws about homosexuality. From the very beginning the Gay Movement stressed the importance of adopting a positive attitude towards homosexuality, and they themselves coined the word 'gay' as a symbol of this attitude.

Two things developed from the Gay Movement which particularly helped gay people to be more open about their sexuality: a massive growth in the commercial gay scene — clubs, bars and so on — which made it easier for gay people to meet, and the development of a series of self-help groups plus counselling and information services.

As these facilities developed so did the gay community, and this in turn helped many gay people to come out. A homosexual no longer needed to feel isolated, but instead could get support and confidence from the many other homosexuals — it has been estimated that in some countries from 5 to as much as 20 per cent of the population is gay.

The existence of an open gay community means that a young person becoming aware of his or her homosexuality today is much more likely to find friendship and acceptance, as well as positive images to identify with. But the flourishing of this community has not just helped the young; many men and women in their sixties and seventies have been able to come out and say, 'I have been a homosexual all my life but I've never felt able to

The process of coming out falls into at least three stages. Stages 1: The gay person has begun to identify his sexual feelings but probably feels confused and isolated.

tell anyone until now.'

In coming out, a homosexual's commitment to be open about sexuality is half the battle, but it would be misleading to say that there are no problems — it is practically impossible to predict what people will say when they are told. In many cases friends, colleagues and family do reject homosexuals, perhaps even refusing to have anything to do with them.

If this occurs, homosexuals should try to remember that it probably took them quite a long time to make the decision to come out so other people may need some time to come to terms with it as well. In fact, most gays find that after an initial shock the majority of the people they tell soon learn to accept it. Many people will even feel closer to them because they have been honest.

It may help to add that in the few cases where people cannot learn to accept homosexuals, there is probably something lacking in the relationship. If there was a basic liking and respect in the first place, then trying to understand such an important part of someone's life should come as a matter of course.

In certain situations it can be particularly difficult for homosexuals to make the decision to come out — for example, if they are married. Many gay people marry as a way of trying to escape their homosexuality, hoping that if they do what heterosexuals do, they will 'get over it'.

Stage 2: He may begin to play a part in the gay community, going to gay pubs and discos to meet people.

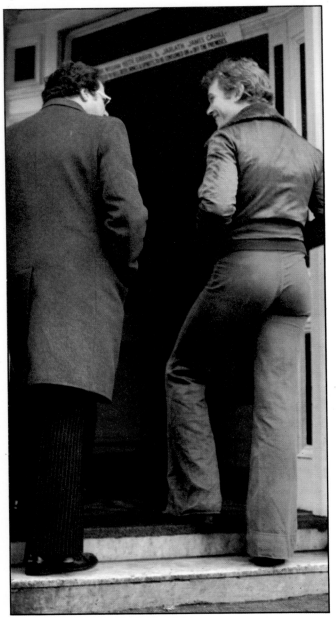

Many other people discover the strength of their homosexual feelings only after they are married and perhaps even after they have children.

Here homosexuals are faced with three choices: whether to be open about their sexuality and risk breaking up the relationship; whether to try to lead a double life, risking possible exposure all the time; or whether to try to suppress their feelings and risk continuous emotional frustration.

This decision would be easier if the gay partner felt unable to gain anything more from the marriage. But in most cases the marriage is still valued by both partners and the gay partner does not want to hurt or reject a cherished companion. The prospect of separation or divorce in this situation is probably at least as painful as in any other marriage, if not more so.

The problems are compounded if the couple have children. Until recently it has been usual practice for the divorce courts to give custody of the children to the heterosexual partner. So, the gay parent must consider the possibility of losing contact with his or her children, a risk many people do not want to take.

No one can tell a person in this situation what to do — it will be difficult in every case. However, it is worth pointing out that neither frustration nor deceit is a sound basis for a continuing relationship. If a gay partner chooses to lead a double life enormous tension can develop: lies have to be told to explain mysterious absences; there is constant fear of being discovered; and there is always the possibility that gay involvements will become deep emotional attachments that threaten the marriage.

If the gay partner is a woman there may be even more difficulties. A married lesbian faces all the problems a male homosexual does, with the added worry that if she comes out she risks losing not only her home and probably custody of her children, but also her income: men still tend to earn more than women and many women do not work at all.

A fresh start

Despite all these difficulties many people find that honesty can lead to a fresh start and a new kind of relationship. Some people prefer to dissolve the marriage amicably, remain friends and share responsibility for their children. Other couples opt for what is called a 'mixed marriage'. This means that the couple reach an understanding which

Stage 3: At this point, he will feel that he can be almost totally open about his sexuality.

allows them to lead more or less independent lives while maintaining a close involvement, perhaps even continuing to live in the same house.

Coming out at work can also be difficult. Many people find that not only do they have to contend with prejudice from work colleagues but also with discrimination from their employers. The latter tends to occur in certain areas of employment more than others — for example, homosexual teachers sometimes lose their jobs because they might influence young children and homosexual civil servants are often not promoted because they are thought to be open to blackmail. For this

reason, many homosexuals who are quite open with friends and family will decide that discretion is better and remain silent at work. Yet some gays do decide to come out at work and many of them find that everything works out well. It is very rare for there to be just one homosexual in a factory or office, so sometimes coming out leads to new friendships and often it helps other people to come out as well.

It would be wrong to say that whatever the problems everyone must come out. On the other hand being open with yourself and other people can be a very liberating experience. There is no doubt about the fact that gay people who have come out are much more relaxed than those who feel guilty about their sexuality.

Am I a lesbian?

If a woman discovers that she is sexually attracted to a female friend, her first reaction, given the widespread prejudices against homosexuals, may well be one of fear and disgust. However, lesbianism is neither 'sick' nor perverted, and many women have found great happiness and fulfillment in loving members of their own sex.

Many people worry, at some time in their lives, whether they are sexually 'normal', usually when they are finding it difficult to form close relationships with members of the opposite sex. For some, however, the problem takes the form of a specific, and sometimes frightening, question: 'Am I homosexual?' In the past, anyone confronted with this worry was forced to cope alone, because physical love between members of the same sex was frowned upon by society. Nowadays, though homosexuals still face discrimination, there is tolerance of what people choose to do in the privacy of their own homes, and a greater awareness that some may feel sexually attracted to members of their own sex.

With the recent wider public discussion of female sexuality, some women are beginning to express their sexual desires more openly. A number are now choosing to have sexual relationships with other women, and are finding that such partnerships can bring both emotional and sexual fulfilment. However, for many women, lesbianism is still taboo, an object of fear and suspicion. When 30-year-old Penny found herself attracted to her friend, Elaine, her first reaction was to feel disgusted with herself and to wonder whether she was ill. A friend in whom she confided advised her to discuss her fears with a woman counsellor:

Like many other questions of women's sexuality, lesbianism has been, for many people in our society, a 'hidden issue', to be whispered about rather than discussed openly. So, when we look at sexual love between women today, we have to consider it in the light of these attitudes. The fact that women have been forced to keep their love for each other secret is, I think, one of the reasons why so many women come to me admitting fear and disgust about their desires.

It might help you if we began by exploring your feelings towards other women. When did you first become aware that you felt sexually attracted to another woman?

'Last year I joined the local community group, where I worked with other women to campaign for children's playspaces in my area. There I met Elaine. At the time I had a steady boyfriend and, though our relationship wasn't very exciting, I felt fairly content with him.

However, the more I worked with Elaine, the closer we became, until I realized that I was more interested in being with her than in working for the campaign. I found her company much more enjoyable than my boyfriend's — there are things you can share with other women far more easily than you can with men. It was like finding the sister whom I had always longed for as a child.

At the same time, my feelings for my boyfriend changed: I couldn't bear him to touch me and we stopped making love. It was then I realized what I had been trying to hide from myself — that I felt more sexually attracted to Elaine than I had ever felt to a man.'

The feelings which you describe are more common than you might imagine. As I have said, lesbianism is not generally discussed openly, but if it were, many women might admit to feeling like you — at least some of the time.

These desires are often hidden, not only because of society's attitudes, but also because women have traditionally been rivals, forced into competition with each other for the love of men. Very often women are encouraged to make themselves beautiful or desirable in order to 'win a man' or to prove their superiority over other women, and these competitive feelings affect their relationships with each other.

This is beginning to change. Women are now working together far more often, not only in women's liberation groups, but also in community work — like you — or as mothers in nursery or toddlers' groups, or simply out at work, where they are able to discuss the problems common to women. The more time they spend together working for a shared aim, the less rivalry women feel, and their natural feelings of affection for each other begin to surface.

In some — but by no means all — situations, this closeness develops further, but many women deny their affection, feeling that it is 'unnatural' or dangerous. After all, until recently homosexual relationships between men were illegal in many Western countries and even now male gays must still take care to avoid prosecution.

Teenage 'crushes'

'Do you think that there is a difference between feeling very close to a woman friend and feeling a strong sexual desire for her?'

It really depends on the individual's sexual personality. There are some women whose strong feelings for other people — whether men or women — are naturally expressed in sexual love. On the other hand, women who do not generally express themselves openly in a sexual way may love another woman just as they might love a sister: with a great deal of emotion and strong affection but without sexual desire.

'As a teenager, I had very strong emotions towards one of my schoolfriends and also, like many of my classmates, I had a 'crush' on one of the female teachers. My mother laughed about it, saying it was perfectly natural phase for a girl of my age and that I would grow out of it in time.'

Most people share your mother's attitude towards schoolgirl crushes — that they are just a phase on the way to 'mature' love for a man. However, some psychologists believe that these crushes are really an expression of sexual love that shows up in teenagers because adolescence is both a time of sexual awakening and intense romantic feeling. It is also a time when a person is more open to experimentation and less concerned with fitting into a conventional sexual relationship.

In most cases, of course, teenage crushes do not lead to lovemaking; usually it is enough for the two women involved to be together, touching each other in a sensual (holding hands, for example) rather than a directly sexual way, and most girls do go on to have sexual relationships with men.'

Bisexuality

'Is it possible to be a lesbian and at the same time have sex with men?'

Some woman do find that they are bisexual, that is, capable of sexual love for both men and women. Sigmund Freud thought that everyone is born with the ability to love sexually both men and women though he argued that this changes in adolescence into sexual desire for the opposite sex only.

It is often difficult to love both a man and a woman at the same time, because the two sexes demand different kinds of love. However, some women find they can manage to do so, if only because their partners seem to feel less threatened by competition from someone of the opposite sex.

Other women discover that there are times when they need the love of another woman rather than that of a man, and other times when they long for the specific kind of love that only men can give. The problem is not that they feel sexual love for both men and women, but rather that they might feel guilt or anxiety about expressing desires that are considered 'abnormal'. There is a great deal of prejudice against bisexual people, not only from those who consider themselves sexually normal, but also those who have moral or religious objections to homosexuality.

Some lesbians feel that women who want sexual relationships with other women should stop making love with men — they consider that these women should make a choice and should not try to have 'the best of both worlds.' This attitude is understandable since many lesbians are trying to fight the prejudice that still exists by 'coming out'

and being unafraid to admit their love for other women. However, I think that for lesbians to criticize bisexual women is merely showing the prejudice that they are trying to fight against.

What happens in a lesbian relationship?

'Is there much difference between lesbian partnerships and those between men and women?'

It depends very much on the individuals involved. Of course, there is a major difference in the way that the partners make love. Many women tell me that they find lesbian sex more satisfying because other women understand their bodies and sexual responses better than most men can. Incidentally, gay men say much the same thing about the way they make love — there is a very close physical understanding. Women also say that the relationship is more equal because they are giving and taking pleasure from someone like themselves, rather than relying on a man to have an erection in order to make penetration possible.

On the other hand, there are strong social pressures which place a strain on a lesbian relationship. In some professions, such as teaching, homosexuals of both sexes may face discrimination at work. A mother who leaves her husband to live with a female lover may face the prospect of losing her children if her husband goes to court to obtain custody.

In other respects, lesbians behave very much like other lovers. They can have the same passionate quarrels, the same worries, the same jealousies, the same need for reassurance. Some set up home together much like a heterosexual couple, with one

partner, for example, doing most of the cooking and the other the house repairs — though some lesbians feel that such a partnership mirrors traditional heterosexual roles too closely, and believe that female homosexuals should try to develop new, more equal partnerships.

Responsibility

'Before I came to see you, I was undecided whether I really wanted a long-term sexual affair with another woman, or simply wanted to try it out. I was worried that the strong attraction I felt for Elaine might be wrong. But is it possible that I could have an affair with Elaine and then go back to having normal sexual relationships with men?'

It is very difficult for me to predict. You may find that your attraction towards Elaine is similar to that you might feel for a man with whom you would like to make love, but who you wouldn't necessarily consider as a long-term partner. Even if Elaine's feelings are as intense as yours, and she wishes the relationship to continue, you might find it difficult to carry on in the face of prejudice and opposition from family, friends and possibly even people at work.

You would also have to come to terms with the prying attitudes of some ignorant people, who are fascinated by what women do together when they make love. (There is a whole range of pornography on the subject, which shows more about men's sexual fantasies of lesbianism than about the reality that women experience.)

And I think I should end with a warning that you should not experiment carelessly with lesbian relationships. They should not be treated as enjoyable 'adventures on the side' while maintaining a long-standing relationship with a man, nor are they opportunities for a new kind of sexual thrill. Any sexual relationship involves the emotions and affects the lives of at least two people — possibly more — and should be entered into only with careful forethought and consideration.

Bisexuality

People who are sexually attracted to both men and women are bisexual. In the past, bisexuals hid their feelings because they feared society's disapproval. Today, they can be more open about their relationships. But many of us are unsure what being bisexual involves and whether it is really normal for some people.

We have all read about famous people — singers and actors mostly — who have announced that they have made love with both men and women, some saying their actions aren't really so odd since, 'We're all bisexual really'. There has, it seems, almost been a fashion for bisexuality and this has caused some confusion among people who don't claim to be bisexual themselves and don't know anybody who does. After all, it is sometimes difficult to know what bisexuality actually implies. Does it just mean that you enjoy sex with both men and women? And do bisexuals, like some pop singers, always look androgenous (mingling characteristics of both sexes)? Is bisexuality in fact just a contemporary fad or is it really normal for some people?

What is a bisexual?

The best way to begin to answer these questions is to look at two examples. On the surface, John is an ordinary young man. He fits easily into his social world: he enjoys playing football and looks conventionally 'masculine'. However, since he was a teenager he has been sexually attracted to both men and women. Although he has homosexual friends, he does not see himself as gay because he still wants sexual relationships with women. He admits he doesn't relate in quite the same way to men and women: with women he is always aware of the physical differences and finds sex more of an effort; with men he feels a greater sense of physical balance and sex is easier and somehow more detached. He finds emotional relationships with women easier and expects that one day he will begin a stable partnership with a woman, but he has no intention of suppressing his sexual attraction for men and is quite open about his bisexuality. His chief difficulty is not in switching between men and women but in meeting other bisexuals. For John, bisexuality is not a fashion or

even a simple choice: it is just the way he feels.

Linda is the same age as John and already married. She is very fond of her husband and their sex life is satisfactory. Recently Linda became involved in a women's discussion group where she soon became aware that she was emotionally and sexually attracted to one of the women. Linda doesn't feel that this makes her lesbian, though she doesn't mind the description; on the contrary, the group feels that women should be able to relate openly to each other without necessarily accepting labels, whether homosexual, heterosexual or bisexual — 'It's the person who counts'.

Linda's husband finds this rather difficult to cope with, but he has come to realize that Linda has needs which he alone cannot fill. The result has been an opening-out of their relationship and the recognition that they may have been too possessive in the past.

These brief accounts show three things. Firstly, there are different ways of being bisexual and it does not necessarily have anything to do with men feeling they are not properly masculine or women not being feminine. Secondly, there is quite often a difference between the male and female experience of bisexuality. It seems to be true that in our society women are more used to close emotional relationships than are men, and in today's more liberal climate these may become physical. Thirdly, supportive friendships are very important. Linda is luckier than John in this way since her woman's group understands her feelings. Despite his openness, John feels a bit isolated in a world which still finds the homosexual side of his nature puzzling.

Is it a natural state?

Human beings have been interested in the idea of bisexuality throughout history. In ancient mythology the original human was believed to have been half man, half woman. Today, sexologists increasingly recognize that characteristics we regard as 'masculine' and 'feminine' are not so much products of nature as of the particular types of culture in which we live. We are still not really sure, however, of the exact way in which the young child adopts male or female behaviour or comes to be heterosexual, homosexual or bisexual. Some experts think it is caused by our hormones, but others believe it is the result of social pressures. However, perhaps Freud has provided the most influential explanation.

Freud argued that everyone was born both bisexual (having qualities of, and able to relate emotionally to, both sexes) and polymorphously perverse (capable of all kinds of sexual activity). It is only through growing up and our relationships with our parents that the kinds of people we are attracted to, and the sexual relationships we desire, are narrowed down. In other words, our culture demands that we give up bisexual feelings and relate sexually to the opposite sex only.

Of course, this process rarely works smoothly in practice. If it did, there would be no homosexuals or bisexuals, and there would not be the range of sexual desires that exist. We can, however, draw two conclusions. First, when we are very young, bisexuality is our truly 'original' state. Second, our sexual feelings towards the opposite sex develop at the expense of our homosexual feelings, but neither of these feelings is more 'natural' than the other and we all retain some of both in greater or lesser degrees.

Some of these conclusions were confirmed by Alfred Kinsey who interviewed thousands of Americans in the 1940s. He found that over a third of the men had had some sexual contact with other men to the point of ejaculation at least once in adulthood. The figures for women were lower:

one in eight admitted they had had 'significant' homosexual contact, but even this figure is large compared to the one per cent who saw themselves as exclusively lesbian. These figures do not necessarily apply to all societies, but they suggest very strongly that there is a vast amount of bisexual behaviour.

The problems of bisexuality

Bisexuals have problems not because of their bisexual feelings — as far as anything can be said to be so, these are natural — but because our society demands that we think all the time in a rigid way. We divide the world into two sexes, men and women, as if there were an iron curtain between them. As a result, many people sneer at those who do not fit in with these conventional ideas — the gentle, passive man or the forceful, active woman. We forget that, as Freud suggested, we all have within us qualities which are both active and passive, masculine and feminine. The difficulties get worse when we talk about sexual behaviour, since we talk of being 'normal' or 'abnormal', and that usually means heterosexual or homosexual. Heterosexuality is so firmly fixed in our institutions, such as marriage, the family and parenthood, that those who can't accept this framework feel guilty and rejected.

On the other hand, it is often equally difficult for the bisexual to fit easily into the gay world. Because homosexuality has been the object of so much disapproval, the gay scene tends to be rather defensive and a little suspicious of those who are not willing to come right out and say that they are gay. Many people exclusively attracted to their own sex may feel that they are being used for casual pleasure and that if things get too difficult, the bisexual can always retreat to the safety of the heterosexual world. The different cultures of the heterosexual and homosexual worlds tend to harden the divisions and make it difficult for the bisexual to fit easily into either camp.

Adolescence

There are two periods in life when particular problems can arise for the bisexual. The first is during adolescence. During their teens, young people want to explore their sexuality in a variety of ways, and this often takes the form of sex play with members of the same sex. Even very conservative people are prepared to see some of this as 'natural' and to treat it as a passing phase.

The difficulties arise when the young adult feels the need to go on having homosexual contacts or to be actively homosexual. The young individual might now feel really isolated and anxious, and needs all the support that can be given. It would be wrong to say that in our society it is easy to be openly bisexual. On the other hand, some people do lead sexually fulfilling lives as bisexuals, 'loving them both', as one writer has put it.

Marriage

The second difficult period can come if the bisexual gets married. Here bisexuals are faced with some hard problems: for instance, should they be honest with their partners? Should they be sexually faithful, or should they try for an open relationship? There can be no easy answers.

Consider Arthur for example. He is forty, married with two children, and has had a good sex life with his wife, Cathy, since they were married twenty years ago. However, during this time he has also had a number of casual sexual encounters with men whom he meets in the local gay pub. He has not dared tell his wife, who would, he says, 'never understand'. But, at the same time, he very much wants to be honest with her and feels that he

has important needs that are not being openly expressed. His difficulty with Cathy is that he always has to take the initiative in their sex life. In his encounters with men he feels that he need not take the lead or that the lead can be taken alternately. Yet he is still very attracted by the female body, so different from, but as desirable as, the male's.

Is honesty the best policy?

Arthur's problem is that a double life imposes strains of its own on top of anxieties about his sexuality, since he has a constant fear that somehow Cathy will accidentally find out about his bisexuality. There is no easy solution, though men in similar positions have found that it is possible to be more honest with their partners. This means taking risks, of course, and there is always the danger that the partner and children will not understand. The alternative, however, can be equally risky, and many people have found that their marriages have taken on a new lease of life,

both emotionally and sexually, when both partners are open about their deepest feelings.

Changing attitudes

Attitudes are changing and people are finding it somewhat easier to come to terms with themselves sexually. One of the great results of this change has been the growth of organizations and groups where individuals who are anxious about their sexuality can talk to sympathetic people. In most Western countries there are groups that can help worried teenagers and give advice to isolated or married bisexuals, though these organizations can only help people to help themselves.

It would be wrong to say that we are all really bisexual, or that everyone should experiment with bisexuality. Many of us are firmly attached to heterosexuality, but perhaps one of the major results of the relaxation of some of the old taboos is that bisexual people can now be more honest about their sexuality.

Coping with a bisexual partner

*Learning to cope with bisexuality can be very difficult for both
the bisexual and the heterosexual partner. But many couples
manage to overcome these problems and develop a relationship
that allows both of them to lead lives which are
nevertheless happy and fulfilled.*

The subject of homosexuality is discussed more openly today than ever before. Being a homosexual means feeling sexually attracted to someone of one's own sex, as opposed to the *heterosexual* attraction between a man and a woman. Many people now recognize that homosexuality is widespread and needs to be understood and accepted by society.

This new tolerance and interest is allowing many men and women, who some years ago would have led miserable, secret lives trying to hide their homosexuality, to develop their personalities and lead happier lives. Many of these people will have led apparently happy lives in heterosexual relationships although they were denying — to both themselves and society — that they had deep homosexual feelings as well.

Today's attitudes have allowed these *bisexuals* — people who desire relationships with both their own sex and the opposite sex — to begin to explore this aspect of their character and lead a less anxious life. For the bisexual this may be a positive experience but for the heterosexual partner it can be very difficult and a great strain is often put on the relationship — particularly if the partner had no idea about the lover's 'secret'.

Most heterosexual people will talk quite happily about homosexuality but few of them will have to come to terms with it in their daily lives. When it comes to the crunch many people find it much more difficult to cope with.

Understanding homosexuality

It can be easier to understand homosexuality — and bisexuality — if you can remember how during early adolescence almost everyone has closer friendships with members of their own sex than with members of the opposite sex. Boys shun girls, sticking together as a group and later picking out individual boys who they can admire, talk to and share secrets with. Girls ignore boys, have schoolgirl crushes and make close friendships with one or two other girls.

This natural part of growing up can even include some kind of sexual expression — most men will tell tales of comparing the size of their penis with others and some will have masturbated together. Most girls will have had similar experiences — even if it is just cuddling up with their best friend when they stay the night with each other and share a bed.

At this early stage a child will feel that there is

nothing wrong with this expression of a close friendship. But he or she will learn very quickly to identify it as something that they have heard adults talk about as 'bad'. Powerful social conditioning teaches adolescents to reject physical experience with their close friends, and instead go out in search of more acceptable heterosexual relationships — the homosexual (or 'gay' as it is often called today) side of a person's nature is repressed.

A few adolescents will hold out against the social pressures and learn to affirm their sexual and emotional preferences for members of the same sex, but the vast majority of gay people will only come to terms with their homosexuality after

many of whom also marry and have children like 'normal' heterosexuals.

The effect on a marriage

Discovering that one partner is bisexual will usually rock a marriage to its very core. But often the couple will recognize that it is a serious problem and will try to face it as rationally as possible.

Ann and John had been happily married for 14 years. John had known ever since he was 15 that he had strong gay inclinations but, as he was also perfectly able and willing to enjoy sex with women, he hid the homosexual side of his nature. Like many others he thought that if he did nothing about it, it would go away.

For a while their marriage seemed to be fine — their sex life was good, they enjoyed each other's company and in time they had children. However, after a while the relationship seemed to get worse; they talked it over and decided that they needed to look beyond each other for satisfaction, so they made new friends and did new things.

This worked well for Ann and she soon felt happy again. But the period of mutual soul-searching prompted John to start thinking about the things he really wanted from life. He began to realize that the gay side of his nature had by no means 'gone away' and now he felt that he needed to express the other side of himself, none of which affected the fact that he still dearly loved his wife and children.

One day John met another man, an ordinary businessman called David who made no secret of the fact that he was attracted to other men. John was amazed by David — he had always thought that he was unique, and that all other homosexual men were 'camp' or effeminate, and did not hold down ordinary jobs or dress in an ordinary way.

Suddenly John realized that he was far more in love than he had ever been before — the strength of his emotions deeply disturbed him and he knew that he would never be the same again. David felt very much the same way about John. Ann mentioned to John that he seemed to be more relaxed about life, but meanwhile he kept his secret — thinking that he could run his love affair and his marriage as well.

It was David who finally brought things to a head. He began to resent the fact that John always went home to his family and he asked him to explain things to his wife. John just could not find the courage to upset his marriage so he did not tell Ann. David felt that this put such limits on their relationship that he reluctantly put an end to their affair.

several attempts at establishing heterosexual relationships. Whichever way a gay person discovers their sexual identity it can be a difficult task which requires a considerable amount of courage.

Some gays use bisexuality to keep up a 'heterosexual front' — they have fallen into a heterosexual lifestyle and when they rediscover their homosexual nature they cannot admit that this is really all they want. But many other bisexuals feel that they want both types of relationship — a life without both would not be full for them.

In the final analysis no one can be certain what makes a man or woman gay. But it seems that there always have been and always will be homosexuals,

John was extremely upset and Ann began to sense that something was not right. Some time later he felt he had to get it off his chest and he explained the whole affair. Ann was deeply shocked and the marriage ended in divorce.

It was too late for this couple to begin to resolve the problem they faced — the relationship had been too badly damaged by the secrecy surrounding such an important aspect of John's character. If John had come to terms with his bisexuality before he ever met Ann he would not have been torn about telling her what had happened. He would have been able to tell her from the start of their involvement that he felt the need to have relationships with both sexes. She may not have accepted this in which case the marriage might never have taken place. Alternatively, she too may have felt the need to have an 'open marriage' in which case the relationship would have suited them both and would have stood a better chance of lasting.

This is all much easier said than done — it can take a great deal of courage to 'come out' and admit to yourself that you have a desire for relationships with people of your own as well as with the opposite sex. Most gays do not 'come out' until much later in their lives, but it is never too late, especially if they have an honest and open relationship with their heterosexual partner. If they are able to communicate with each other about most other things then talking about homosexual desires will be much easier.

The heterosexual partner

The most familiar reaction to discovering that your partner is having an affair — whether it is homosexual or heterosexual — is total rejection and a feeling of failure at your inability to keep your lover happy. Most people are absolutely shattered if they find that the third person is a member of the same sex.

The familiar weapons of war used to win back a husband or wife seem useless to a partner facing competition from another man or woman — a husband making threats against his wife's *female* lover just does not have the same air of masculinity about it. And what point is there in a wife thinking about new clothes, hairstyles or any other traditional feminine wiles when her rival probably has stubble in the morning?

Both husbands and wives can go through a period of severe depression, feeling totally uncertain about themselves and their acceptability as a man

or woman. Probably the worst part of the heterosexual partner's distress is the discovery that someone so close has an entirely hidden side to their character. It can hurt greatly to know that your partner has kept such a closely guarded secret when you thought you were very open and honest with each other.

It will be very difficult to cope with the sudden discovery of bisexuality, but above all else it is important to remember that bisexuality is not abnormal — people are not freaks because they have such feelings.

After the initial shock many husbands and wives decide that competition from a same-sex affair is really no competition at all — 'after all it is not love in the real sense, is it?' Or is it? Homosexual feelings can be just as strong and intense as heterosexual emotions so it can be a grave mistake to treat one partner's gay desires as light-hearted jaunts which he or she will get bored with.

Coming to terms with bisexuality

If the heterosexual couple are to reach any understanding, it must be acknowledged that the homosexual relationship is just as 'real' as the heterosexual one. Simply dismissing homosexual feelings may make the bisexual partner feel that it is all going to be too complicated to resolve and make the easy option of breaking away from the marriage seem preferable to trying to find a way to work things out.

It is all-important for the heterosexual partner to approach the problem with interest and understanding — despite the emotional stress felt inside. Just expressing pleasure at the fact that the bisexual partner has confided long pent-up emotions can be very reassuring.

If the couple manage to reaffirm the mutual bond that they have probably spent years developing then it is quite possible to work out a new way of looking at each other. Many couples end up leading a full and happy life together, even though they may not be quite so close as they were earlier in the relationship.

Some couples find the problems too difficult to deal with on their own: they should seek advice from their doctor who will be able to refer them to a marital counsellor. Counselling can often help the couple resolve their feelings. They may decide that they cannot live together any longer, but at least they will feel they gave it a try and their future relationships will probably be happier for that.

'How do I tell my wife I'm gay?'

Today, with the increasing acceptance of homosexuality, some people in heterosexual relationships, who have hidden their gay feelings, are finding it easier to be honest with those close to them. Such a revelation may well change the relationship, but need not cause permanent unhappiness, if the couple can work out their feelings together.

In the past, homosexuality was regarded as either, at best, a 'problem', or, at worst, a 'perversion', and so many people, fearing the reactions of family and friends, were forced to suppress the homosexual side of their natures. Today, however, with the increased honesty about sexual differences, most people recognize that homosexuality is not a disease and that the best 'treatment' is to help the homosexual to come to terms with his or her own feelings without shame or guilt. As a result, some people, who may have heterosexual partners, now finally feel that they can admit that they are gay.

Len is 30 and has been married for 10 years. He and his wife have two children, aged five and seven, and until recently were happily married with a full and rewarding sex life. However, since he was a teenager, Len has been strongly attracted to other men, and in the past few years these long-suppressed feelings have surfaced strongly. Recently Len went to a gay club for the first time and was shocked at how much he sexually and emotionally desired the men he met there. He wants to be honest about his feelings, but fears that the truth will permanently harm his relationship with his wife, whom he still loves very much. In an attempt to sort out his feelings, Len went to a counsellor:

Is honesty always best?

'I have known ever since I was a teenager that there was a strong homosexual side to my nature, but I always hid it, as I was very disturbed by the idea. Have I been wrong to keep it a secret, especially from my wife?'

In this situation it is difficult to generalize, but attitudes have changed so much over the past few years that my answer to that question is very different from what it would have been some years ago. These days I would say that — as long as you have a loving and trusting relationship with your partner, as you have — you should not hide your feelings, but calmly and reasonably discuss your fears and problems with her.

In your case, however, I can see that when you first experienced homosexual feelings, social attitudes made it impossible for you to be honest with your friends and relatives. And today, although you may feel able to be open with your wife, you may find it more difficult to discuss your homosexuality with others close to you, such as your parents or other relatives.

I see a lot of men with a similar problem, who have been forced to suppress the gay side of their natures, and the result is that these feelings show themselves very strongly later in life. I am sure you feel, as they do, that your homosexuality will not go away, that you have been hiding it for too long, and that if you don't do something about it now, you never will.

Betrayal and hurt

'Yes, that's it exactly. I know that telling my wife I am gay may cause a change in our relationship, possibly for the worse, but I feel I must take the risk, as the tensions building up inside me are forcing me to lead a double life. However, I am still worried that she will be very hurt and I am not sure she will want me to stay with her.'

When you tell your wife she will probably be very confused for a number of reasons, and if you can reassure her that you still love her and that you are willing to try and work things out together, she will become more understanding as she gets used to your homosexuality. After all, you have revealed a new side of your character.

Indeed this may be one of the reasons why she will probably also feel betrayed and hurt: she thought she knew you, having been married to you for so long. You should try and explain how difficult it would have been in the past to reveal your feelings; tell her you need her help now.

She will also almost certainly have a very bad mental picture of homosexuals since she will probably only have seen the stereotyped effeminate man shown in films and on television. You must explain that gays are just like everybody else, except that they relate sexually to members of their own sex.

Reassurance

'*Now I have accepted my feelings I have lost interest in my wife sexually, and I am not sure it is fair on my wife to stay if I cannot satisfy her any more.*'

Again, this is not an unusual reaction. The long-suppressed desires take over very strongly when you allow them out into the open. Obviously, you are very concerned about your wife and you should discuss with her what she wants and her inevitable feelings of rejection. If you both decide that the best thing to do would be for you to leave home, then you will have made a joint decision that suits you both. Why do you think leaving home might be a possible solution?

'*I suppose nothing else occurred to me. I feel I am letting my wife down and that if I can no longer make love to her I should let her find someone else.*'

I suspect you feel you must be able freely to explore the homosexual side of your nature, and that you are really trying to justify what you consider to be an unreasonable desire to leave home.

But remember, the blow to your wife's self-esteem has been hard. To be deserted for another woman is bad enough for most women, but when the object of her husband's affections is another man, a wife can feel very lost indeed. During this stage of bewilderment you should try always to reassure your wife that you still love her but that you have sexual needs which she cannot satisfy. The more you talk about it, the easier things will become, and eventually you will be able to discuss your homosexuality without pain or anger. Until then, you must be prepared to give support and reassurance to your wife — admittedly difficult when you are still struggling to come to terms with an aspect of your sexuality which you have only just admitted to yourself.

Leaving home

If you feel that it would be best to leave home, make sure that you see as much as possible of the family. Go home often and spend time with the children. Take your wife out to the cinema, for meals or for visits to friends. Then, even though you no longer live at home, your wife will see that you still care very much about her and the children.

Other cases like yours have shown that, once the conflict about sex has been resolved, if the husband leaves home but stays in close touch with the family, a better relationship between the couple often develops, albeit very different from before.

However, if your wife decides that she does not want to see you, try to reason with her along the lines I have suggested, but don't force the issue. She probably needs time alone to adjust to the sudden change thrust upon the marriage. Quite often, in your situation the wife's initial reaction is one of horror and disgust, but given time most women's attitudes do change and they generally want to keep in touch with their husbands.

Staying together

The other option would be to stay at home and explore the gay side of your nature, with your wife's full knowledge and consent. By now you have probably met quite a few homosexuals, and although you have realized that they are ordinary people just like yourself, your wife may be sus-

picious of them. Ask your friends to meet your wife, on neutral ground at first, like the local bar, restaurant or social club.

If you form a relationship with another man, explain both to him and your wife exactly what the situation is: that you still want to live at home, that you are emotionally attached to both of them, but sexually only to the man. If you have an understanding wife and lover, this kind of arrangement can work quite well.

However, do not be surprised if, in time, your wife decides to take a lover to whom she can relate sexually. After all, although you may well still love each other very much, sex is now impossible between you, as you have said, and your wife will, after a time, almost certainly feel sexually frustrated.

If your wife does find someone else, be prepared to accept her actions — just as she will have to accept yours after you have told her. The blow to your self-esteem — even though you may have anticipated the situation — will be harder than you expect. However, a lover for your wife could well make life much happier, with everyone staying friends. If, and when, your wife can find sexual and emotional comfort from her boyfriend and you are happy with a male lover, the time is probably right for you to split up — while, of course, still remaining good friends with your wife and keeping in touch with your children.

As you can see, there are different ways of approaching the problem. Which one you choose depends on how well you know your wife and how you think she will react. Is she very emotional, or does she think things through before she acts? In the first case you will need a lot of tact and compassion for her feelings. In the second you can try to be as rational as possible, but it will still be hard at first, until time has given everyone an opportunity to get used to the changes in your lives.

Telling the children

'I still feel fairly emotional myself, but I think my wife will still see me as her husband and will decide to help me through this crisis. I think that she may be worried about the children, though.'

If you are going to continue living at home, there is no need to explain everything to the children until they are old enough to understand what has happened. However, if you leave, you should tell them that you have to go away, probably only for a while, until you can sort out some things that

have been worrying you recently. Reassure them that you still love them very much and that you will come and see them often. Make sure that they feel that you love and want them.

'I intend to keep in touch with and support my wife and children financially if I have to leave, but I think my wife may be more worried that our children will follow my example and grow up to be gay.'

Some people think this is the case, but research has shown that, although parents are an important influence on their children's lives, children do not necessarily copy their parents' sexuality. Gay parents do not always have gay children, any more than heterosexuals produce heterosexual children — after all, most gays have straight parents!

'Do you think that when they are older my children will accept what has happened?'

It is, of course, impossible to predict what will happen in future, but it is to be hoped that, if present trends continue, social attitudes will have so changed that, by the time your children are grown up, the idea of homosexuality will be accepted by the vast majority of people.

If we could be more honest about our feelings without fear of censure from those around us, many difficulties would be resolved more easily, and homosexuality would not be seen as a problem, but merely as a facet of some people's characters which causes them to have certain sexual needs and emotions. In the past few years women have shown that they are not the naturally domestic, emotional creatures that they were for so long assumed to be, and equally there are signs that men are beginning to demand their own 'liberation' from being thought of as inevitably cold, rational beings with selfish interests.

Because of the changing climate of ideas on sex and the differences between men and women, the revelation of your homosexuality to your wife could well be the trigger that leads to a broadening of your understanding of each other, if you respect each other's feelings throughout.

Abnormal Sexual Inclinations

What is considered normal varies a great deal in different societies and at different times. At one time any type of extramarital sexual activity was severely punished, sometimes by death. In some Islamic societies this can still happen. In modern Western societies many activities once considered abnormal are now judged to be a matter of individual choice or preference. Nevertheless there are still some types of sexual behaviour that are universally condemned.

What is normal?

Sex is such a private occupation that comparing practices is often difficult. Many men and women wonder if what they do is 'normal'. But what is normal?

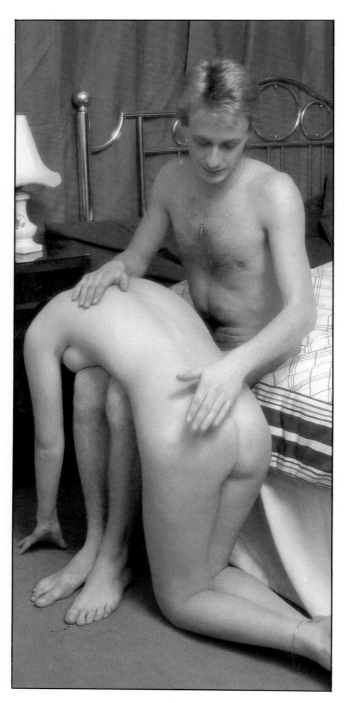

Normal means both 'conforming to standard, usual, typical' and 'free from mental or emotional disorder' but it does not necessarily have any moral connotations. What is considered normal in sexual behaviour varies from culture to culture and time to time. It will be reflected in the society's education, social pressure, medicine and ultimately the law. Laws in various countries penalize rape, sodomy, adultery, prostitution, indecent assault and exposure, obscenity and incest. However, since most sexual activity takes place in the privacy of people's homes, and does not come to the notice of the police, what is considered normal and what will be tolerated by people is very often up to the individual.

In Western society today there are three definitions of abnormality upheld by the medical profession and sexologists. The first is almost universal, and is also considered morally wrong. It is the use of physical aggression in sexual behaviour which can take the form of rape, indecent assault and violent attacks on homosexuals. The condemnation of such acts is also reflected in the law — although rape and indecent assault are not recognized within marriage. Any form of sexual behaviour which is forced on an unwilling partner is also considered abnormal and morally wrong: this may involve physical aggression or more subtle forms of humiliation, such as forcing a woman, either physically or emotionally, to have oral sex.

Another definition of abnormality is when a certain type of sexual behaviour — and presumably this would include homosexuality — becomes a substitute for full heterosexual intercourse. Some experts believe that although there is nothing abnormal about sex games that do not lead to penis-vagina penetration, people who indulge in them exclusively are usually unable to form close relationships, probably as a result of traumatic childhood experiences.

This does not mean that the person is immoral or that sex games are perversions, but simply that the person does not have the confidence to manage 'straight' sex — sex games are crutches to help the individual express his or her sexuality. But if the person is sexually satisfied by the sex games and does not harm anyone else, then there is no need to agonize about 'normality'.

Thrills and frills

Taking types of sexual behaviour that tend to worry people, it is possible to determine the dividing line between normality and abnormality, and whether this matters.

Being sexually excited by certain objects or types of clothing is called 'fetishism'. Black or scarlet female underwear — push-up bras, scanty briefs, suspenders and black stockings — along with high-heeled boots and shoes, leather and fur are common male 'fetishes'. The underwear may be associated with early experiences with prostitutes or excitement felt when looking at 'girlie' magazines as a teenager — or even as a reminder of exciting childhood sights involving glimpses of a mother or sister undressing.

Many women enjoy wearing these special clothes for their men but others may feel uncomfortable if they are requested to wear high-heeled boots or black panties as a prelude to lovemaking. But the reason for the request may be a sign that their partner has secret fears of impotence and feels that, without the excitement caused by the boots or the panties, he might not be able to have an erection.

If the fetishism is only mild, when a man's confidence grows, he might be able to rid himself of his dependency on the boots or panties for sexual stimulation. But if his partner refuses to wear the garments or suggests that he ought to be able to manage without them, he may feel his masculinity is further threatened and retreat from her altogether — using the boots or the panties alone for his sexual excitement and satisfaction. The boundary between the normal and the abnormal would then have been crossed.

Another form of stimulation used mainly by men, but sometimes by women as well, is reading pornographic or erotic magazines and looking at pictures and films of couples making love. There is nothing dirty or abnormal about this, as long as it leads most of the time to sexual intercourse. But when a man or a woman can reach orgasm only by

masturbating to such a stimulus it would be termed 'abnormal'; then again, if there is no other partner to consider and it is done in private, it does not really matter.

Transvestitism is another form of abnormality — it is not 'usual' and it certainly has elements of mental or emotional disorder. A transvestite is usually a heterosexual man who, for one reason or another, loves to stroke and wear female clothes.

A wife who discovers her husband is a transvestite may be bewildered and horrified, but if she can overcome her initial response, and try to understand why he does this there may be the possibility of a working relationship.

Another form of deviant sexual behaviour which

may prompt the question 'Is this normal?' is sado-masochism, in which the partners take up extreme roles, one being dominant and in complete control, the other submissive and helpless. The roles may be reversed from time to time. Pain or acts which seem cruel are used to stimulate sexual excitement. The practices vary in severity. A couple may experiment with pinchings and bitings, or light strokes across the bottom while extremists may whip each other, dressing in uniforms, leather garments or hoods. Mystery and fear plus a sinister atmosphere are needed as well as pain.

The practice of these activities is rare and usually occurs among people who have suffered severe anxiety as children and have learned to use sexual

excitement to make fear more bearable. It is abnormal only when the behaviour causes one partner distress, when the pain inflicted is excessive or when it does not lead to intercourse.

Oral sex, anal sex and masturbation, although considered less weird, still cause worries. These practices only become abnormal when they become a substitute for penis-vagina penetration. For example, if a woman likes having her clitoris licked to the point of orgasm but refuses penis penetration, she is abnormal because she fears intercourse. If sex is mutually satisfying, this will not matter, but at some stage the couple may realize that they are missing the physical closeness of penetration or they may want to try for a baby.

Practised occasionally, anal intercourse can be exciting and daring, but over-indulged in, it often loses its appeal. Compulsive anal intercourse in preference to vaginal intercourse would be considered abnormal. It should only be attempted with the aid of lots of lubricant applied to the penis and the inside of the anus — and with, of course, the woman's full consent. Penetration must be very gradual and gentle, since the line between pleasure and unbearable pain is very fine.

Cleanliness is also very important: the bowels should be emptied and the man should wash himself immediately afterwards. He must *never* insert his penis into the vagina after anal intercourse because this can cause vaginal infections.

Masturbation is both normal and natural. Not only children masturbate but adults too — even those with good sex lives. And masturbation need not be solitary — partners can masturbate in view of each other as part of lovemaking.

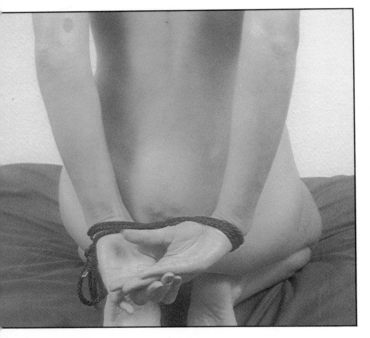

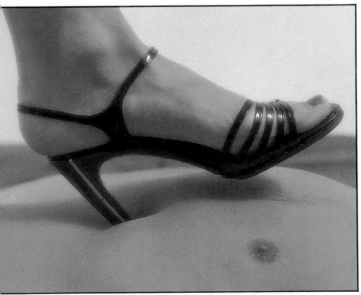

So what is truly abnormal?

True deviants are people who cannot form close relationships with others and inflict their sexual behaviour on unconsenting partners. These include the 'peeping Tom' or voyeur, the 'flasher', the person who has sex with children or animals and above all, the rapist. However, there are many forms of mild 'abnormal' behaviour which do not harm anyone and are simply crutches for people who cannot manage straight sex with sufficient confidence. Nevertheless, if a sexual practice or preference goes beyond what one partner thinks is normal or acceptable, then help should be sought from the family doctor who can give advice and arrange further help with a specialist counsellor if necessary.

Unusual sexual urges

Flashers, Peeping Toms and strangers who 'touch you up' in crowded places, all get their sexual satisfaction in what appears to most of us as 'kinky' ways. But to what extent do we all share these unusual sexual urges — and how abnormal are they?

We all have something of the exhibitionist, voyeur or frotteur in us. Haven't most of us, at one time or another, made an exhibition of ourselves by showing off or by dressing to attract attention to ourselves and our bodies? How many men and women can honestly say that, if they suddenly caught sight of someone naked, or of a couple making love, they wouldn't linger over the sight for at least a moment or two before turning away? And isn't it true that, however much we may dislike rush-hour crushes, sometimes the accidental contact of an attractive stranger's body against our own can be both warming and exciting, whichever sex we are? But for most of us, that's as far as it goes. Our sexuality is something personal, to be shared only with an intimate partner. We find it difficult to understand those people who flaunt their sexuality in antisocial, and what seems to us unfulfilling ways; indeed, we tend to refer to them as 'perverts'. Why do they behave as they do?

The 'flasher'

Exposing the genitals and/or masturbating publicly is known as behavioural exhibitionism and, in most countries, is forbidden by law. It is often thought that women are the sole victims of this offence (also called 'indecent exposure'), and this is usually though not always the case.

This kind of exhibitionist, commonly known as a 'flasher', exposes his penis to a woman, in the hope that she will react with horror, disgust or even excitement; he uses the most primitive and childlike way of displaying his virility. It is a natural part of growing up for boys and girls to say to one another 'I'll show you mine if you'll show me yours', and for adolescents to compare notes with friends of their own sex. Most of us, however, move on to realize that it is not the size and shape we are, but the way we behave which makes for mature adult relationships.

Behavioural exhibitionists get stuck at the childish stage. They suffer from a deep-rooted sense of sexual inadequacy, a feeling of unattractiveness or of sexual deprivation. Married men who have been caught exposing themselves may claim to have happy relationships with their wives, but in reality are likely to feel weak and insecure as lovers. Exposing themselves reassures them that, even if they are unable to lead a sexually fulfilling life with their own partner, their potency is at least sufficient to shock other women.

Outlets for exhibitionism

Behavioural exhibitionism occurs very little among women because the conventions surrounding female behaviour are still much stronger than they are for men. However, the conventions governing female dress are much weaker than they are for men's dress; women have a far greater outlet for socially acceptable exhibitionism when it comes to plunging necklines, slit skirts, transparent fabrics and skin-tight trousers. They also have more opportunities to work in jobs which allow them to flaunt their sexuality: they can become showgirls, hostesses, strippers or topless waitresses. Like their male counterparts, women with strong exhibitionist tendencies may feel sexually inadequate and may need the reassurance they get from the reactions of others — in this case, men lusting after them.

Nowadays men are also finding new and more socially acceptable outlets for any exhibitionist tendencies they may have. It is no longer considered effeminate for a man to take care with his appearance or to wear sexy clothes. And now that women are less inhibited about their own sexual needs and desires, men have the chance to become sex objects if they so wish. An indication of this can be seen in the increasing number of male strippers whose acts are extremely popular with female audiences.

Why then does a woman feel distressed when a man exposes himself to her in public, yet might feel quite happy, even sexually excited, when watching a male striptease show? Quite simply, the shock a woman feels is probably due to a fear of physical assault and rape, rather than disgust at the sight of the man's penis.

The voyeur or Peeping Tom

The voyeur's source of sexual satisfaction stems from watching people who are naked or having sex. When this is done without the other party knowing, the voyeur is usually referred to as a Peeping Tom.

Curiosity and a desire to see how we measure up sexually makes everyone voyeurs to some degree, even if it is confined to sneaking an inquisitive glance at someone undressing in a communal changing-room of a department store or in a locker-room. But, like exhibitionism, voyeurism can only be regarded as a deviation when it becomes a substitute for more conventional forms of sexual gratification.

Compulsive voyeurs have got stuck in the pattern of their childhood days, when they watched or heard their parents making love, and have somehow intertwined this subconsciously buried erotic experience with feelings of inadequacy. Women are not generally thought of as voyeurs, nevertheless some women who move into more uninhibited sexual areas, such as group sex, discover that they can be very turned on by the sight of other men and women making love.

The frotteur

Frotteurism consists of 'touching up' or genital rubbing up against another person (usually a complete stranger) in order to become sexually excited. Here again, there is a fine dividing line between what is normal and what is not. After all, touching and rubbing is an important part of the sexual play between two partners. But the person who compulsively rubs up against others in crowded places tends to be emotionally undeveloped.

Why do people become sexual nuisances?

Exhibitionism, voyeurism and frotteurism all have their roots in a disturbed childhood. If a person has been excessively indulged and spoiled, then the attention has been withdrawn suddenly, the withdrawal shock may cause the child to get emotionally stuck at that traumatic point, and he or she may well develop any of these tendencies in later life as part of a childlike attempt to gain attention from others.

By and large, these kinds of sexually maladjusted people are harmless enough. Like other sexual nuisances, such as obscene telephone callers — but

unlike rapists — their behaviour is based on a deep fear of participating in full, one-to-one sexual activity. However, they can seriously frighten young children who have not been forewarned about them (though it is worth remembering that hysterical adult responses to a child's reported experience are as likely to disturb the child as the experience itself). People who are sexual nuisances can be treated; psychotherapy and hypnosis, for instance, have both proved successful in helping those with antisocial exhibitionist, voyeuristic and frotteuristic tendencies. Provided such people can learn to recognize why they have come to behave in the way they do, they can be encouraged to move on to develop more adult and fulfilling patterns of behaviour.

Sexual deviations

Many people who regard certain sexual activities and fantasies as shocking, kinky or perverted do not realize that in a minor way they may in fact be using them to add excitement to their sex lives. So when exactly do certain types of sexual behaviour become really deviant?

Among the articles on sale in some sex shops, you may notice pictures, magazines, sexy clothes and sex aids associated with deviations. The emphasis is likely to be on sadomasochism, fetishism and transvestism. Today, popular opinion about these sexual activities is mixed. To some people, they are sick, sinful or weird, while to others they are no more than diversions which add excitement to sex. Some sexologists believe that what you do is less important than whether anyone involved (including yourself) is upset — if they are, then something should be done about it.

What are sexual deviations?

These opinions are important because quite a lot of guilt feelings arise from 'deviant' activities and fantasies, although virtually all of us enjoy such activities and fantasies at a modest level. This may surprise those who regard their love lives as conventional, yet a moment's thought will probably convince them that this is true. No one who affectionately smacks their partner's behind during lovemaking is thought of as sadistic, nor does a girl who undresses provocatively in front of her lover think of herself as a exhibitionist or of him as a Peeping Tom voyeur. If a man likes his partner to wear sexy underwear sometimes during sex, she will be unlikely to think of him as a fetishist. If sometimes she likes to be pounced on and seduced whilst she struggles gently and whispers 'Get off, you beast!', she won't be thought a masochist. But if sexual arousal entirely depends on such activities, or if fantasies about them are necessary before the person gets turned on, then doctors describe the activities and fantasies as true sexual deviations and the person who is dependent on them as sexually deviant.

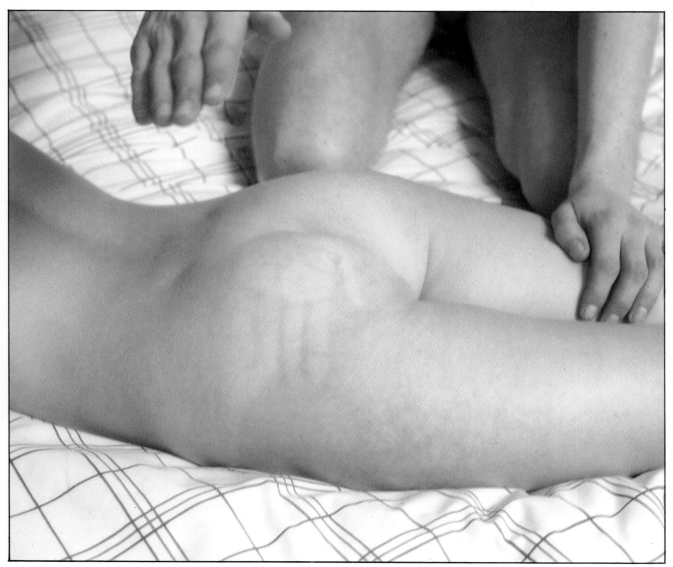

Why are men more deviant than women?

Women are beginning to realize that some of these more modest sexual deviations can occasionally be pleasurable. However, research has shown that few women feel the powerful attraction of a particular sexual variation in the way that some men do. Men, it seems, are more likely to have deviant fantasies than women. This is not because women are too shy to tell researchers about their fantasies, for wide-ranging surveys show that women do have sexual fantasies, but seldom are they of the 'kinky' type.

Why is this? Research shows that men are more sensitive to what they see (which has a lot to do with fantasy), and that their arousal, even when very young, is felt in the penis, causing erections, even when the reason for the arousal is not directly sexual, such as hunger or heat. This arousal may make a baby scream and his mother might smack him. The visual image of an angry mother is more easily remembered and associated with the smack, which can also increase the arousal. If this is repeated often, the association of sexual arousal with smacking may be reversed and the child may come to think that the smack causes the sexual pleasure.

Sexual reactions

This kind of association has also been demonstrated in a controlled experiment with adults. Men with conventional sexual interests were shown slides of a woman's shoe just before slides of sexy nude women. At first, the shoe produced no sexual reaction, but the nudes did and the men began to get erections. After several showings, however, the men began to get erections whenever the shoe was shown, even if the nudes did not follow. The expectation was enough — and the shoe had become associated with sexual pleasure. These examples show that the chance of picking up a random image and labelling it as sexual is greater for a man than for a woman.

Of course, if this stimulus-response mechanism were the only reason for sexual deviance, most men would become deviants, because most get smacked as children. Deviance is, however, much more likely if parents and other people in authority make the child believe that sex is 'sinful'. As a result, the youngster never learns to relate successfully to the opposite sex.

Boys also have more difficulty in developing

their own sexual identity than girls. This is because boys learn most of the rules on how to behave from their mothers (because mothers have traditionally been the ones to bring up the children), but then they have to break some of these rules and learn new ones in order to conform to society's idea of masculinity. These changes can be confusing. On the other hand, young girls learn the model for female behaviour from their mothers and they can retain that model for life.

Tradition also influences male and female behaviour during adolescence. The boy is supposed to make the first sexual moves and the girl has the

UNDERSTANDING SOME SEXUAL DEVIATIONS

Many people are unclear about what sexual deviations involve because they hear misleading catch-phrases and jokes about them. A deviant relies entirely on certain fantasies or activities for sexual arousal. Here are some definitions to help towards a clearer understanding.

Sadism can mean cruelty in general, but research shows that sexual sadism exists more in fantasy than fact, unless a masochist is involved or the person is deeply disturbed. Fantasies are of spanking, tying up and other dominating activities.

Masochism is complementary to sadism. The masochist enjoys being dominated even if it involves physical pain. A person can be both a masochist and a sadist.

Fetishism is having to rely on 'props' such as underwear, shoes, rubber, leather for sexual excitement. Unlikely non-sexual objects can arouse some people: handbags, prams, safety-pins. Also parts of the body — a breast or foot.

Transvestism is a wish to dress in the clothes of the opposite sex. This may be done for sexual stimulus or because the person really wants to 'belong' to the opposite sex, with very little arousal being involved — in which case the person may be a transexual.

Voyeurism is the desire to look at sexually exciting scenes without becoming involved. For example, a Peeping Tom peering in through a window at someone undressing, and some members of the audience at strip clubs and blue film shows can be called voyeurs, but only if it is their sole means of obtaining sexual satisfaction.

Exhibitionism ('flashing') is the counterpart of voyeurism, being a compulsion to expose the sex organs without becoming involved in any sexual activity.

Paedophilia is the ability to enjoy sex only with children. Fantasy plays a large part in the sex lives of paedophiles.

---

right to accept or reject him. Consequently, it is the boy whose amorous advances can get blocked — and if he already has alternative fantasies or activities that arouse him, he will tend to turn away from straight sex towards these alternatives if he is rejected often.

An interesting question is to what extent the influence of social tradition will decrease if present trends continue and fathers become more intimately involved in looking after and bringing up their children, and if women become less inhibited about being the active partner in sex.

What sort of men are deviant?

It is perhaps unfortunate that the popular image of the man with a special sexual liking is always so bad. He is either a creepy little fellow in a dirty raincoat or a crazed psychopath unable to control his desire to mutilate or kill his sex partners. But research has shown that these images are far from the truth, although it also shows that such men are different in some ways from others.

They are likely to be shy and reserved, to have been obedient when young, to be worriers — especially about relationships with others. They may feel lonely, be dissatisfied with their sex lives and have a tendency to depression. But when they do develop good relationships with women they are likely to be eager to make them happy. However, when it comes to sex itself, they are usually far more submissive than the average man. This may appeal to women who have fantasies of being adored, but not to those who like a more dominant man. But, even so, this picture is rather different from the popular idea of the sadistic unbalanced 'pervert'.

Treating deviants

There are of course sexual variations which are unacceptable. The compulsive exhibitionist (or 'flasher') and the Peeping Tom are usually harmless — they are actually scared of real sex, but they can be offensive and frightening. The person who desires sex with children (a paedophile) can be in an extremely serious state, as is someone who mutilates his sex partner before (or after) sex, or who lusts after animals, corpses or other inappropriate objects. These people have problems which possibly only a psychiatrist can tackle. However, nowadays many sex problems can be successfully treated by simple therapy. Modern methods are not always successful, but the chances of success are particularly good if the deviant person can establish a reasonably happy conventional sex life after his deviation has ceased to be attractive.

Treating sexual deviations

A dependence on a sexual deviation such as sado-masochism, fetishism, or transvestism can cause much unhappiness between partners. However, there are a number of modern treatments which have generally proved successful.

Many couples like to add a little extra excitement to their lovemaking: a man may be turned on if his lover wears stockings and suspenders, or she may be excited when he describes his favourite fantasy. However, for most people, such activities are not essential for enjoyable sex; they simply add spice to pleasure.

There are other people — usually men (see pages 177-178) — who depend on sado-masochistic, fetishistic or transvestite behaviour and fantasies if they are to be turned on. When such activities are essential, doctors call them sexual deviations.

It's difficult for most of us to understand the pleasure others get from what seems very strange behaviour. If we found out that a friend, neighbour or workmate liked to wear the clothes of the opposite sex, dress in a rubber catsuit, or be tied up and beaten during sex, we would at best think him (or her) rather pathetic or, at worst, morally evil.

However much a person enjoys his particular deviation, he cannot help but be aware of opinions like these. Although some people, and their partners, are happy with the deviation and reject the idea of a 'cure', many are very unhappy, fearing rejection by their families and friends. If a person wants to break his dependence on the deviation, modern treatments, which have generally proved successful, are available at psychosexual clinics.

Types of treatment

Modern treatments are based on the commonsense idea of the 'carrot and stick'. If you punish one kind of behaviour, it will decrease, whereas if you reward another kind of behaviour, it will increase.

Dominance and slavery are often a part of sexually deviant games and fantasies.

Aversion therapy

One of the first techniques used was called *aversion therapy*. The patient was shown slides depicting his favourite deviation. As soon as his penis became erect, he was given a harmless electric shock, usually between two fingers. Not unnaturally, the patient lost his erection. The process was repeated until the unpleasant electric shock was associated with the pictures of his deviation. He was no longer excited by the deviation and, it was hoped, would turn to more conventional sex as a permanent substitute.

Covert sensitization

There are obvious ethical objections to punishing people, even with their consent, and so doctors have devised other treatments. The method known as *covert sensitization* involves the patient imagining possible unpleasant consequences of his deviation — 'What if I were found out by my wife, neighbours, workmates or the police?' When he imagines his favourite activity, he moves on to the unpleasant consequences and an erection is less likely. In time, the deviation fails to produce an erection and is abandoned.

Thought stopping

In another treatment, called *thought stopping*, the patient fantasizes about his favourite deviation, then stops (sometimes by literally saying 'Stop!' to himself) and thinks of another, more acceptable, fantasy. This technique is practised in therapy until, when the fantasy intrudes in real life, merely saying 'Stop!' will prevent it, allowing the patient to connect pleasure with more conventional ways of making love.

Fantasy reshaping

These treatments can sometimes be distressing to the patient and, because they use the 'stick' rather than the 'carrot', demand quite a lot of will power. So an alternative and quite pleasant form of treatment has been evolved, called *fantasy reshaping*, which seems to be reasonably successful.

The patient is first told to masturbate to his favourite deviant fantasy, then when orgasm is inevitable to switch to another fantasy, previously agreed upon with the therapist as being more acceptable. After a time, the acceptable fantasy is switched in during masturbation a few seconds earlier so that some of the pleasure of orgasm becomes associated with it. In subsequent sessions, the acceptable fantasy is brought in even earlier, until it has totally displaced the original deviant fantasy. This treatment is successful because the patient himself controls the speed of change and so his pleasure in orgasm is never diminished.

Therapy may help the patient in more general ways besides dealing with a particular deviation. Research has shown that the man whose sex life is upsettingly deviant is generally more reserved, anxious and lonely than the average male, and is therefore likely to be sexually inhibited. The incidental advantages of therapy — being allowed to talk freely about sex, to masturbate, look at explicit pictures and to enjoy sex without disapproval — can make the patient feel less shy about sex and help give him the confidence that has much to do with happy lovemaking.

The partner's role in treatment

In the end, therapy by itself can only do so much. Good lovemaking involves two people. We are more likely to do things if they have pleasant consequences, so if a man visits a therapist to get rid of some deviant behaviour that embarrasses him and frightens his wife, and the therapy is successful, he must be rewarded with lots of love and sex from his partner. She may have to take the lead for a time in lovemaking, which may be difficult if she herself is inhibited and shy.

Nevertheless, if a man completes therapy and announces he is no longer addicted to the deviation that had previously been a bone of contention between him and his partner, and then gets a cool response, his 'cure' is not likely to last very long. After all, the therapist has taken away from the patient a great source of pleasure, and if alternative, equal pleasure is not substituted, it won't be surprising if he reverts to his previous deviant ways.

Is treatment always necessary?

Recently some doctors have suggested that it may not always be necessary to 'cure' someone who is sexually deviant. Sometimes partners tolerate or have been turned on to the deviation themselves and co-operate enthusiastically. In cases like this, when couples involve no one else, should doctors interfere and perhaps destroy the relationship? It is a difficult question, but it's clear from the few interviews with people who are happy with their deviation that some couples hotly reject the suggestion that they are 'ill'. After all, doctors cannot force people to accept treatment.

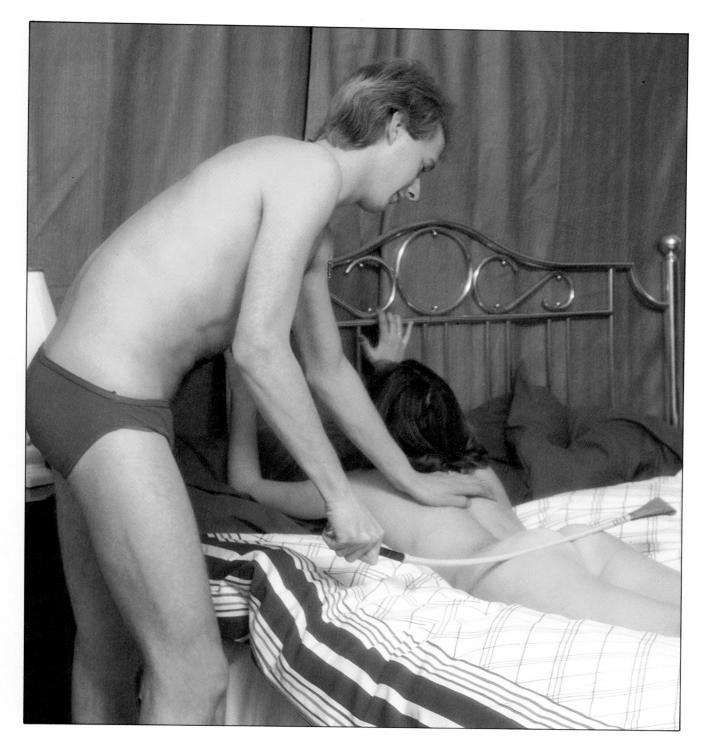

Tolerance and co-operation

It seems that the attitude of the partner is the key to how happy a person is with his deviation. Surprisingly, it seems that the partner need only tolerate the activity; co-operation in acting out the fantasy is of course welcome, but not essential. Only if the deviant person is too frightened to tell his partner about his desires, or has done so and received an angry, bitter or disgusted reaction is

For some people, deviation is a natural part of their relationship, but for others it can be very destructive.

there deep loneliness, frustration and unhappiness on both sides. But, on the other hand, research has shown that if the partner can accept the deviant as he is, realizing that he is not merely trying something new for kicks, but that his liking has existed since childhood, the situation is likely to be far better for the couple.

Why a man rapes

The horrifying crime of rape exists in all human societies, but the more we understand why men commit rape, the better the chance that we can create a healthy climate in which there is harmony, rather than fear, between the sexes.

Few subjects are surrounded by as much myth and lack of understanding as rape. For all the TV and newspaper coverage and public discussion, little is known about why some men rape. What we do know is that it is the most primitive expression of male hostility towards women.

Various motives for rape have been given, but they are sometimes based on prejudice and myth, rather than on fact. All too often, investigation of rape has concentrated on the woman's behaviour — what she was wearing, why she was out alone — instead of on the motives of the rapist. It is, in any

case, often difficult for researchers to collect evidence about rape because neither victim nor rapist wants to help analyze what happened.

Understandably, a raped woman usually wants to forget her experience as soon as possible. Given that she will often forgo the chance of punishing her attacker by complaining to the police (only 15 per cent of all rapes are believed to be reported to the police), it is not surprising that a woman is often reluctant to talk to researchers. She may well wonder what caused the man to rape her, but she will naturally be more concerned about her own

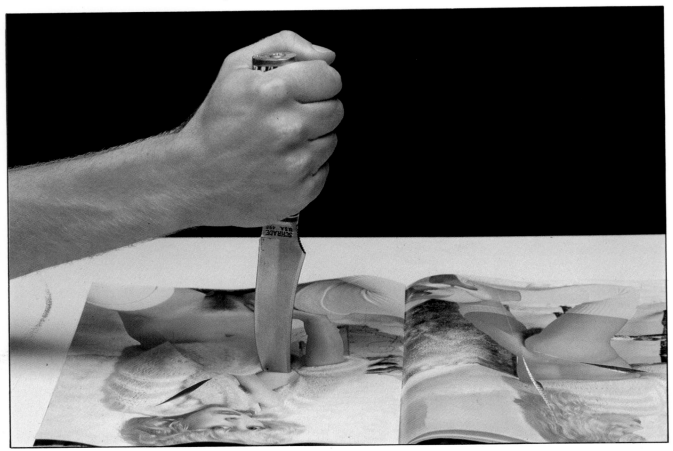

psychological, and sometimes physical healing.

Rapists themselves can also be unhelpful to researchers. Some rapists are keen to boast about their exploits, often telling misleading and exaggerated stories of the numbers of women they have raped. Others refuse to admit they have committed a crime, perhaps because they think that women 'ask for it', or because they want to escape the informal punishment dealt out by other prisoners, who often regard rape, particularly of older women and young girls, as the worst of crimes.

The mentality of rapists

Some studies of rapists have found that they express more rage and violence than other men — though such studies are sometimes carried out in the violent environment of prison — but there is little evidence that rapists' sexuality is in any way different or abnormal, or which supports the view that rapists are impotent and can only achieve erection and orgasm by forcing unwilling, frightened women to have sex.

There is no generally accepted psychological explanation for why a man rapes. Some psychologists believe that the key lies in the rapist's early relationship with his mother, and that a man who has always felt dominated by women, from his mother onwards, may rape to revenge himself on the female sex and to assert himself. Other experts think that a man rapes to convince himself that he is not homosexual. However, while these theories may be true for individual rapists, there is as yet no way of proving that they apply to every man who rapes.

Are rapists sick people?

It is still a common belief that rapists are psychopaths — mentally sick people who cannot control their violent urges. However, rape is not usually committed on the spur of the moment; some organizations have estimated that at least 70 per cent of rapes are planned. Instead of acting on impulse, the rapist can be a devious schemer who lays careful plans to rape a woman when she is alone in her home. Although such men's behaviour may seem obsessive, only a small minority of convicted rapists — in some countries under 3 per cent — are considered by the courts to be in need of psychiatric help in special hospitals.

A rapist is also not necessarily a stranger who rapes a woman in a dark alley. At least 50 per cent of rapes take place in the victim's home and some organizations which help rape victims believe that at least half the men who commit rape know their victims, as boyfriends, husbands (though the law often does not recognize that a husband can rape his wife), family friends and neighbours.

Is there a typical rapist?

In the hope of preventing rape, many people have tried to define what kind of man rapes. However, it seems there is no particular pattern to rape. A rapist may be young or old, he may come from any social class or background, may be married with a family or be single; he may rape once or several times, alone or with other men.

What does seem to link rapists is their lack of respect for, sometimes hatred of, women. They talk about their victims as if they were objects or property that they have a right to possess. However, some men who are not rapists also talk about women in this way — it is an old idea that women are the chattels of men who consequently have a right to control their sexuality — so these attitudes do not necessarily predict that a man will commit rape, though they make it more likely.

'Accidental' rape

The idea that men have stronger sex drives and so have a right to have sex with women is probably behind the idea that women often say 'No' when they mean 'Yes'. In his defence, an arrested rapist will frequently claim that there was a misunderstanding between the woman and himself, or that he was 'led on' by a provocative woman. There are people who believe that rape is a physical impossibility: if a woman doesn't want sexual intercourse, there are ways of preventing it.

There are, of course, times when a woman is rather reluctant to make love and does so to please her partner rather than herself. And some women can be provocative and teasing — in our society women are still encouraged to behave in this traditionally 'feminine' way. However, there is a world of difference between this and encouraging rape. There comes a point at which it is perfectly clear what a woman means: even if she cannot fight off her attacker, fear makes her vagina become dry and tight.

However, it is often difficult to prove rape in court since the law in Britain and many other countries demands that the man must believe that the woman did not consent. The line between reluctant consent and consent through fear is unclear precisely because the man has superior strength. He does not need to threaten directly — the woman knows he can hurt her if she does not co-operate. Faced with the choice between injury, or possibly even death, and rape, it is not surprising that many women give in.

Violence against women

Most studies of rape show that it is rarely simply a case of 'sex gone wrong' but a crime of violence against the victim. Apart from the brutality of forced penetration, which causes severe pain and internal tears and bruises, at least one third of rapes are accompanied by other types of sexual abuse and violence. Some rapists also punch or stab their victims, even after the terrified women have agreed to intercourse, and rapists who prey on courting couples often force the woman's boyfriend to watch, or even to participate.

Many rapists are also verbally violent towards women, saying, 'It's only what they deserve', and 'They want it anyway'. The violent images of much hard-core pornography reinforce this view, and some people (very often men) have said that women secretly want to be brutally violated and dominated by men. While some women have fantasies involving submission and domination, it is quite another thing to live out these fantasies in a brutal and degrading rape.

The connection between violence and rape is most clearly seen in gang rape. Men who would not

rape by themselves are encouraged to do so when they are with a group of other men; the group seems to release its members' inhibitions and to encourage them to prove that they are 'real men'. This explains the frequency of rape in war time, when raping the women of the defeated enemy is regarded as one of the fruits of victory.

Just as the presence of other men may encourage rape, so alcohol and certain drugs can release inhibitions. Gang rapes by groups of men who have been drinking and playing 'dare' games are fairly common in many societies.

Some studies in the United States have shown that there is a connection between rape and less serious crimes like burglary and common assault. This is especially true for men who are connected with the criminal underworld. Within this sub-culture, all kinds of violence, including rape, are much more accepted than in normal society — indeed, they may be the only ways in which a young man can prove himself.

Do rapists enjoy rape?

Rape allows a man to have sex on his own terms, without emotional commitment, and to act out the sadistic fantasies he would not dare to suggest in normal sex, but it is hard to tell whether a rapist actually enjoys the orgasm for its own sake. Women of any age are potential victims and their attackers usually dwell on the violence used or on their own sexual prowess, rather than the sexual pleasure they may obtain.

There is a small number of rapists whose enjoyment seems to come primarily from planning the crime and hiding from the police. These are perhaps the only genuine psychiatric cases: exhibitionists who seem to enjoy being notorious and feared more than they enjoy sex. They are also more likely to murder their victims in bizarre ways (it seems that the vast majority of rapists do not intend to kill their victims).

Social attitudes to rape

Rape is unique among serious crimes in that the victim is often considered to blame. The rape of a young, attractive woman is regarded by some people as almost understandable, while rapes of a child or an 80-year-old woman are viewed with horror and disgust.

Unfortunately, although rape arouses public horror and disgust, it also excites a kind of voyeurism — sensationalized details of sex crimes are a proven way to sell newspapers. This helps to create a climate in which the rapist is sometimes seen as a 'black hero', to be portrayed in books and films. Since many rapists are young men at an impressionable age, it is possible that they are influenced by these images.

There are no easy solutions to the problem of rape. However, it is clear that social attitudes to rapists and their victims must change so that the myths surrounding rape are swept away. In the end, though, what needs to change is the idea that sex and violence go naturally together. The more that people are encouraged to be loving towards each other in sexual relationships, the greater the chance that rape, one of the blights of our society, can be eliminated for ever.

Paedophilia

Caring parents are naturally anxious to protect their children from being sexually molested, and warn them not to talk to or accept sweets from strangers. However, much myth and ignorance surrounds paedophilia. Why, then, do some people have this sad sexual interest?

In many countries in the world paedophilia is against the law, the adult who is involved usually being charged with gross indecency. Psychologists and doctors have found it difficult to investigate paedophilia, not only because it is a crime and this prevents paedophiles from admitting their sexual interest, but also because it arouses such strong feelings of anger and disgust in most people. However, recent research has helped experts to understand paedophilia better, and has shown that some strongly held beliefs about the subject are based on myth and ignorance.

What is paedophilia?

It is surprising to many people to learn that, strictly speaking, the word 'paedophilia' does not mean 'sex with children' but 'love of children', and research does seem to suggest that very few paedophiles want actual intercourse with children. Although there are cases of intercourse between an adult and child, one expert has said that, as far as girls are concerned, 85 to 90 per cent of all sexual experiences with adults take the form either of exhibitionism, such as 'flashing', or of having their bodies touched and that the percentages for boys are probably the same. Other research has found that there are some paedophiles who have never wished for direct sexual contact with children. Instead, they are generally satisfied with affectionate cuddling.

Who are paedophiles?

Much myth and confusion surrounds paedophiles themselves. Many people think of them as 'dirty old men', and it is certainly true that paedophilia, like other sexual deviations, attracts men far more than it does women (see pp. 177–178). However, by no means are paedophiles all elderly. It seems that they can be divided into three age groups: adolescence, the middle to late thirties and old age—the last, surprisingly enough, comprising the smallest category.

While most paedophiles are men, there have been cases of women seducing children, and some people have suggested that our social customs may perhaps lead us to ignore paedophilic behaviour in women and to accuse men wrongly. In our society, it is acceptable for a women to talk to, kiss, or cuddle other people's — sometimes strangers' — children; if a man, who simply likes children, does this, he risks being labelled paedophilic.

Most parents believe their children to be in the greatest danger from strangers. However, research has shown that the majority of paedophiles are known to the child. A study of 79 cases found that 34 per cent of the adults involved were teachers or social workers, 30 per cent were religious figures such as clergymen, choirmasters or Sunday school teachers, and another 20 per cent were youth leaders or scout masters. Only 2 per cent were complete strangers to the child — most of the remaining 14 per cent were either family friends or relatives known and trusted by the child.

Like other sexual deviants, paedophiles may not be exclusively attached to their deviation. Some at least can, and do, maintain relationships with adult partners, though their main sexual interests will be directed towards children. (Although recent research suggests that, in a few cases at least, it is possible to increase the paedophile's interest in adult sexual partners.)

Though some studies have found evidence of psychological disturbance, there is little evidence to suggest that paedophiles are psychologically different, except for their sexual likings, from the rest of humanity. They seem to be generally physically healthy, and most studies have found few signs of aggressive behaviour or severe personality disorder.

The causes of paedophilia

Psychological abnormality does not seem to be the usual cause of paedophilia, but some psychologists have suggested that paedophiles may differ from other people in the way they regard the world of adults and children. Paedophiles seem to see people chiefly in terms of whether they are innocent or sophisticated, submissive or dominant. To a paedophile, adult women seem especially dominating and, to some extent, sophisticated and therefore frightening. In contrast, he sees children as submissive and innocent.

There is no evidence that people are born with tendencies to paedophilia. Studies of paedophilia and other sexual deviations indicate that such attitudes are more likely to be caused by events in childhood, which make paedophilic behaviour likely but do not produce it unless a person's normal sexual development is in some way blocked in later life (see page 177). For instance, the paedophile may lack the social skills necessary to put him sufficiently at ease with adults to attract them sexually. In support of this idea is the fact that the peak ages at which paedophilic behaviour occurs — adolescence, the approach of middle age and old age — are those when normal sexual outlets are likely to be blocked, though without the necessary childhood experiences, it is unlikely that paedophilia will develop.

The victims

A recent survey in Britain found that some people believe that paedophiles can be sexually interested in children as young as two years old. In fact, a paedophile is usually attracted by the pre-pubertal

In our society, women, unlike men, are not suspected of paedophilia if they affectionately cuddle children.

child of between seven and 14 years. It seems that the pre-pubertal appearance of the child is very important, and when a paedophile can also sustain a sexual relationship with an adult, he will most often choose a slightly-built person. In addition, there is evidence that many paedophiles are very much turned *off* by children who are growing pubic hair and by boys whose voices are breaking.

So the man who is turned on by the school girl image is not a paedophile. He is more likely to be a fetishist who is mainly interested in the traditional gym-slip uniform. In his fantasies the girl will be between 16 and 18 years old and will always be wearing school uniform — a fantasy girl

without clothes will not attract him half so much.

Both boys and girls can be victims of paedophilia, though some people have suggested that a paedophile is more likely to be a homosexual. However, homosexual paedophilia may seem more common simply because of the number of offences committed by men who work with boys — scout masters, schoolmasters, youth workers — who may have little chance to meet young girls. Because these men hold positions of trust with children, their crimes may appear more shocking and so may be more highly publicized than similar crimes against girls. Other people have argued that since we do not know how many paedophiles there are in the population, hetero-sexual paedophiles might just as easily be in the majority. We simply do not know.

When paedophilia takes place it is seldom simply a case of rape or assault of a child by an adult which the child could not have avoided. This does happen of course, but one study has concluded that in most reported cases of paedophilia, the children could have avoided the experience.

This is not to say that children initiate or encourage sexual involvement with adults — though there are almost certainly a very few such sexually precocious children. Children may allow the attentions of adults simply because they do not realize that what is happening is wrong and that they should object. Most parents warn their children not to talk to or accept car rides or sweets from strangers, but rarely explain exactly why strangers are dangerous.

Children are capable of sexual feelings (see Child sexuality, on pages 8-12) and they may not connect a sexual experience with their parents' warnings. The situation is further confused because so few paedophilic assaults are in fact committed by strangers. We tell our children to obey older people because adults know best, so it is not really surprising if children do not reject the sexual advances of, say, the local clergyman or social worker, who is not only an adult but is also a trusted figure in the community.

A child victim need not be affected in the long term by paedophilia and usually grow up quite normally, just like any well-adjusted child.

The effect on the child

Ideally, a sexual relationship should take place between equals, and so in cases of paedophilia — even when the child does not resist — there is an imbalance which some people believe may well harm a child's later sexual development.

Many psychologists today believe that such harm can be considerably reduced if any investigation into an incident is carried out unemotionally and calmly. It may be difficult for parents to remember this when they discover their child has been sexually molested, but it does seem to be true that when there is a dramatic family scene, with mother crying and father threatening to kill the man involved, the effect on the child of this tension is likely to be more disturbing than that of the sexual experience itself.

The research which has produced this evidence is very recent, and it may be that the effects of this kind of childhood experience may not appear for many years. However, when children whose parents behaved calmly are compared with children whose parents did not, it appears that the advice to keep calm is extremely valid.

Treating paedophilia

Many of the techniques used to treat other sexual deviations (see pages 179-181) have been used successfully in cases of paedophilia. However, with deviations such as fetishism and sado-masochism, the therapy is designed not to remove the deviation entirely, but to give the man alternative ways of obtaining sexual pleasure and the ability to come to terms with his deviation. There can be no such compromise in treating paedophilia, since it is a crime in many countries.

As a result, therapy must not only remove the paedophilic behaviour but also replace it with allowed sexual activity. In some cases, training in social skills has been given to help the paedophile make normal sexual approaches to adults. However, although success has been reported with convicted offenders in prison (where, perhaps, any sympathetic treatment would be helpful), little is known about whether any improvement is maintained in the outside world. In short, although doctors and psychologists have had some success in treating paedophilia, and research into the area is continuing, we still have a very long way to go before it is possible to 'cure' every case of paedophilia.

Incest

Sex between close relatives is forbidden in most societies and for centuries has been regarded with horror and fascination. But few of us really understand why incest arouses such strong emotions, why it happens and why it is forbidden.

In most societies, including our own, there is some kind of 'incest taboo' which bans sexual activity between people related by blood. 'Incest' can describe many kinds of relationship, from adolescent experimentation to life-long involvement. Some relationships — such as marriage with a niece — are against certain religious laws, but in some countries are not illegal in the eyes of the civil authorities and very few people would judge such relationships to be truly incestuous; when most people speak of incest they are thinking of sex between brother and sister, or parent and child.

How common is it?

Actual figures for incest have only become available since it was made illegal. In many countries this has happened within the last hundred years and during that time it seems to have declined. But because it is such a taboo area, many cases are never reported and so no one can say definitely how common incest is. Activities, such as heavy petting, stopping short of intercourse may not be illegal, and while children may be taken into care if they are felt to be in danger, these cases will not appear in the incest statistics.

It is likely that incest is more common in families living in isolated country areas. There are less likely to be inquisitive neighbours to report their suspicions to the authorities; children have fewer opportunities to make friends outside the family; and the occasional child born as a result of incest can be more easily passed off as belonging to a married couple in the family.

Brother-sister incest

This is the kind of incest that parents are most likely to encounter, although it happens in only a small minority of families. Most psychologists agree that it is less damaging in the long term than incest between parents and children.

Children are very curious about sex, especially at puberty: they want to explore their sexuality in the company of others. This kind of sexual experimentation is not 'sinful' but a natural part of growing up. If they have few friends brother and sister may turn to each other.

Parents who discover such a relationship should try to end it, but they should not over-react as this will do more harm than good. Psychologists have concluded that sex play between brother and sister is no more harmful than the same kind of behaviour with children outside the family. Long-term harm is more likely to be done by the punishment inflicted by the shocked parents rather than by the sexual activities themselves. If children who have always played, dressed and bathed together are suddenly separated, the resulting loneliness will be a hurtful childhood memory.

Innocent sexual exploration between brother and sister usually ends when the children find friends outside the family. Long-term damage can happen when they fail to do this, either because there are few young people in the area or because possessive parents prevent them from making friends. In these circumstances, brother and sister can discover a sexual attraction for each other and an emotional bond develops, sometimes leading to a life-long relationship, which can never be really fulfilling because of their guilt.

Father-daughter incest

It's very common for a man to be surprised, and perhaps a little shocked, to find that his daughter is changing from a child into a sexually desirable woman. He may even feel supplanted in her affections by her boyfriends. This of course does not mean that he would like to make love to her, but the situation can arise if the man's marriage is unhappy or if he is sexually inadequate.

If he is widowed or unhappily married, a man's natural affection for his daughter may be confused with his sexual desires, and the daughter may seem to be the ideal substitute for her mother. Sometimes a man finds adult women frightening and feels he can only assert himself with much younger girls. If, in addition, he is afraid to seek partners outside the family, he may turn to his daughter. Incest may first happen when the father is drunk, loses control and makes love to his daughter. Unless the girl has the courage to resist the first time, it can easily happen again.

Sometimes, however, the girl is a willing partner. At puberty a girl's instinct is to reject her mother — she may well see her as a rival — and to test her charms on a mature man. If the girl's natural feelings are exaggerated by bad relations with her mother and marital difficulties between the parents, the situation may develop into incest.

Mother-son incest

Mother-son incest certainly occurs, but prosecutions are rarer, perhaps because most people consider an adolescent boy to be less vulnerable than a girl. It usually occurs in families where the father is absent for long periods, the son is an only child, and the mother has not broken the habit, started in early childhood, of letting the boy sleep in her bed. Sometimes a woman who has a poor relationship with her husband may try to hold on to the affections of her son, particularly if he is about to leave home and she sees herself alone in an unhappy marriage. Unless the son rebels against his mother's smothering love, she may find herself responding to his virility.

Does incest produce damaged children?

The 'incest taboo' is very ancient and we can only guess at its origins. Many people still believe that the ban exists because children of incestuous relationships are likely to inherit all the genetic faults of their parents, resulting in deformities, idiocy and stillbirths. There is some evidence that where

Incest with a parent disrupts the family and causes immense unhappiness, guilt and hatred.

a related couple themselves have inherited some abnormality they are more likely to pass it on to their children. However, recent research has shown that closely related healthy parents are no more likely to have damaged children than healthy people who are not related.

Family relationships

A more likely reason for the almost universal ban on incest is that it is concerned not with 'sin' but with social survival and order. Incest disrupts the family as a whole and hence the society in which its members live. Family relationships will clearly be harmed if a daughter becomes her mother's rival for the father's affections, or if father and son vie with each other for the mother's. Perhaps because it is less destructive of family relationships, brother-sister incest is held to be less damaging.

The Oedipus complex

The idea of incest has had a strong effect on the human mind and has inspired myth and legend.

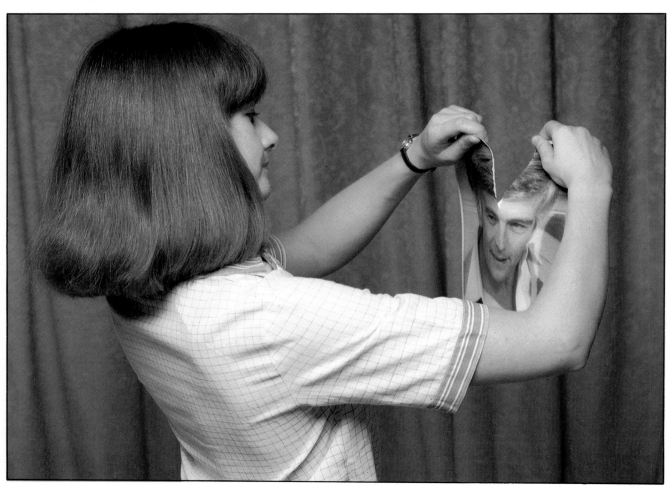

A person involved in incest will find it difficult to form happy relationships like those shown here.

According to one of the most famous incest myths, a shepherd in Ancient Greece was ordered to kill the baby Oedipus, but failed to do so. When he grew up, Oedipus returned home and unwittingly killed his father and married his mother.

During his investigations, Freud identified the instinct which makes children want to form sexual relationships with their parents and named it the Oedipus complex after the Oedipus myth. The child is sexually attracted to the parent of the opposite sex, seeking assurance of the parent's love and protection from the world outside the family. As a normal part of growing up, the child learns that he or she must fulfill any sexual needs with a partner outside the family. The Oedipus complex is dealt in detail with on pages 26–30.

Confusion and guilt

Incest, particularly with a parent, makes it much more difficult for the child to break away from the family. The child feels confused because, while he (or she) loves and wants to please the parent, he realizes that the parent has involved him in something that most people consider to be wrong. He may come to hate the offending parent and may feel guilt since, however impossible it was to refuse, he may feel the situation is all his fault. These emotionally damaging feelings of guilt can often be carried into adulthood.

People who have been damaged in this way can be helped by psychotherapy to resolve their difficulties, but it is a long process and so anyone who is worried about incest should seek professional help immediately at a psychosexual clinic attached to a hospital.

Transexuals

Today, we are told that we should accept each other for what we are, rather than for what we appear to be. Why, then, do transexuals still face being branded as 'freaks' if they, too, claim that right and want to live as the sex they feel they really are?

Transexuals are people who physically belong to one sex but who are totally convinced that they belong to the other one. They are *not* effeminate homosexuals. They are quite certain that nature has made a terrible mistake and placed them in a body of the wrong sex, making them male when they feel they are female, or vice versa.

Transexual or transvestite?

Transexualism is thus probably not the same thing as extreme transvestism, although there is still some controversy over the point. In transvestism, people merely enjoy wearing the clothes of the opposite sex because it either increases their sexual arousal or relaxes them and allows them to express characteristics and attitudes shown by the opposite sex. In transexualism, however, the person simply wants to *be* of the opposite sex.

There are other ways in which transexualism differs from transvestism. The urge towards transvestite behaviour comes and goes: in transexuals, the compulsion is continuous. Transvestites still value the sex organs with which they were born: many transexuals hate and despise their own sex organs, and will sometimes go as far as mutilating them in an effort to rid themselves of the evidence of their original sex. Also, most transvestites are males, whereas transexualism is shown by both males and females.

Yet, despite all these differences, the distinction between transexualism and transvestism is not absolute. This may seem unimportant to anyone who is neither transvestite nor transexual, but nowadays it is possible to have what is popularly called a 'sex-change' operation which radically alters the appearance of the sex organs from that of one sex to the other. Obviously, it is important that irreversible surgical procedures are not carried out on a person who might regret the change later, however much he or she desires it at the time. After all, the transexual starts life on one side of the gender fence. He or she is not a *hermaphrodite,* a person showing the sexual characteristics of both male and female.

However, some people mistakenly believe that they are transexuals. An example of such unwitting self-deception has been cited in the case of a man requesting a 'sex-change' operation who lived up to all the standards by which a transexual is judged to be genuine. Some almost intuitive feeling nevertheless told the man's consultant that something was not quite right: accordingly,

observation was continued while the patient was given tablets containing a female hormone which, among other effects, would encourage the development of breasts. This in time occurred, but with this development the patient surprisingly abandoned his desire to have a 'sex-change' operation and stated that he no longer believed himself to be really a female.

Learning to live and dress as a woman often becomes an important part of a male transexual's life.

Are people born transexuals?

The question arises of whether a person is born transexual or acquires the desire to change sex as a result of experiences in childhood, but this cannot yet be answered for certain. There is a feeling among researchers that the cause is at least partly physical, but evidence has been difficult to find; no signs of any differences in the genes (which carry from parent to child most of the instructions concerning our physical make-up) and few convincing differences in the hormone levels between transexuals and non-transexuals have been found, making it look as if transexualism is purely psychological — all in the mind.

Reports showed that some males who had had 'sex-change' operations were no happier after the event than they were before. The cause of transexualism was therefore thought to be due to an unusual upbringing.

Recently, however, research has shown evidence that a substance called *H-Y antigen* is present in the skin of male-to-female transexuals but not in ordinary males. This substance also seems to be present in normal females but not in that of female-to-male transexuals. Research is in its infancy, but it does reopen the issue of whether transexualism is 'born in' or acquired.

Towards the 'sex change'

We know that no persuasion, expert or otherwise, is likely to alter the transexual's determination to change sex. No deep analysis or behavioural therapy is likely to assist in keeping the transexual content with his or her sex. Therapy is therefore geared towards helping him or her learn to live as a member of the opposite sex and to deal with other people's reactions.

As the technique for female to male 'sex-change' surgery is rather more individual than male to female surgery, this article deals with the pre-surgery preparation and the operation itself from the point of view of a male transexual who wants to become a woman. Female transexuals will get a clearer picture of their own particular possibilities if they discuss their case with a specialist.

The male transexual will in all probability already have been practising behaving as a woman, in dress, make-up and manner. Although treatment can modify the voice quality, much will already have been achieved by voice control.

Indeed, the performance of female impersonators on television or in the theatre demonstrates the ease with which a female voice can be produced by many males.

Taking oestrogen — the principal female hormone — also assists feminization to some extent if continued for some time. This hormone lowers the sex drive, calms the personality, softens the complexion and encourages breast development, increases the size of the nipples and decreases the growth of body hair. Growth of hair on the head is often improved: facial hair, unfortunately, is not much affected, and generally has to be removed by electrolysis.

Interestingly, having reached this stage, many transexuals never go beyond this point and actually have a 'sex-change' operation. Instead, having learned to pass as women, they gradually sever connections with their previous life as a male; they usually move from home and begin a **new life as a woman. There is no reason why the** accomplished transexual should be recognized as such.

In certain cases, however, a consultant may consider that the 'sex-change' operation would benefit a male transexual, but it will be made clear that the words 'sex change' are not entirely accurate, because although much change can be achieved, the result never enables the transexual to function totally as a woman in the sexual sense. The transexual who has become a woman will obtain pleasure from breast stimulation, can have intercourse as a woman but, being without ovaries or a womb, will never menstruate or become pregnant. Whether she will wish to have sex is another matter because the sex drive of the transexual is usually low. And, of course, she remains male in chromosome terms: to change that would mean changing every cell in her body.

The 'sex-change' operation

There are three main procedures in the operation. The transexual is castrated — that is to say, the testicles are either removed completely or surgically put out of both sight and action, the penis is amputated, and an artificial vagina and labia (vaginal lips) are created by plastic surgery.

Testicle removal is straightforward, but some surgeons prefer to retain them but move them (still connected) from the scrotal sac to inside the abdominal wall where they will be invisible and cannot be touched; they can no longer function in reproduction but they can still function as a gland — there is some evidence that the testicles in transexual men produce more oestrogen than is normal, and so the feminizing influence is strengthened.

Removal of the penis is also simple, but care has to be taken that the urethra (the tube in the penis through which the urine is discharged) still functions adequately in spite of its greatly reduced length, and does not close up as the scar tissue heals after surgery.

The creation of a vaginal-type opening, complete with vaginal lips made from the skin of the scrotal sac, is complex. A pouch or cavity about eight or nine inches long is prepared in the perineum (behind the scrotal sac but in front of the anus) and the channel is lined — often with the skin of the amputated penis turned inside out. Using this skin is better than taking skin from other parts of the body because it has no body hair and has nerve endings which increase its resemblance to a female sex organ. Whatever the technique, however, much aftercare must go into ensuring that the vaginal opening does not gradually close up as time goes on. The orifice has to be stretched regularly, either with the fingers or by artificial means, otherwise it can close up completely and a new operation will be necessary.

After the change-over

Whether or not the transexual undergoes a 'sex change' operation, there comes a point where she presents herself to the world as a woman, living a woman's life and displaying the femaleness which she has always thought of as being her real nature. She will for some while periodically visit a psychiatric counsellor so that any problems arising from her new personality, or from adapting herself to her new way of life, may be fully discussed.

It is only too easy for others to point to these visits as evidence of instability, but, almost inevitably, the changes in life-style involved in changing a sex-role bring stresses that cannot be relieved simply by a quick chat to a friend. Many of the transexual's former friends will in any case have now been discarded to make the change-over as discreet as possible, and not many new friendships may yet have been sufficiently established to help with the transexual's unusual experience.

Yet even experienced researchers are wary of talking about the average transexual's emotional state, since there are so many differences in their lives *before* they cross the bridge between the sexes, that making too many general statements about them would be unwise. However, it would seem from clinical experience that transexuals who try to live quite ordinary lives, who find themselves a job and become part of 'normal' society, generally acquire a better self-image and have fewer problems than transexuals who remain detached from life around them.

Nowadays, the transexual is less alone than she used to be. Quite apart from official helpers from the counselling world, there are societies in many countries formed exclusively for (and by) transexuals and transvestites whose combined experience and support can do much to help with any difficulties. The organization of such societies varies, but will always provide ways in which members can correspond, talk to each other and meet socially. Even the most conventional of us knows how useful it is to have someone to talk to when problems arise, and the rarer the difficulty, the more valuable that sympathetic someone becomes.

The transexual can form long-term relationships and can find as much contentment as other people do, but the road to that contentment is not easy. He or she will need as much understanding and as little harassment as possible.

Sex in Later Life

Ageing brings emotional and physical problems that can affect your sex life. Some people even think there is something unnatural or 'wrong' in sex after a certain age. However, many couples find that as their understanding of each other deepens with age so does their sexual relationship become more satisfying. Where there are problems these can usually be resolved, and there is no reason why older couples should not enjoy sex as much as the young.

The female menopause

The menopause is simply another chapter in a woman's life – so why do so many fear it, feeling that the door to everything that gives them pleasure is about to be slammed in their face? By coming to terms with any changes she may experience, a woman can enter middle age enjoying life to the full.

It's a good thing that the expression 'change of life' is disappearing and the sooner we get rid of it altogether the better. Women are changing all the time, both physically and emotionally, and the menopause is one of the stages all women go through. The word menopause actually means the end of the monthly periods, when the ovaries stop producing a monthly egg and stop secreting oestrogen. When this happens the woman is no longer able to conceive, and because she has to adapt to a diminished supply of hormones (the body's level of progesterone has also reduced) she may have to put up with some uncomfortable symptoms until the body readjusts itself to its new state.

Facing up to the inevitable

The menopause does not mean a total 'change of life' nor does it herald the onset of all kinds of frightening diseases, as old wives' tales would have us believe. A woman should be used to changes in her body. They are inevitable because there is nothing static about the human body and the more a woman understands what is happening the less worried she will be. The onset of puberty — the time when periods first begin — rarely causes anxiety and the girl usually takes the whole enormous business of growing into womanhood in her stride. Pregnancy and motherhood is another tremendous change which the majority of women sail through with little difficulty. The menopause, however, is often presented as something horrifying which spells the end of all the pleasant things of life. The age at which the menopause begins varies considerably: it generally starts between 45 and 52, although it can begin as early as 35 or as late as 55. If a woman has had a hysterectomy it doesn't mean she is menopausal even though she will no longer have periods.

The first signs

The first sign of approaching menopause is the changing in the pattern of periods, and this can happen in various ways. The loss of blood may remain the same, but the intervals in between periods may become increasingly longer or the periods may be regular but lighter. It is also quite normal for a woman's periods to become irregular — perhaps even stop for a year — and then return to normal, or stop suddenly without having become scanty or irregular.

There are other patterns which are not strictly due to the menopause, none of which are necessarily serious, but all need medical attention because they can make you feel ill and depressed. You should consult your doctor if your periods appear every two or three weeks, are much heavier than usual or you experience flooding with large clots. Also watch out for bleeding, spotting or a brownish discharge in between periods; periods lasting much longer than usual; blood staining after intercourse, or on straining; bleeding after an interval of a year — this may well be the final period, but let the doctor decide. The causes of most of the disturbances are usually quite easily dealt with.

How it can affect you

The ending of the periods is the only thing that is common to all women at this time. There are other symptoms experienced by a great number of women — but by no means all — and some of these can start long before any change in the periods.

The most common of these are hot flushes, and they may average six or more a day. There is no way of telling how long they will last, and sometimes they do not appear until well after the periods have finished.

A hot flush can range from a warm glow to the kind of heat that sends sweat pouring all over your body. It can appear on the face only, or creep up from your legs over your back and chest and finish at the neck. Or it can appear unexpectedly as sweating of the face, body and head.

It is not known exactly what causes hot flushes, but they are due to a large extent to a lack of oestrogen, the sex hormone we begin to lose at the onset of the menopause, and to over sensitivity of the nervous system.

The other most common complaint is vaginal dryness. This is the result of a reduction in the secretions of the vaginal wall, and it usually occurs when the menopause is well advanced. It can be particularly distressing, especially as the vagina narrows and the vaginal skin becomes thinner, often causing intense irritation and making intercourse painful or even impossible, but it responds quickly to medication.

There are a number of other symptoms that some women experience at this time, but because the hormone imbalance can affect us both emotionally and physically it is difficult to separate what is due to natural ageing and what is

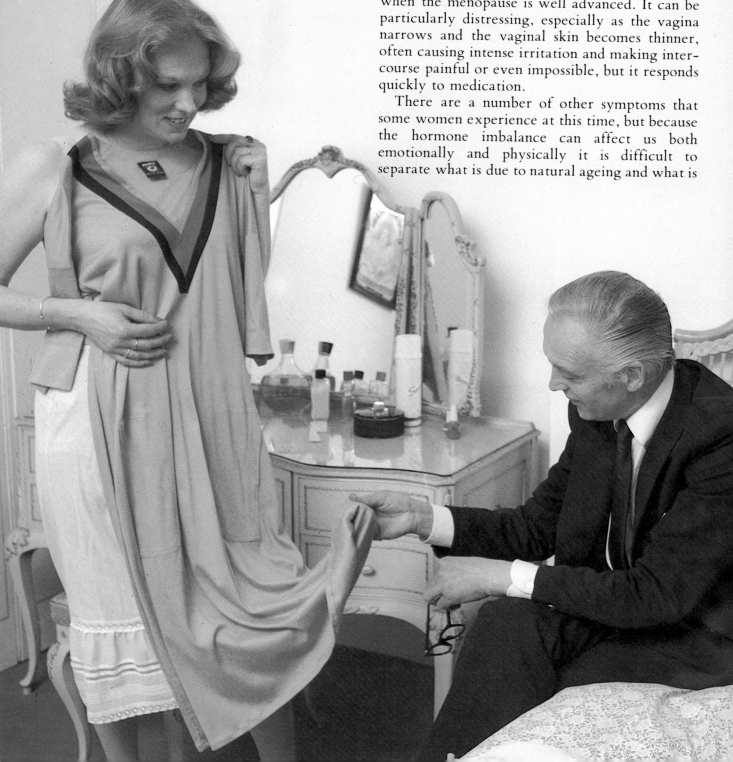

caused by the actual menopause. It is as well to know what symptoms you may encounter, however, because most of them respond well to treatment, and you need not fear you have some horrible illness! Some common symptoms are: palpitations, dizziness, itching all over the body, aches and pains in the joints, loss of healthy bone (osteoporosis), sleeplessness, swollen ankles, fatigue, depression.

Treatment

Doctors are now more sympathetic to the problems that can arise at this time, and they no longer believe it is all in the mind, telling a woman to pull herself together, take a holiday, or prescribing large doses of tranquillizers and tonics. But medical opinion varies considerably on what symptoms require treatment, and what treatment should then be given. Women who suffer severely from menopausal symptoms may be given Hormone Replacement Therapy, which involves taking the hormone oestrogen (and possibly progesterone) in the form of pills, injections and creams. HRT will only be given where it is absolutely necessary.

It is generally accepted that the body loses vitamin E just at the time when it most needs it and nutritionists often agree that an additional intake at the time of the menopause can help with hot flushes, sleeplessness and depression. Some people believe that combined with vitamin B and ginseng, vitamin E may produce a feeling of well-being.

Hot flushes are common but distressing – relaxing when you feel one coming on can certainly help.

Nevertheless, it should not be taken indiscriminately, particularly if there is a history of diabetes or high blood pressure. It is important to remember that even vitamins taken in excess can be harmful.

To have the least possible trouble during and after the menopause, you need to keep yourself as healthy as possible, and this means watching your food intake very carefully. Increased calcium is vital because calcium is lost owing to the lack of ovarian hormones, and you need calcium for healthy bones and to discourage osteoporosis. Calcium is present in many fresh foods, particularly cheese, milk and milk products, potatoes and fish. But you also need vitamin D to enable the body to absorb the calcium, and cod liver oil tables are highly recommended as a valuable source of both vitamin A and D. These two vitamins prevent premature ageing and help with the circulation.

Women also have a poor mineral intake at this time and this can be corrected by taking treacle (molasses). It is also a splendid source of iron, excellent for women who suffer from anaemia.

Constipation can be a problem, and here again it should be tackled by eating plenty of roughage in the form of wholemeal bread, bran, and plenty of uncooked fruit and vegetables.

Learning to live with the menopause

For many women it is the fear of losing their sex appeal that worries them most. Particularly those who have had a hysterectomy, when they believe that the removal of the womb means the end of all sexual feelings. This is *not* true. The womb's only duty is to house and nourish a baby, and its removal has no effect on sexual desire. In fact, a woman's sex life often improves once she no longer has to worry about becoming pregnant. It has been discovered that women have a special need for sexual love at this time. So the taboos about when love-making should stop can seriously restrict a husband and wife's attitude to life. Sexual intercourse and a loving relationship can and does go on well into old age.

Perhaps too much has been written about the negative aspects of the menopause in a worthy campaign to bring the distress many women suffer to the attention of the medical world. In fact as many women as one in four notice very little change, and although most women do suffer some troublesome symptoms many do not require medical attention at all. Because it is an individual

Telling yourself that you are still attractive, and finding new interests, makes all the difference.

experience it varies with different women and the emotional aspect is sometimes the most difficult to overcome without medical help.

The menopause is not a disease and should not be viewed with dread. The normal processes cannot be halted, neither can a woman remain young forever. To grow older is nothing to be ashamed of, nor should it be fought in the interests of husband and family by resorting to plastic surgery to retain a youthful appearance. But that does not mean you should let yourself go and lose interest in your appearance. Although you will undoubtedly change somewhat, you do not have to lose your looks, your figure or your sexual attractiveness as you get older. It is the loss of confidence that does most damage at this time, and the menopause is often used as an excuse to bemoan the loss of looks, the husband's lack of interest and the futility of everyday life. In fact, the root of these troubles can often be traced back to earlier years, when too little attention was paid to diet and skin care. As one should prepare for pregnancy, so should one prepare for middle age and ultimately old age. Regardless of her circumstances, a woman must ultimately look to herself for help. An effort should be made to read more, take up new hobbies, develop new interests and seek new friends.

The menopause is often a time of moods and depressions, and these are more difficult to cope with because they come so unexpectedly. A once placid woman may find she has developed all kinds of complexes about herself and other people, and

Get as much exercise in the open air as you can.

she may have strange panicky feelings that persist for no apparent reason. Other women complain of blurred vision, a dry mouth and muzzy headaches. It can be a difficult time for the family too, and they need to be made to understand that the menopause is a passing phase.

Making the most of life

Tell yourself you're an attractive woman, that you've got more to offer and that you're going to make the most of the next thirty years. If you get hot flushes, try to keep a sense of humour about them. Many women who have previously suffered from the cold find them a lovely source of inexpensive heat in the winter, and others tell themselves it's cheaper than having a Turkish bath! It's possible to 'go along' with them too. When you feel one coming on ride with it, don't fight it, and you will often find it doesn't develop into an all enveloping sweat bath because of the lessening of tension. If you have friends going through the same thing, try laughing about it together.

It is, of course, more difficult for women who go out to work to laugh off a hot flush when they are in the middle of talking to a customer or having an important board meeting. They feel it undermines their authority or makes them an object of fun. Yet, in fact, these things are hardly noticed or, if they are, they are more likely to be regarded as a flash of anger or irritability. It is well known that women often blush and to the disinterested a hot flush is simply that.

If you don't want the dreaded middle aged spread, watch your food intake and don't blame your glands for your putting on weight. Eating more food than your body needs is the usual cause of weight gain, although you are more likely to fluctuate at this time. Get into the open air as much as you can and walk as much as possible. You don't need any extremes of diet or exercise but you must have a regular, healthy pattern of living.

After a while, the body adapts itself and you will regain your equilibrium. It may take a matter of months, or be spread over a number of years so that just when you feel it's all over you get another hot flush! If you have not wasted your time fretting over what has happened you will be well adjusted to middle age and able to make full use of your life. Do you really want to miss out by believing that the menopause is the end of everything when you are virtually right in the middle of your life?

Hormone replacement therapy

The middle years should be a time of fulfillment for a woman – her children are grown up and she has more opportunity to be with her partner. Sadly, the menopause can make it a depressing and uncomfortable time. But some specialists believe that hormone replacement therapy can help. What are the pros and cons of this recently developed treatment?

Hormone replacement therapy, also known as HRT, is a relatively new, and still controversial, form of treatment designed to combat some of the health problems surrounding and following the menopause (also called 'the change of life') in women. Before deciding whether or not this treatment really can help, we should first understand what happens during the menopause.

The menopause

The menopause occurs gradually in women aged between 45 and 55, although it can begin as early as 35. The ovaries become less responsive to stimulation from the pituitary gland in the brain. This means that they secrete less of the hormone oestrogen. The body's level of the hormone progesterone also decreases.

These changes in hormonal balance cause the symptoms of the menopause: periods become irregular, less frequent and finally cease altogether; breasts decrease in size; the womb (uterus) and ovaries shrink and become inactive; the vagina narrows, is less well lubricated and more easily irritated; bones become lighter and more brittle and the skin thinner. The woman may experience unpleasant physical symptoms such as hot flushes, sometimes accompanied by tingling sensations and drenching sweats, which can cause depression and, if they occur at night, loss of sleep.

What is hormone replacement therapy?

Some women find that the menopause passes easily and they experience few of these symptoms. Others, however, have a difficult menopause and

they can now be treated with hormones. This treatment is called hormone replacement therapy because it involves replacing the hormone oestrogen over several years, making it seem as if the menopause had never happened.

The treatment consists of a daily pill of either oestrogen and progesterone, or oestrogen by itself, for three weeks out of four — rather like taking a contraceptive pill. It is usually prescribed at the beginning of the menopause. After a while, the dosage will be reduced and treatment gradually ended. But, for some women, reducing the dose below a certain level will make symptoms reappear, and these women may end up having HRT on a permanent or semi-permanent basis.

However, HRT may be begun years after the menopause has finished, either for medical or cosmetic reasons.

The pros and cons

HRT is a relatively new treatment and its supporters make a number of claims which are disputed by those who oppose or disapprove of the treatment. So, we will now examine the claims made in support of HRT, and look at the evidence for and against them at present available.

●*HRT stops the skin from ageing.* After the menopause, the decline in oestrogen causes the body to reabsorb the slight layer of fat under the skin, which helps give it its soft appearance. However, skin ages regardless of oestrogen levels — it is different when a woman is 40 to what it was when she was 20, even though the oestrogen level is much the same during these years. Changes in the skin are the result of ageing and HRT will not get rid of wrinkles or eliminate a double chin.

●*HRT restores the vagina's elasticity and lubrication.* Loss of oestrogen causes changes in the vagina in nearly all women, and in some cases these changes can be distressing. The vagina becomes less elastic, dryer and more vulnerable to infection (vaginitis), though regular sexual intercourse appears to alleviate these symptoms. Oestrogen, taken either as tablets or used as an ointment, can prevent or reverse these changes. It need not be used permanently as its effects are usually long lasting.

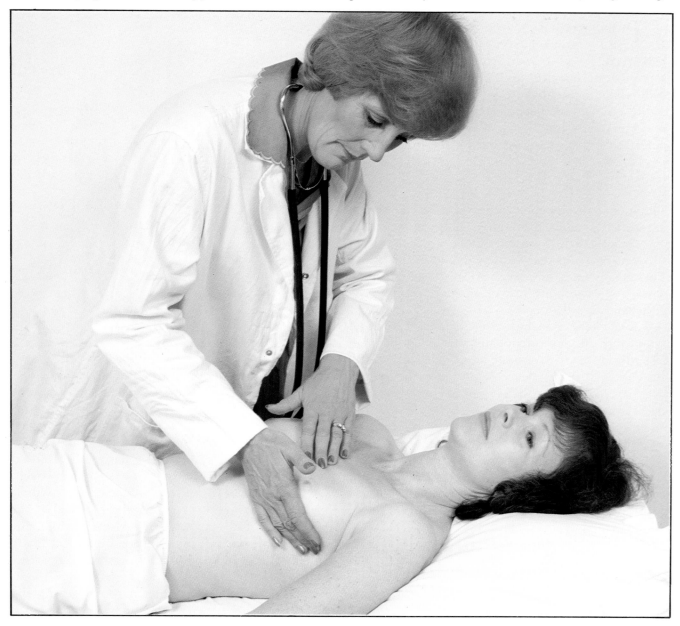

●*HRT ends hot flushes.* Most women experience hot flushes during the menopause and these can be helped by HRT. The therapy is usually prescribed for a few weeks or months and then gradually reduced and ended. About 5 to 10 per cent of women find that hot flushes return after they finish HRT and they may prefer to continue the therapy indefinitely.

●*HRT prevents some forms of bone disease.* This is a major claim made by those in favour of HRT and it seems to be supported by the evidence presently available. After the menopause, women's bones may become brittle and more likely to break. This condition, which is called osteoporosis, is also found in men but is three times more common in women, about one in every four or five developing it after the age of 55. Opponents of hormone replacement therapy say that it is unlikely that oestrogen deficiency is a cause of osteoporosis and point to the fact that men, who have little oestrogen, rarely get the disease. Instead, they recommend that sufferers take extra calcium in their diets.

This can, however, do more harm than good. Women with osteoporosis are losing calcium from their bones, which passes through the kidneys and is excreted in the urine. In a small proportion of women this calcium may cause kidney stones. Taking extra calcium may therefore increase the chances of stones developing. But even the opponents of HRT admit that large doses of oestrogen will help a woman with osteoporosis. The condition cannot be reversed, but there is convincing evidence that oestrogen treatment can help prevent it from becoming worse, or at least slow it down considerably. It has also been shown that, provided the treatment is begun soon after the menopause, osteoporosis can be delayed or prevented.

●*HRT prevents 'masculinization'.* Supporters of HRT say that the hormonal changes at the menopause in effect 'castrate' women, causing them to become 'masculine', with facial hair and gruff voices. It is perfectly normal for the ovaries to secrete a small amount of male hormone (androgen), just as the testes in men secrete a little female hormone, and it is this natural amount of male hormone which causes many older women to grow facial hair. Taking oestrogen will prevent this happening, but it will not reverse growth because once the hair follicles have been stimulated the hair will continue to grow. HRT is, however, a very extreme measure to treat what is in most women a mild symptom, best remedied by pulling out the hairs with tweezers or, in more severe cases, by waxing or electrolysis. Deepening of the voice is extremely rare in women of any age, but fortunately responds well to oestrogen treatment.

●*HRT protects women from coronary heart disease.* Supporters claim that HRT does this by lowering the levels of cholesterol in the blood. It is certainly true that before the menopause, women are protected by their hormones. However, there is no evidence that doses of oestrogen given after the menopause have the same effect; in fact, since the contraceptive pill causes an increase in the risk of heart attack and thrombosis in the legs, HRT might have the same effect. The risk seems to be related to the dose and to the woman's lifestyle: if she is slim, has normal blood pressure and does not smoke, she is probably safe; if she is overweight, has high blood pressure and smokes, the risk can become very high.

●*HRT protects women from cancer.* It has been suggested that HRT protects women from all forms of cancer, particularly of the breast and the lining (endometrium) of the womb. Opponents say that, on the contrary, HRT increases the chances of cancer of the womb. The available evidence does seem to indicate that, with the exception of certain cancers which are dependent on oestrogen, HRT does not cause breast cancer and may make it less likely. It now seems certain that oestrogen in combination with progesterone can actually protect a woman from cancer of the womb, though there is evidence that oestrogen on its own is less safe.

The drawbacks

There are drawbacks, some less serious than others, for women taking HRT.

●*Gall bladder disease.* This is the most serious problem associated with HRT and the only way in which the therapy seems to be undoubtedly harmful. The risk is multiplied by two to three times. As with cancer of the womb, gall stones are associated with overweight in women.

●*Bleeding.* When oestrogen is given to a woman after the menopause, bleeding rather like a light period occurs, though the woman does *not* become fertile again. It can be irregular, though taking HRT in a four-week cycle makes it predictable, and older women may find it embarrassing to have to buy sanitary protection. More serious than the inconvenience is that the bleeding might mask bleeding caused by the onset of cancer. Reducing the dosage of oestrogen, and introducing progesterone into the dose during the third week before the forth week off the therapy, allows the lining of the womb to be shed. This means that irregular bleeding which occurs at any other time

can be identified. Regular health checks are also advisable.

●*Nausea and water retention.* Nausea usually disappears after a few weeks of the therapy, along with water retention, which often gives a bloated feeling and causes an increase in weight. If these symptoms do not disappear, the woman should go back to her doctor who will change the dose or prescribe a different preparation. Water-losing tablets (diuretics) are not advisable as these can cause side-effects of their own.

●*Inconvenience.* Some women find it hard to remember to take a daily pill for twenty-one days out of twenty-eight. HRT also involves visits to the doctor, laboratory tests, and either private fees or prescription charges.

HRT for men?

If you are a man, you may be wondering whether some kind of hormone replacement therapy would help you over your middle years. Despite 'rejuvenating tablets' sold in sex shops, men have no need of HRT since there is no male equivalent of the menopause. People sometimes talk of the 'male menopause', but this refers to a mid-life crisis when a man may wonder whether he is as successful as he might be or if he is still as attractive to young women. These doubts can lead to depression, but the cure, like the cause, is psychological, not physical.

Should I take HRT?

If you are approaching the menopause, actually experiencing it or even if it is well behind you, you may be considering hormone replacement therapy. As can be seen from this article, there are no easy answers; it's up to you and your doctor to decide, weighing the claims and counter-claims of the supporters and opponents of HRT. There are a number of physical conditions (such as gall stones, fibroids, liver disease, diabetes and high blood pressure), which would lead doctors to be wary about prescribing HRT, and there is little evidence to support exaggerated claims for its youth-giving properties. But, on the evidence now available, it seems that HRT can alleviate distressing symptoms of the menopause such as vaginitis and hot flushes, can prevent or postpone the onset of common conditions in older women, such as osteoporosis, and can help women over what can be, but need not be, a very difficult time.

The male menopause

The menopause in women is a well-known condition, but what about men? Is there such a thing as the male menopause, and if so, what are the symptoms and how can they be treated?

When a woman says that she is going through the menopause, doctors know what is happening and what she means. With the change in hormone levels, she is having hot flushes and night sweats. Often she reports other symptoms such as depression, irritability, anxiety, insomnia and palpitations.

Recently, it has been suggested that some men go through a similar change at about the age of 50 called the male menopause. However, when a man is described as going through the menopause it may mean a number of different things. He may be having difficulty with erections or ejaculations or, in rare cases, he may be undergoing some of the physical symptoms that menopausal women describe, such as hot flushes, night sweating and palpitations. Or it may mean that he has suddenly become depressed, fed up with his domestic situation or anxious about his job.

Most doctors and scientists doubt that there is really a male menopause as it is known in women. It is simply a case of the male suddenly becoming aware of physical changes that have been occurring for some time and coming under social, psychological, job and domestic pressures that occur inevitably during middle age.

Symptoms

The symptoms of male menopause fall into three main categories — physical, sexual and psychological. The physical changes are apparent enough: sudden unexpected hot flushes and palpitations, and sometimes sleeplessness. The man may tend to wake up bathed in perspiration.

And he may experience erection or ejaculation difficulties, developed gradually or suddenly. Loss of interest in his partner, or any sexual partner, is another common symptom, although just the opposite may occur: some men find that they are more interested in sex than before. Many men report that they are increasingly sexually aroused by young attractive women. Leaving wife and family for a younger partner is far from rare at this age and may be because the man needs to be reassured about his 'performance'.

Emotional changes are by far the most common symptoms of male menopause. The man suddenly becomes depressed about his job, family or future. He begins to lose concentration and his memory fails him unaccountably. He may become irritable, forcing his family and friends to become more careful about what they say to him. Often he is very critical of those around him, resentful of his superiors at work and of the demands made upon him by his wife and family. He may report feeling 'trapped' by his commitments. At times he may become lethargic and withdrawn while at others he appears more active than usual. Some men become hypochondriacs and start fussing about their health. Food fads, such as health food or vegetarian diets, may be introduced.

The fact that these changes are observed over a wide variety of ages and that a large proportion of men do not suffer from any of the symptoms makes the male menopause, if indeed it exists, very hard to define. But there are certainly many men who do notice these symptoms in their late forties and early fifties, although they rarely seek professional help.

Hormonal changes

In women the onset of menopause coincides with hormone changes. At the age of approximately 50, because the level of oestrogen produced becomes unstable, physical symptoms such as hot flushes occur. Psychological effects are directly or indirectly a result of the same change in hormone balance and usually continue until the oestogen level drops permanently. The effect, like the change in hormone levels, is sudden. In men, however, there is no equivalent change: there is no sudden increase or decrease in hormone levels. Certainly there is some decline in hormone production as men become older, but this begins at about the age of 40 and continues gradually for 20 to 30 years. A tiny minority of men, perhaps one in 100, do show some marked hormonal changes at about the age of 50, but the symptoms are far too common for this explanation to be generally the correct one.

What is happening?

It has been suggested that the flushes that men of this age experience are simply a result of changing blood pressure, which does fluctuate with age. At the same time, flushing (like blushing) is related to the emotions — we all go red when angry or sometimes when embarrassed — and it may well be that all the other changes that are occurring at this age make the man more easily angered, upset or irritated. Many of the night sweats may simply be a result of greater anxiety and tension. The changes in sexual abilities, drive and interest may simply be a result of growing anxiety about ageing. Men reach their sexual peak physically in late adolescence and from that time on, in theory, it physically decreases. However, confidence, enthusiasm and experience tend to maintain sexual abilities in old age if nothing happens physically or emotionally to interfere with them.

As men get older, it may take longer for them to achieve their erections and more stimulation may become necessary. Many become very upset that their erections are no longer an automatic response to their partner's touch, and they find that erections may not be as hard or as full as they were. This trend may be noticed by men at any age.

Ejaculation is also affected. It can take longer to achieve and becomes less powerful with increasing age. The delay is welcomed by men who reach orgasm prematurely, but is often regarded as irritating and frustrating by others. This is particularly so if the partner is only having sex out of a sense of duty. Men may also find that the time between ejaculating and gaining another erection gradually increases.

These are continuing processes that begin when a man is in his early twenties. But it is often only when he has doubts about other aspects of his life that he really notices the changes. A man does not, for instance, look at the changes in his physical features or his ability to run 100 yards every day, but when he reaches a milestone such as his 30th or 40th birthday, he might think back about how he has changed. He may also do this on important occasions during his life (the day of his wedding or the start of a new job) or when he is feeling depressed or miserable. If things are going badly, all the other aspects of his life seem to be affected and it is easy to understand how a man who is worried about his future suddenly feels that nothing, including his sex life, is as it used to be.

Once he starts to worry how his sexual capabilities have changed, he may try harder to overcome the difficulties. As expected, the harder he tries to improve his sexual response, the worse these difficulties become. A sudden panic about the difference between how hard his erection is now at age 50 and how it was when he was 20 could make him so anxious that he loses his erections altogether. Some men attempt to reassure themselves that they are still the 'same men they once were' by seeking other partners; others decide that it is easier to avoid the risk of failure by not having sex at all. In the latter case it may seem that not only is their sexual capacity reduced but also that their drive has disappeared.

In fact all that has happened is that the man has suddenly become aware of the gradual natural changes in his sexual response, and instead of coming to terms with it he has decided that as he cannot respond as he used to he will avoid sex altogether.

Drugs can also affect male sexual performance and drive. As men and women get older, they are more likely to be afflicted by such ailments as diabetes and high or low blood pressure. These will have their own direct effects on male erection and ejaculation, but the drugs that are given to combat them have side effects which influence sexual abilities too. Drugs given for depression (more common in older males) will certainly, in high enough doses, affect a man's ability to gain an erection and will delay his ejaculation. Thus middle age is a time when the man is likely to start reducing his sexual activity, if only because of the other bodily changes that are occurring.

The partner

At the same time, a man's partner may be undergoing changes herself. She is no longer as physically attractive as she was, just as he may be less attractive to her, and physical changes, illness or drugs may be affecting her own sex drive and abilities. This can, in turn, affect her attitude to sex. If the relationship is a long-standing one, the sexual rituals may have become very predictable and boredom often sets in. Sex can, under these circumstances, become a chore for both partners and they may therefore decide to abandon it altogether.

However, there may be another, more subtle, reason why an older man avoids sex. A woman often becomes more sexually interested when she experiences the menopause. This is not simply the

result of changes in her hormone levels, but also because the menopause tells her there is no longer any danger of becoming pregnant. Many couples, unhappy about the use of a sheath, an intrauterine device, the Pill or other precautions, can now enjoy sex without using them. And those who do not, for religious or other reasons, want to use any contraception can now have sex without worrying about the possibility of pregnancy. For women especially, this may provide the opportunity to relax during intercourse for the first time in many years. It is easy to understand how this can result in a woman showing more interest in having sex and being more inclined to take an active role. Some couples report that because of increased relaxation this is the period when their sexual relations are the most enjoyable.

Unfortunately, for some men, this increase in interest and initiative may be difficult to cope with. If they are worried about their own sexual abilities they then worry about whether they can cope with their partner's new sexual demands. This can result in the man opting out of sex altogether, deciding that if he cannot have full control of the sexual relationship and dictate how often and when intercourse takes place, he will have no sex at all.

Outside factors

At about the age of 50, many changes occur in a man's life which will have direct and indirect effects on his sexuality and psychological state. For instance his attitude to his job changes, and he will start thinking about retirement.

If he is self-employed there is a great deal of pressure on him to accumulate sufficient money for a comfortable life when he retires. If, on the other hand, his pension is based on his last year's salary, then he must get as high up on the salary scale as possible. In any case, work becomes a high priority. He comes home tired, especially because he no longer has the same physical energy he had when he was younger. This will affect his sexual performance and interest markedly and also make him more irritable.

The search for lost youth

Although in some men anxiety, depression, sexual difficulties and loss of confidence lead to lethargy and acceptance, others try to fight it all the way.

Certainly many men attempt to 'regain their masculinity' by having affairs with younger women. If they are having sexual difficulties with

their wives, these men are often trying to prove that they are still capable of sexual functioning by having a relationship with someone else. They are also attempting to convince themselves and others that they are still attractive enough to be desired by a younger woman.

Indeed, many of these men are more successful with other partners. This is understandable: new relationships with new sexual patterns often produce a stronger and more passionate sexual response than older ones. But they fail to realize that as the new relationship progresses, they will probably once again find themselves with the same difficulties.

Many men do not go as far as having an affair. Instead they adopt a young hair style, wear 'trendier' clothes and often take up vigorous sports. What they do not realize is that these activities simply draw attention to the difference between their real age and the image they are trying to project.

Unlike women, many men pass through life without experiencing any of the symptoms of the menopause. Among those who do, however, there are two types that seem to appear particularly frequently.

The first is the man who is obsessed with his work and is therefore generally more aware of the drop in his performance. He struggles valiantly to keep up but discovers that he cannot. In an attempt to do so, he works harder and harder for longer hours and becomes even more tired and depressed. He is usually very aware of what is going on in his home life and becomes depressed and feels guilty about how little time he spends with his family.

The second type is the man who is very dependent on what other people think of him. He worries about his appearance and his activities, and when these are affected by increasing age he either becomes depressed and loses confidence or tries behaving like someone 20 years younger.

Treatment

Since the male menopause is unlikely to be caused by changes in hormone levels, there is little that drugs can do to help, although, in common with sexual problems at any age, anxiety-reducing drugs will help in a small percentage of cases.

The first step in resolving most sexual difficulties is to discuss the problem with the partner. Does she want to have sex? If she does not, this is often enough to interfere with the man's ability to

obtain an erection. What does she expect from him? This may change as they become older.

She may not want the man to struggle to keep up the role he once took in intercourse. If he is having difficulty getting an erection (a natural consequence of increasing age) then a change in sexual habits may help. Satisfying her own sexual impulses by masturbation or the use of a vibrator may reduce the pressure on him to 'perform'. Further help may be received from one's doctor — if he is trained to deal with psychosexual problems — or by referral to a psychosexual clinic.

Understanding and reassurance

A marriage may be at its most vulnerable at this age, both partners resenting the need for understanding by the other. Often all that is needed is for the couple to talk about their frustration, depression and anxieties and recognize that they both need reassurance about their attractiveness and sexual abilities. Unfortunately, since *both* are undergoing difficulties, they usually fail to see that the other partner also has problems.

Just as in sex, changes in the daily routine may be necessary. For example if one partner does not wish to participate in social activities for a while, there is little to be gained by pressure from the other partner. Compromises such as staying at a party for an hour or going out for a quiet drink can help.

Now more than ever before in the marriage it is important for each partner to understand what the other is going through. The temptation in either partner to nag or find fault should be firmly resisted: criticism that was merely irritating in earlier years may now become intolerable. The wife who criticizes her husband every time he looks at another woman, for instance, may push him along the way to a more serious interest, and it may be all he needs to decide that he has had enough of his marriage. And the husband should understand that what he regards as nagging may simply be his wife's need for more security and reassurance as she copes with her own menopausal problems.

Problems arising from the male (and female) menopause are common, and a couple will often benefit from having an independent observer to help them work through their difficulties. Marriage counsellors and, if the problems are sexual, psychosexual therapists are trained to do this; their advice can be invaluable.

Sex and the menopause

The psychological effects of the menopause on a woman can cause difficulties in a couple's sex life – especially if it coincides with her husband's own mid-life crisis. But with mutual understanding they can overcome fears of growing old and doubts about sexual performance.

The onset of the menopause in a woman is often regarded as being the time when she is likely to lose interest in sex and, although a man does not go through a physical menopause as such, his late forties and fifties may also be the beginning of changes in his sexual activity. However, these changes in both women and men mainly happen for psychological rather than physical reasons.

The female menopause

The menopause marks the end of a woman's child-bearing years, but it has little effect on her ability to respond sexually and enjoy lovemaking. However, there are some changes that can lead to slight discomfort during intercourse.

The vagina may expand and contract less easily so she or her partner may find that it feels more 'slack' than it used to be. This can be improved by exercises known as Kegel exercises similar to those given to a woman following the birth of a child, where she learns to tighten the vagina by squeezing certain pelvic muscles. Regular intercourse will also help.

The vagina may not expand as much in either length or width, and this can make intercourse slightly painful and uncomfortable. Again, more frequent sexual intercourse can put this right, but a more tender and gentle approach to lovemaking and a change in sexual position may be necessary.

A decrease in vaginal secretions will also happen, making penetration during intercourse less easy. This is part of the normal ageing process, but a marked decrease in natural vaginal lubrication is caused by the menopause itself. A simple solution to this problem is the use of a water soluble lubricant.

Lack of sex drive

Despite the possible discomfort of penetration, it is more often a loss of sex drive which affects women during and after the menopause — although some women do in fact experience an increase in sexual drive during the menopause.

The menopause can cause women to lose confidence. When periods stop and they can no longer become pregnant, some women feel that they have lost their femininity. This can often result in a loss of confidence and the feeling that they are no longer attractive. At this time, a woman's children may be leaving home, and this may also emphasize her sense of loss because she feels deprived of her role as a mother. Not surprisingly, all this can lead to depression which reduces sex drive.

Is there a 'male menopause'?

A man does not go through a physical menopause as such — there is no sudden decline in male hormones or in the rate at which sperm is produced, but rather a slow decrease in these does occur from about the age of 40. It may not be until his fifties that a man notices that he takes longer to get an erection, and that his erections are less hard or full. It may take him longer to ejaculate and the refactory period — the time between one ejaculation and the capacity for a second one — generally increases, and some men do not feel the need to ejaculate every time they make love.

However, most of the sexual problems in men of about 50 and over are due to anxiety about sexual performance, fear of sexual failure, and to a deteriorating marriage.

For the first time since early marriage the couple are likely to be alone together, their children having left home. At a time when they need to 'get to know each other' all over again, both partners may be absorbed in their own crises. Even if they realize that the other also has problems, their own difficulties may be so great that they feel unable to help each other.

If resentment and frustration have built up in the marriage this may cause the couple to critize each other's lovemaking techniques or to reject sexual advances, so destroying whatever remains of the sexual relationship. Some couples stop physical contact altogether for fear that a partner will want more than a 'quick cuddle' or that they themselves will not be able to finish what they start sexually. This can add to feelings of isolation.

Some solutions

There is no simple solution for the couple with a marriage that is in a disastrous state, or who have severe psychosexual problems, short of seeking specialist advice, though this may not be as daunting as it sounds. People who previously have had a good life can usually be helped very easily. However, here are some self-help suggestions.

Say how you feel and sympathize with your partner's problems. A simple agreement that each partner will listen for 15 minutes without interrupting the other is a good way to start communication. Sex will never be good if the rest of the relationship is poor.

Spend more time doing things together — and apart. Often couples maintain rigid routines which have become boring and depressing. Resignedly watching the television together in silence is not likely to make a couple feel positive about life or each other. Simply going for a walk together is a good start.

Make an effort with appearance and change your sexual habits to take changes in sexuality into account. It will take much longer to arouse both partners and so more time should be taken over foreplay. Enjoy touching and caressing for their own sake, even if intercourse does not take place. In view of the changes in the woman's vagina, the man must be gentler during intercourse and a lubricant should be used. The woman should try to understand that a man may not need or wish to ejaculate each time they have intercourse.

'My husband chases younger women'

The happy marriages of many middle-aged couples are
threatened when the husband starts to flirt or have affairs
with younger women. Some relationships break up under the
strain, but if the situation is dealt with calmly,
the marriage can be saved.

The man whose eyes wander constantly from his wife towards younger women may be a devoted husband seeking innocent diversion, or a frightened man looking for a boost to his sexual pride. Whatever the cause, his wife will often find his behaviour very difficult to cope with. Along with natural jealousy of the other women and the fear that her marriage may be threatened, a wife may feel inadequate because she knows she is no longer young.

Some men chase younger women all their lives, believing that in this way they can stay young themselves. However, the most common situation is that of a long-standing marriage put at risk when the husband — often after years of happy marriage — begins to flirt or fall in love with someone younger. At this point many wives — like Susan, whose husband, Ray, was having an affair with Joanne, a much younger work colleague — seek the help of a marriage guidance counsellor:

'For the past 20 years we've been married, Ray has been faithful, though recently he's started flirting very obviously at parties. I thought this was fairly innocent and put it down to his depression since our two children left home, but I was shocked when he told me that he was having an affair with someone at work. At first I thought it wouldn't last — he's nearly twice Joanne's age — but he now says that, though he still loves me, he loves her too and won't give her up.'

Thousands of women everywhere are sharing your problem at this moment. Many — less fortunate than you because their marriages have not been so stable — grow used to their husbands' behaviour and seem prepared to tolerate it in order to keep their marriages together.

These women know that husbands who chase younger women are very often, despite appearances, loyal and devoted to their wives, so although it is a frightening and difficult situation for you, it is worth fighting to save your marriage. Many women who come to me with this problem have been married for more than 15 years; it seems that this is a crucial period for many couples — a time when some men begin to mourn their lost youth and try to prove to themselves and the world that they are still sexy.

It is, of course, perfectly natural for men and women to be sexually attracted to people other than their partners, and most flirtations are harmless. However, when a man reaches early middle age

such behaviour may grow more extreme. Some wives tell me that their husbands have started to make fools of themselves: flirting outrageously at parties — as your husband had begun to do — or buying expensive presents for younger women. Sometimes that is as far as it goes, but today's more permissive attitudes mean that some younger women are prepared to have an affair with an older man, even if they know that he's married.

'My family are telling me to leave Ray for a short time, just to teach him a lesson and bring him to his senses.'

Walking out on your husband won't solve the problem unless you are prepared to end your marriage. In the past, women did use this as a final threat, but easier divorce now means that Ray could marry Joanne if he thought you had rejected him. And since he is used to the comforts of a secure home, it is quite possible that he would rush into marriage, if only to get a replacement for you.

I think that it would be far more constructive to look at the reasons why he has fallen for a younger woman, to try to come to terms with your own feelings and to look for ways to bring you both together again.

The 'male menopause'

Why do men chase younger women? The most obvious explanation is that they are really chasing their lost youth. Your husband may be trying to prove that he is a 'real man' because, deep down, he is afraid he is no longer as sexy as he once was. This has been called the male menopause, the time when the prospect of old age becomes a reality and some men feel the need for a 'final fling'.

More common divorce might also mean that Ray is a little jealous of some of his friends, who have embarked on second marriages with younger women. From his point of view, a long, stable marriage makes him seem middle-aged.

It might help you to take a critical look at your past together and your relationship now. You say, for instance, that he calls you 'Mother' rather than 'Susan' — maybe he's grown to regard you more as the mother of his children and less as a lover and friend. Perhaps in the past you concentrated too much on the children, neglecting each other's needs and taking each other too much for granted — the husband who buys large bunches of flowers for younger women often wouldn't dream of making such a romantic gesture to his wife.

In a long marriage, routine may be a source of security and happiness, but it can be boring at times. We need surprises even more as we get older and begin to regret lost opportunities. Since Ray has until now been faithful, he probably feels he has missed out on the 'permissive society'. Being with younger people at work will only make his regrets sharper.

Jealousy

'I have tried to be understanding and look at the situation as you advise, but I can't stop feeling angry and jealous, especially when I think of Ray making love to Joanne. It seems to cheapen our life together, particularly as our lovemaking has always been very satisfying and passionate for both of us.'

That is a perfectly natural reaction, but it could lead you to actions you will regret. Thinking about the problem calmly and sharing your worries with me and sympathetic friends will help you get the problem into perspective. Ray's affair is naturally a shock to your self-confidence — you have trusted him and you feel he has betrayed you.

'I have thought of having an affair myself — if only to let Ray know that I'm not just old 'Mother', who will always be waiting at home for him. I also think that if I had someone else I would worry less about being lonely if our marriage does break up.'

Many women in your position drift into an affair, but that will not help you to win back your husband. Remember, two wrongs really don't make a right. Not only would you be using another person in your attempt to get revenge, but you would also be sacrificing a marriage which could be saved with some effort.

'But I feel Ray owes me something; if anyone changes it should be him. I'm the one who lost my beautiful figure having children, who missed years of sleep when they were young, and who gave up a job that I enjoyed to look after them.'

It is natural to feel like this, but relationships cannot be weighed on a scale and guilt and blame shared out in the way you are trying to do — it takes two people to make or break a marriage.

Relationships are like sensitive plants that need to be carefully looked after. It seems to me that you have both neglected this care, believing that giving love to your children is the same as showing your feelings for each other. You say Ray has been a good husband and that you still love him, so try to suppress your anger and hurt pride and think positively about the situation.

Saving the marriage

The first thing to do is to find out whether Ray still loves you and wants to share his life with you — the chances are that deep down he does, after 20 years of happiness. Like many men who have affairs with younger women, he may have absolutely no intention in the long term of endangering his marriage.

Then, if you think it is worth trying to win him back, work out how this can be done. Hasty action and angry scenes will only drive him further away from you. I know it is hard to tolerate an affair, but since he has been honest enough to tell you what's happening — many men hide their affairs and even enjoy their deception — try to be honest with him. Tell him how you feel, choosing a calm moment when you both have time to explore the problem in a rational way.

If your husband is willing to try to save the marriage, perhaps he would be prepared to see me, together with you, and we could explore why he is unhappy and why he feels he needs a younger lover.

'When Ray first told me about his affair, I did all the things a wife in my position is always told to do: I had my hair done, bought a sexy nightdress, and cooked romantic candlelit dinners. I also started reading sex manuals, but he just said he didn't want to make love.'

Trying to compete with your husband's younger lover is just fighting a losing battle. However much you try to preserve your youth, there will always be someone younger and more attractive. Of course, it is important for your self-confidence that you look after your body and keep your mind alert, but it won't win back your husband if he is looking for new emotions and excitement.

Try to think about what you can give each other. Affairs with younger people can provide passing excitement and boost your self-esteem, but they are no substitute for a long, loving relationship in which each partner is aware of the other's needs. Any woman can cook your husband romantic meals or wear sexy nighties; only you know him well enough to help him to come to terms with growing older and to work with him to build a

partnership that will survive into your old age.

I am sure he knows that a younger woman may well tire of him eventually and look around for someone of her own age, perhaps someone to have children with. Since your husband is proud of and loves your own children, it's unlikely he would want to deal with the ever-present demands of a young family at his age.

Think positively of how to transform your relationship. Try to show him that there can be as much excitement in rediscovering each other as in having an affair with someone else. Because you have known each other for so long and shared so much, the thrill of exploring new aspects of each other will be even greater. A relaxing, luxurious holiday together might give you the chance to sort out your relationship; or you could move to a smaller house now that your children have left to set up their own homes.

Many middle-aged couples discover that shared interests — such as choosing and decorating a new home, joining a club or learning a new hobby — will repair a rift in their partnership by bringing them closer together.

Self-respect

At the same time, you must consider your own needs. You will only feel resentful and he will lose respect for you, if you try to win back Ray by pandering exclusively to his emotional desires.

You have shared your leisure time with your husband for so long that most of your friends are probably the wives of Ray's friends, so you are naturally afraid that if he leaves you will be very lonely. Try to make friends of your own — join a club or try voluntary work. Such effort will not be wasted if Ray decides he wants to stay with you; you will be more self-confident and secure when you realize that people value you for yourself, not just because you are Ray's wife.

Provided both partners are deep down committed to each other and their life together, a marriage can be saved when the husband chases younger women. However, if you find the situation grows more difficult, be prepared to consider a separation — it will save you much unhappiness in the long run. At the moment though there is still plenty of hope, and while Ray continues to come home to you, you know that in his heart of hearts he still loves you in his own way.

Staying sexy

The media often suggests that youth and sexiness go hand-
in-hand. But sexiness is difficult to define — and personality
is as important as being young and attractive.

Firm flesh, smooth taut skin, health, vigour, optimism and freshness are the characteristics of youth and, in many ways, go hand-in-hand with sexiness. But the natural attractiveness of youth is only one aspect of sexiness — almost everyone can point to older men or women who, outwardly at least, seem to possess none of these things, and yet still describe them as sexy. So if sexiness is not the prerogative of youth alone what are its qualities, and does it increase or fade when middle-age approaches?

What is sexiness?

Sexiness means different things to different people. Some men find women with full bosoms or a provocative way of dressing sexy, while some women find men with small bottoms and slim hips sexy. But true sexiness is much more than an attractive physical appearance. Anyone, of any shape, size and age can give off an aura of sexiness, for it is a complex quality that is made up of many different factors.

The sexy image

The association of sexiness with youth and physical beauty tends to concern women far more than men — largely because of pressure and conditioning by a traditionally male-oriented society. As a result, most men do not worry too much about their physical attractiveness fading as they get older. Although they may not be happy when their hair falls out, or their clothes no longer fit, they are confident that they are still considered sexy by women of all ages. And the media treat the middle-aged male very differently from his female counterpart. As such, it is women, far more so than

men, who are made to feel self-conscious about their sexuality and physical appearance, particularly as they begin to grow older.

In magazines and films and on television, the attractive women shown are almost always young and flawless. Advertisements that offer remedies to keep wrinkles at bay, dye to cover grey hair and aids to fight flab conspire to play on insecurity and foster a belief that signs of age are unattractive, and that physical perfection is all important.

Indeed, older women could be forgiven for thinking that once they are no longer young their days of being attractive to the opposite sex are numbered. But to believe this is to believe that the generally presented images of sexual stereotypes hold true in real life. In reality it is the personal make-up of individuals that is much more important than youth and looks alone, as the following examples show.

The empty beauty

Sandra is twenty five and has the looks of a model, with the kind of glamour that turns heads at parties, but none of the men who work with her find her remotely attractive. She created a stir when she arrived at the office, but that has been almost forgotten after two years. The main reason is that she is disgruntled: everything is a bore, she only speaks to complain, and her tone of voice is weary with a hint of a whine. She is always immaculate and beautifully dressed, but her sole contribution to life is her physical appearance.

Because men have always sought her out and responded to her good looks, it has never occurred to her that she needs to make any other effort. Her looks may be an instant magnet to men, but her total lack of anything else to offer means they find her totally lacking in sex appeal once they have the opportunity to get to know her.

The sexy older woman

Sylvia is fifty, and younger women are frequently surprised by the amount of attention men pay to her at parties. She is by no means slim, and although she is fairly well preserved, she never tries to hide her age. The main attraction is her amusing and warm personality. She has a tremendous sense of fun and gains pleasure from keeping people amused.

She is happily married and although she makes no obvious attempt to flirt, she always shows a genuine interest in other people and makes them feel they are very good company. She makes no attempt to apologise for her size or to disguise it. She dresses expertly and flamboyantly in a way that always draws attention to her elegant wrists and hands, and her shapely legs and slender ankles. She approaches the world as a woman confident that she is sexually attractive, and the response she always encounters proves her to be right.

Sexual experience

Many men find the expectation of the young and inexperienced difficult to live up to. A young girl who expects lovemaking to be an unforgettable experience each time, but is unable to give any indication of what turns her on, can prove to be a disappointing partner.

A woman who has had a few lovers will be a more understanding and technically competent lover than a younger girl. Not only will she know more about men and their bodies, but her attitude to sex will be more realistic. She will not expect 'bells to ring,' or the 'earth to move' every time she makes love. She will know that not all men are sexual athletes and that the occasional bout of impotence or lack of interest in sex is common.

An older woman is also more aware of what she finds sexually stimulating and is less afraid to communicate her desires to her partner. And an older woman who has come to terms with her own sexuality, is more likely to radiate a sexiness that is not assumed, but quite natural.

Knowing how to flirt

Flirtation is an important indication of sexiness. And experience can teach an older women how to flirt in order to say what she means.

Young girls often flirt dangerously and indiscriminately and either get themselves labelled as 'cock-teasers', or else become involved in situations they have difficulty getting out of. A common mistake the younger woman often makes is to dress and behave provocatively simply in order to get reassurance that she is attractive. Once com-

plimented on her appearance however, she simply drifts off to find some other man who will also tell her how attractive she is.

An older woman has learnt to do quite the opposite when she flirts. She makes the man she is with feel unique and desirable. She doesn't need to be told that she is attractive, but if she receives a compliment she accepts it gracefully. Experience has also taught her how to pitch her flirtation: how to indicate that it is just a game to make each other feel good at a party; and when to signal that she hopes for more than just one brief meeting.

The attraction of maturity

Growing old usually brings with it the benefits of increased maturity and wisdom. There is something attractive about a woman who has had to take charge of her life and cope with the ups and downs of living. A woman who has successfully brought up a family amid the stress of family life, or one who has juggled a career with her private life — both have a lot to offer in terms of wisdom, compassion and commonsense. If this is coupled with confidence, then many men find the combination very sexy indeed.

An older woman has also had the opportunity to learn the art of making the best of herself. She is fully aware what her best features are and knows how to emphasize them, while at the same time minimising what she sees to be her faults. She is also aware that fashion is only a guideline and the only rule she must follow is that what she wears, and how she makes-up or wears her hair, should be simply what looks best for her.

The un-sexy woman

Sexiness, therefore, is very much an attitude of mind — and many women simply refuse to be sexy. They choose to take little interest in their appearance and mentally adopt a staid and 'middle-aged' attitude, even if they are barely out of their teens. Their conversation is continually peppered with phrases such as, 'I'm going to grow old gracefully' or, 'Well, when you get to my age . . .' Women who behave in this fashion may well be loved and respected by friends and family but are rarely considered to be sexy — indeed, should the label of 'sexy' ever be applied to them, they would undoubtedly feel insulted and consider it to be in extremely bad taste.

These women often use growing old as an excuse to cease any sexual contact with their partners, though in fact, after the menopause when a woman is liberated from the fear of pregnancy, many women find that their sex life can take on a whole new lease of life and be more exciting than at any time previously.

Looking to the future

We are living through a time when the traditional lifestyles thought to be suitable for a woman are rapidly changing. Women are now much more career oriented and many women now hold top jobs. The sexual double standard of virgin wives and experienced husbands is disappearing and much more attention is now being paid to the woman's point of view.

Once the media begin to portray the older woman as an attractive human being in her own right, women will start to loose their fears that after a certain age their sexual life is over.

All this is not to say, of course, that older people tend to be sexier than the young or vice versa — simply that each age has its own qualities that should be recognised for what they are, and that no age group has a monopoly on sexiness.

'Am I too old for him?'

Most couples are affected by what other people think of their relationship. This is especially true in the still relatively unusual marriage between a younger man and older woman. But the disapproval of outsiders need not harm a relationship if the couple deal with the situation together.

It is still generally accepted that, when a woman marries, she will be younger than her husband. And even if the age gap is particularly wide it rarely draws comment or criticism. But the woman who links herself with a younger man is still relatively rare, though this kind of relationship is becoming more common with the increased rate of second marriages and as women delay marriage to concentrate on their careers. Despite this, such relationships often attract disapproval, which may cause hurt and worry to the couple concerned.

Barbara, a 36-year-old widow, had lived with Sam, her 26-year-old boyfriend, for two years. Their relationship was good and they had recently decided to get married. Since then, they had been flooded with advice from their families and friends, much of it being that they would be making a great mistake because of the 10 years' difference in their ages. Barbara decided to see if a counsellor could help her resolve the doubts she now had about her relationship:

'Getting married is a big step for anyone — especially the second time around — and I can't help worrying about the age difference between us, especially after one of my friends said younger men marry older women when they are looking for a 'mother figure'. Can this be true?'

It is certainly true that *some* younger men want to be mothered by their older wives. Many of these relationships work very well indeed if both partners accept and enjoy their roles. Trouble comes when either the woman tires of looking after a 'son' and wants a more equal partnership, or the man 'grows up' and tires of being submissive. In

this case, unless both partners can adjust to changed circumstances, the relationship may be threatened.

However, the 'mother–son' relationship is only a generalization which probably does not apply to your relationship. From what you tell me about your fiancé, he is a mature man who regards you as an equal partner and lover, not as a mother.

Younger rivals

'Even if he loves me now, I can't help fearing that soon he may be attracted to a woman nearer his own age. I know that I am reasonably attractive and I'm told I look young for my age, but I have stretch marks and wrinkles, and although our sex life is good, it is no longer as passionate as it was when we first met.'

I think there are two separate worries here. Sooner or later, the vast majority of sexual relationships lose their initial overwhelming passion, but happy couples, like you, find that their relationship gains in tenderness and quality — after all, by now

you understand each other's likes and dislikes, and know each other's bodies intimately.

Whether your man is attracted by younger women now or in the future is another question altogether. Many quarrels between partners are caused by the myth that after you fall in love, you never desire or admire another person again. This is unrealistic — you probably see other men whom you find sexually attractive or perhaps fantasize about, but that doesn't mean that you seriously consider going to bed or starting an affair with any of them.

If your man had an affair with a woman of his own age, it would not be because of the age difference between you, but because of deeper problems in your relationship — so if it is happy and healthy,

there is no need to worry. But remember, if you are tense and jealous when you and your fiancé are in the company of other women, or you question him closely about what he does when you are apart, it could cause strain on your relationship. If you love him, you must trust him — as, I am sure, he trusts you.

'If I worry now about the 10 years' difference between our ages, what will happen when I am 50 and he is just entering his forties? Won't there be real trouble and many more problems then?

It would make life much easier for anyone deciding to get married if we could foretell the future, but there is never any guarantee that a marriage will

227

not end in later years. The age difference between you seems large now, but most couples in your position find that age matters less as they grow older. If you were to be ill when you were older, that might put a strain on your marriage — as it would in any relationship — but whether your marriage broke up would again depend on your deeper feelings for each other.

Looking on the bright side, it is worth remembering that, in general, women are longer-lived than men, so you should be able to look forward to spending old age together. When the man is older than the woman, as in the traditional marriage, statistics show that she has a high chance of ending her days as a widow.

Having children

'My fiancé gets on extremely well with my nine-year-old son, and hasn't mentioned wanting children of his own, but do you think he might change his mind in the future? In a few years I will be too old to have children and really, I don't want to wreck my career by taking time off to have another baby.'

I am glad that your son and fiancé like each other as children may cause problems when their mother becomes involved with another man, whatever his age. As to whether your fiancé will want children of his own, only he can say. The fact that you have asked me suggests that you have not discussed this subject with your man. To avoid later unhappiness, you should do this before you go ahead with your marriage plans.

Of course, your fiancé may be satisfied with the contact he has with your son, but he should think carefully about the future and whether his ideas may change. However, you are quite likely to find that he loves and admires you for what you are — a happy, successful career woman — and he may dislike the idea of you as a mother at home with young children.

Disapproving friends

'I think I could cope with my own doubts if I could ignore the reactions of other people. When we were simply living together, our friends seemed to accept our relationship; now that we have told them we're making it permanent, my friends are disapproving and his friends have started introducing him to girls of his own age. Is there anything we can do to stop them behaving in this way and accept our marriage?'

This is an unpleasant situation for you both, but I doubt if most of your friends are being deliberately cruel — indeed they probably believe they are acting for your own good. Talk to your friends and tell them how hurtful they are being. Your fiancé should point out to his friends that their interference is, at worst, tactless and, at best, extremely offensive, especially to you.

If you have not already done so, make a great effort to meet each other's friends so that you can

mixing difficult. While there is only 10 years' difference between yourself and your fiancé, your man may find that he is more than 15 years younger than your friends' partners and that he has little in common with them. You, equally, may have interests very different from those of the wives or girlfriends of your fiancé's men friends. Probably the best solution is that adopted by most successful relationships: see together those friends whom you both like, and see others separately.

Why people disapprove

'Some of our friends have been really spiteful. How can people be so hurtful?'

It is possible that some of your women friends are jealous of you — by comparison with your fiancé, their husbands may seem rather old and unfit, and while your friends could tolerate your man when they saw him as a gigolo figure, out for what he could get, they may be disturbed now that your relationship turns out to be 'the real thing'. Your fiancé's friends, on the other hand, may be less mature than he is and may really be unable to understand why he should prefer an older woman. They may even think that you have somehow tricked him into marriage.

Both of you should tell your friends what the real situation is between you. Then, though it may be difficult, ignore spiteful comments and well-meaning advice. I am sure that true friends will be horrified to realize the unhappiness that their thoughtlessness is causing; those who are not are best ignored.

'It really annoys me that friends think they have a right to interfere. Why should they react so badly to our relationship?'

As long as you do not break the law and you are legally an adult, it is up to you whom you marry, but some people are offended by only slightly unconventional behaviour. Even today, it is still widely accepted that the man should be a few years older than the woman he loves. This attitude is probably based on the assumption — not necessarily true, of course — that the husband will have to support his wife and children, and so needs to be older and established in his career, while the wife should be young enough to bear his children.

Recently people have been more willing to accept that women over 40 can be exciting, beauti-

all get to know each other. They can then see for themselves that you and your man are individuals, not 'the older woman' and 'the younger man'. Do not feel that either of you should cut yourself off from your friends. No relationship thrives in isolation, and it may create problems for the future if either of you feels you have had to forget good friends for the sake of your partnership.

However, do be prepared for the fact that when there is an age gap like yours, some people do find

ful and sexy, but at present it is still true that an older man with a lined face and greying hair has a good chance of being considered attractively 'distinguished', while an older woman is usually seen as a mother or grandmother, rarely as a sexually desirable person.

The idea that sex is only for the young is also still widespread, and so some people think that, over a certain age, women especially should not be bothered with 'that sort of thing', and that if they are, it is somehow dirty or unnatural. It should not have to be said, but both men and women can be sexually active at any age, and women, who reach their sexual peak in their thirties, may well be more sexually compatible with younger men than with men in their own age group.

The trouble is that, whether we like it or not, we are all affected to some extent by what other people think of us, and a relationship like yours has to be basically very sound to cope with the un-welcome attention it attracts. However, if a couple love each other, as you do, and are prepared to tolerate the reactions of outsiders, that is in the end all that matters — and the united front they are forced to display may well be the means of bringing them even closer together.

Ageing gracefully

*Rich or poor, ageing gracefully is something we can all strive for.
Forget any ideas that it is just a matter of luck or the result of
some costly secret formula – looking after ourselves now will set
the pattern for our mental and physical health in later life.*

Rather than living in dread of the irreversible ageing process, learning what changes to expect, and how to prepare ourselves for them, can bring about a new understanding of an inevitable fact of life. This knowledge, coupled with the many advances in modern medicine, can be a positive help, making the onset of old age something we slip into easily and comfortably rather than a trauma from which there is no escape.

There is more than a grain of truth in the saying 'you're as young as you feel' because who can really say how old is old? Some people live for over a 100 years while others die at 75, yet all of them are considered to have lived a long time.

Why do we fear old age?

A certain amount of fear surrounds our feelings about growing old. Most of us know old people who are frail and dependent, but forget that much of this is due to illness which could be treated if the patient did not accept it as an inevitable part of ageing.

We fear loss of sight and mobility because they make us vulnerable. We fear deafness because we don't want to be laughed at, and yet we laugh at old people who are hard of hearing and are forever 'getting the wrong end of the stick'. We shun the lonely, making them lonelier, and fear the day when we will be on the receiving end.

How ageing can affect us

There are three factors in ageing which are very different from each other. One is that the older we are, the greater our chance of dying. The second is that as we get older, there is a greater possibility that our health will deteriorate. We become susceptible to diseases of the circulatory system and to rheumatism. The third factor, the ageing process — such as white hair and wrinkles — is relatively unconnected with either lifespan or illness; grey hair at 20 doesn't mean an early death or a wheelchair at 50.

As we age, our skin gradually loses its elasticity and wrinkles start to appear, especially around the mouth and eyes. The skin also loses its youthful bloom but this loss is very often compensated for by the fact that the older person's face acquires a new type of beauty — character. This is not to say of course, that one must be totally weatherbeaten to achieve this 'new look'. It is always a good idea to avoid too much sun or harsh winds, to keep skin well moisturized and to avoid unnecessary stretching — for example, when applying cosmetics.

Hair turns grey and then white, gradually becoming sparser. The hair loss is more noticeable in men and starts comparatively early — balding is usually complete when a man reaches 40.

Bones lose calcium and become brittle. With women, in particular, the loss of calcium can cause the spinal bones to collapse. This results in the body stooping and in actual height loss, which in severe cases can be up to three or four inches. In addition to these changes, ageing limbs lose their vigour and joints stiffen, all of which make old

AGEING — THE FACTS

- A loss of calcium makes bones brittle and liable to fracture. Spinal bones become thinner, resulting in height loss and stooping.
- Skin loses its bloom and elasticity, causing wrinkling especially around the eyes and mouth.
- Hair turns grey, then white, becoming sparse — baldness in men starts between 20 and 30, and is usually complete by 40.
- Eyesight deteriorates and eyes are more prone to cataracts.
- Loss of teeth, frequently caused through gum disease, alters facial structure.
- The body's balance and gait alters with diminished height and stiffening joints, making the body's carriage less stable.

. . . AND HOW TO SLOW IT DOWN

- Modern advances in hormone treatment can't reverse these changes, but can help to halt or, at least, slow the process down.
- Avoid exposure to the sun and wind. Moisturize and gently handle the skin.
- Keep off certain drugs, like cannabis, in youth — research suggests that this could cause premature hair loss.
- A relatively straightforward operation can cure cataracts.
- Have regular dental check-ups and maintain an effective oral hygiene routine.
- Take gentle exercise regularly from youth to middle age; older people should avoid strenuous sports — such exertions can cause bones to crack.

people slower and less agile. Although these changes cannot be reversed, they can be halted and made less distressing by hormone treatment.

Hearing can deteriorate in old age though it rarely becomes troublesome before the age of 70. Eyesight undergoes a gradual change throughout the whole of adult life. Only in very old age does eyesight start to fade through loss of sensitivity to light and through cataracts. Light sensitivity cannot be replaced, but cataracts can be cured by a relatively simple operation.

One of the greatest changes in old age comes from losing teeth. It gives the face a sunken look, which can be improved by dentures; but prevention is better than cure, and gum disease which causes teeth to drop out in middle age can be prevented by good oral hygiene.

The causes of ageing

Despite intensive research, the causes of ageing are still largely unknown. There is an exceptionally rare disease called *progeria*, whose sufferers age prematurely. Research has shown, however, that people suffering from progeria have a high concentration of a pigment called *lipofuscin* in their cells. This pigment increases in concentration in everyone as they get older. An anti-lipofuscin drug has been produced which is said to improve memory and intellect in old people who suffer from hardening of the arteries in the brain.

Vitamin E has been credited with rejuvenating properties, perhaps because a deficiency of it in-

creases the rate of production in lipofuscin. But since vitamin E is common in many of the foods we eat, it is unlikely that anyone will have a deficiency and therefore taking additional amounts would probably be of no value.

Mind and personality

As we get older our capacity to learn new things may become less. Some employers don't like taking on new staff over the age of 45 or 50 as they fear that they will be reluctant to adapt to new ways. On the other hand, employers sometimes welcome the experience and maturity of older staff members.

Memory tends to fade with age, and the newer the event the easier it is to forget it. Memory in fact consists of three processes — taking the information in, storing it, and retrieving it from the brain. In old people it is the formation of new memory that suffers, whereas events from the past can be recalled with ease and clarity.

Hardening of the arteries (*arteriosclerosis* or *atherosclerosis*) increases with age and may sometimes be associated with senility. However, it is not necessarily part of old age and can be avoided by a diet low in animal fat, plenty of physical exercise and keeping the mind active.

The search for eternal life

Despite a thousand claims, there is no 'elixir of youth' and nothing can be done to prevent the inevitability of old age and death. Nevertheless, through the centuries, various practitioners, ranging from qualified doctors to out and out quacks, have proclaimed 'miracle cures', and they are still doing so today. The practice will never die as long as there is human gullibility and vanity. The 'cures' are often related to virility and fertility, for in many people's minds youthfulness is associated with sexuality. Even today, ginseng, the root of a plant grown in the Far East, is made into a 'tea' which is claimed to be rejuvenating.

There was a fashion among a few of the wealthiest Americans in the late 1950's to arrange for their bodies to be frozen after death, in the hopes that medical science would bring them back to life once there was the technology to do so. Cryobiology — preserving tissues in a frozen state — continues to progress, but so far the best that has been done is to freeze small healthy organs while they are still alive. Thawing out dead bodies needs the ability to bring the dead back to life as well if 're-birth' is to become possible.

Changing relationships in older married life

Among older married couples there exists a whole range of relationships — from the devoted couple who live together in great happiness and harmony to the couple who seem to stay together out of a combination of financial necessity and habit. What they all have in common is that each couple is an economic and social unit, sharing the same home, possessions and friends built up over a long period together.

A couple grow old together, and broadly speaking, men and women grow old at the same rate. The female menopause, however, is a noticeable milestone for which there is no real male equivalent.

One of the greatest prejudices of our society is that sex is an activity for the young and that old people should not indulge in it. Many women may see the menopause as an opportunity to discontinue sexual relationships they have never really enjoyed. Some men may have a similar reaction.

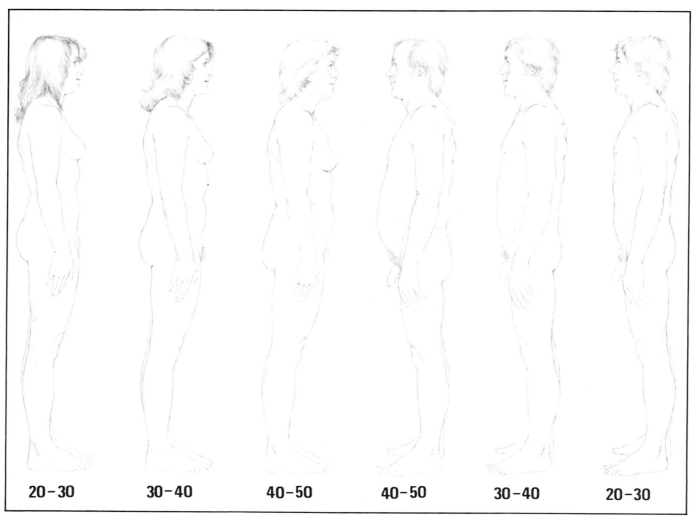

| 20-30 | 30-40 | 40-50 | 40-50 | 30-40 | 20-30 |

When children have left home, some couples will take advantage of this and have a freer and fuller sex life. Many women regard the menopause as a time when they can enjoy sex more fully, as they need no longer fear pregnancy.

Although the Victorian moralist said that too many orgasms would exhaust the body prematurely, the opposite is in fact true. The way to have an active sex life in old age is to have an active sex life in youth and middle age. Impotence in older men usually has psychological or medical causes. Masters and Johnson have proved that sexual interest and activity can persist well into the nineties, and about 30 per cent of married couples are sexually active after the age of 75. Although after the menopause the vagina and vulva shrink in size and are less well lubricated, sexually active women are affected less.

Later life is not the end of attractiveness or desire; nor is it the end of sexual responsiveness and pleasure, and the only factor that should discourage sexual activity in an older person is severe heart disease. Impotence in men and dryness of the vagina in women can be caused by diabetes, and no one should feel embarrassed about going to a doctor who can prescribe treatment.

Grown-up children may find it difficult to accept their parents' sexuality. The remarriage of elderly widowed people is often looked at askance, so much so that the newlyweds hasten to reassure everyone that 'it's just for companionship' — though if they were to live together without marrying there would be a lot of raised eyebrows!

As Maurice Chevalier once said, 'There are ten thousand ways of loving and the main thing is to choose one that goes best with your age.' So bearing in mind the words of a man who grew more attractive with every passing year, always remember that sexuality is part of ageing and ageing is part of living.

I'm too old for sex'

Older people, especially, may have physical and emotional worries which affect their sex lives. However, most problems can be dealt with, and there is no reason why sex should not be as enjoyable for older couples as it is for the young.

Middle age presents many new challenges and opportunities, but it may also be an extremely difficult time. Together with very natural fears about the approach of retirement and the loneliness which follows children leaving home, there may also be sexual worries. An especially difficult situation arises when one partner still wants to make love when the other does not, perhaps believing that sex in middle age is in some way indecent or 'abnormal'.

Alice and Peter are such a couple. Both are in their mid-fifties and they have been married for just over 35 years. Following her menopause, Alice has become more interested in making love, alarming her husband who has always believed that lovemaking naturally ceases as a couple grow older. They love each other very much and are otherwise very happy, so Peter went to see his local doctor for advice:

The end of love?

'I came to see you because my wife insisted, but I really don't think anything is the matter with me; in fact, I think she is the one who is a little sick — to be wanting sex so much at her age.'

First of all, there is absolutely nothing 'sick' or unnatural about *anyone* in their fifties — or sixties, seventies, eighties, or even nineties — wanting to make love. It is still common for people to believe that sex automatically ceases as a couple grow older, but there is very rarely a physical reason why this should happen.

I believe older couples are often affected by those beliefs of our society which seem to suggest that life is only truly worth living when you are young,

and that older people cannot be beautiful or sexy. So older people worry needlessly about the perfectly natural ways in which the body changes with age, and some go to the extremes of plastic surgery or injections with exotic substances to 'preserve' the appearance and vigour of youth.

The truth is that in sex, as in other areas of life, age has its compensations, and lovemaking can be just as — if not more — fulfilling for a couple in their sixties as it is for their twenty-year-old grandchildren or other young people.

'A friend told me that, even if men continue wanting sex as they get older, women usually want to make love less after the change of life. But my wife has recently started suggesting we make love almost every night.'

Some women do give up sex following the menopause, but very often they never liked lovemaking that much in the first place and the menopause provides a good excuse to give up an activity they regard as a distasteful duty. They may have been brought up to regard sex as 'dirty' or they may believe that sex exists solely to produce babies and, when their families are complete, see no need to continue to make love.

However, there is usually no physical reason why a woman's interest in lovemaking should cease. The natural changes in a woman's body during the menopause may make sex difficult or uncomfortable for some women — for instance, the lining of her vagina may grow thinner, making it more difficult for the penis to enter. Such problems are not usually serious, however, and can be remedied by pills or creams from the doctor.

For other women, such as your wife, these physical problems are minor compared to the freedom from worries about pregnancy following

your age. The exercise is of course good for the heart and lungs, but the emotional satisfaction produced by lovemaking may be equally important, since a happy person is much more likely to cope with the ups and downs of life.

'I had a medical check-up at work and the doctor said I was fine, but I feel so tired most of the time and when my wife wants to make love, I just can't be bothered. So what is the matter with me?'

Many older men feel tired simply because they neglect their health. They drive, rather than walk, to work, and spend their evenings and weekends slumped in front of the television. Naturally, when they do take any exercise — such as making love — the effort is more difficult. And of course if you are overweight and drink or smoke, you will feel less energetic and more prone to minor illnesses like coughs and colds, or minor aches and pains.

Why older men worry

Very often, however, simple tiredness is not the true cause of sexual problems. If a man wants to make love, he really has to be exhausted before he cannot perform. In some cases a man has deeper worries and he uses fatigue as an excuse because he no longer feels sexually confident.

The approach of retirement can often be a worrying time, especially if a man has a responsible, enjoyable job and has always seen his role of breadwinner as very important. This is especially so for men whose wives — like yours — have always been homemakers; then the mere prospect of losing his traditional male role at retirement may be a severe attack on a man's self-esteem, and may in turn lead to loss of sexual confidence.

'I suppose I do neglect my health, and I am certainly not looking forward to retirement, but I'm sure I've read that a man is naturally less sexy as he gets older.'

It is true that, as a man gets older, he is less likely to have spontaneous erections — that is, the sight of a pretty girl will not automatically make him physically excited. He may also discover that during lovemaking, his penis will not harden unless it is caressed and that he takes longer to climax. These natural changes may be alarming but they make lovemaking no less enjoyable or fulfilling. There are also compensations: men who have neglected foreplay discover just how enjoyable their partners'

the change of life. Such women often do find they are much more interested in making love. This reaction is probably just as common as an increased dislike of sex, and definitely should not be seen as abnormal, perverted or strange.

Can sex be dangerous?

'Surely fairly violent exercise such as sexual intercourse is more difficult or even dangerous as we get older?'

Some chronic illnesses, such as arthritis or chest problems, are more common in older people and may make lovemaking more difficult — though many sufferers overcome their handicaps to lead very fulfilling sex lives. There are also a few very serious complaints during which doctors believe lovemaking to be unwise.

The vast majority of older people, however, have absolutely no need to worry that making love could be harmful. In fact, most doctors today believe that sex is positively beneficial, whatever

caresses can be and many couples are delighted with the man's greater 'staying power'.

'I suppose, deep down, I know all this, and my wife wants to help — but I don't know what I should do.'

It is very important that your wife wants to help because a problem like yours can only be solved by reassessing all aspects of your life. First of all, it is essential to change to a more healthy eating and exercise programme. Secondly, deal with your worries about retirement by making positive plans. Then you will be in a much better position to tackle your sexual worries.

Healthy living

You are not seriously overweight, so I don't think you need a reducing diet — crash diets are in any case rarely a good idea, especially for older people. All you need to do is eat different foods. For example, there is now quite a lot of evidence that sugar and animal fats contribute to disease, so cut down on these foods and, in the case of animal fats, substitute vegetable oils and margarine. Don't cut out bread and potatoes — these are extremely valuable sources of vitamins and protein — but serve wholemeal, rather than white, bread and preserve vitamins by cooking potatoes in their skins. Eat plenty of fresh fruit, vegetables and salads — as well as being important sources of vitamins and minerals, these foods also provide much of the roughage the body needs; there really is no need to rely on patent medicines.

Start taking gentle, regular exercise. Walk, instead of drive, whenever you can. If you travel to work by public transport, walk to the next bus-stop or station. Go into the countryside at week-ends, then leave the car and walk — you'll not only feel better, but you'll see more of the scenery. It may be difficult at first to drag yourself out of your comfortable chair and so it is helpful if both you and your wife exercise together: one couple I know bought a dog and have felt much fitter

since they have to take their energetic pet and themselves for a walk every day!

After a few weeks of sensible eating and gentle exercise, both of you will look better, feel fitter and so feel more able to tackle your worries. And of course, if you can cut down on alcohol and give up smoking, you will feel even better.

Planning for retirement

'We've no financial worries about retirement, but I can't imagine what I'm going to do with all that spare time I'll have when I stop working.'

If you have worked hard all your life, it can be difficult to think positively about retirement, but try to see it as the beginning, rather than as an end.

Perhaps you and your wife could take up a hobby, join a club or society or enrole at evening classes. Charities are always on the look-out for willing hands, so look around your area — there is certain to be some good cause you could support. Many employers are beginning to recognize the need to help people prepare for retirement and allow employees to cut down their working hours gradually over, say, five years, so avoiding the sharp break at the official retirement date. Find out if your company has such a scheme.

You could also start helping your wife around the house. Many older women complain that they never retire because they still have to continue to run the home by themselves. One couple I know always get the house work out of the way as soon as possible so that they can concentrate on their hobbies and voluntary work.

Loving for life

If you follow my advice, you will probably find that your sexual difficulties will seem much less daunting. However, it is always possible to introduce new excitement into your lovemaking.

'I feel rather ignorant about sex — our love-life was always rather conventional — and as I always took the initiative, I now feel worried when my wife makes the first move. Can you suggest any techniques?'

There is no set programme that I can recommend to bring automatic sexual satisfaction, but I would suggest that you buy a few of the many excellent books on sexual technique and read them with your wife — there is no need to be embarrassed.

If your love-life has been rather conventional, you can begin to explore the pleasures of foreplay. Don't just concentrate on the genitals, though. The inner arms and thighs, the backs of the knees and the nape of the neck, the earlobes and along the spine are just a few areas of the body that respond to stroking, licking or gentle nibbling. No one person has the same responses, so ask each other what gives the most pleasure. If you have never done so, try caressing each other's genitals with the lips and tongue — oral sex is neither unhygienic or unnatural, but a source of great pleasure.

'We both find our usual positions for making love rather tiring. Are there any that are especially suitable for couples at our time of life?'

Of course, some love positions are too strenuous for older couples, but there are many other ways of making love besides the traditional man-above 'missionary position' — which itself may be difficult for some older people. Try one of the many woman-above positions; your wife will enjoy the new sense of freedom and you will be able to caress each other more easily. Standing up to make love will mean that neither partner has to support the weight of the other, but unless you are the same height, face-to-face lovemaking is unlikely to be successful. The problem is solved if your wife leans over a table and you enter from behind, caressing her clitoris as you move inside her. 'Spoons' — the couple lying side by side with the woman facing away from the man — is also enjoyable. Consult your books, use your imaginations and then discover which positions you most enjoy.

Don't think that lovemaking should happen only at night in bed. Your children have left home and you are alone at home, so make love at any time of day anywhere in the house. And allow your wife to control your lovemaking when she wants to; if you have previously been the active partner, you will be overjoyed to discover the pleasure of just lying back and being caressed.

Finally, never forget that making love means more than just sexual intercourse. It also means holding hands, kissing each other, buying each other surprise presents, or caressing the other person because you love her rather than just when you want to have intercourse. Your marriage is good and you love each other, and I am sure that, if you look after your health and prepare positively for retirement, sex will be rich and fulfilling for both of you for the rest of your lives.

Sex after 60

Many couples discover that sex improves as they grow older, but age does bring a few physical and emotional problems that can affect the pleasure of lovemaking. However, most difficulties can be dealt with, and there is no reason why the majority of couples over 60 should not continue to enjoy a fulfilling sex life.

We all have our own picture of old age: growing old gracefully surrounded by healthy grandchildren, or perhaps using the long, free days of retirement to pursue a favourite hobby. What often seems missing from this dream-like image is sex, and this is partly because of the attitudes of society — especially of-young people — to sex in old age.

Myths about sex in later life

When we are children we idealize our parents, and although they become less god-like as we ourselves become adult, we still sometimes find it difficult to believe that the people who cared for us and brought us up also have sexual needs and tensions.

The result is that young people — even today — think that sexual activity and pleasure belong only to the teens and early twenties, and that afterwards, especially if a person is married, lovemaking becomes a dull routine which soon disappears, much to the relief of both partners. The possibility that men and women can, and do, feel desire at 40 rarely occurs to many young people, but if they do stop to think about it, they find the idea worrying and perhaps disgusting. And the thought that any-one older than 60 should be concerned about or want sex is certainly seen as not only disgusting, but quite often as 'abnormal'.

These attitudes, and the myths on which they are based, would be laughable if some older people did not really believe in them. One of the commonest and greatest obstacles to a full sex life in old age is not that elderly people are physically incapable, but that they believe sex at their age is somehow improper and that they should have grown beyond 'all that sort of thing'.

The truth about older lovers

For most people over the age of 60, the reality of love and sex is very different from the imaginings of younger people. In fact, sexual desire continues throughout life for both men and women, though sometimes it may not be as intense as it once was. Similarly, intercourse may not occur so often or so easily as in earlier years, but many couples do carry on making love well into their eighties and nineties.

Older men and women of course vary greatly in their sexual interests and needs, and in how often they have sexual intercourse. There are no rigid rules, either, about what is sexually desirable in later life or about the techniques a couple should use, any more than there should be for young couples. Couples of any age should do what they want, not what they think is expected of them.

A few generalizations can, however, be made. If sex has never been very important, the fifties and sixties will bring even less desire for it, and people who have never really enjoyed or liked sex will find old age a good excuse to give it up alto-gether. In contrast, people who have led a full sex life during their youth will probably continue to enjoy lovemaking as they get older.

Certainly, apart from a very few illnesses in which doctors advise against sexual intercourse, there is no suggestion that sex in old age has any harmful effects or should be discouraged on medical grounds. Indeed, there is some evidence that the physical and emotional fulfillment of lovemaking may help prolong life.

Physical and emotional problems

A number of physical problems, not exclusive to old age but made worse by the advancing years, can, in the short term, reduce the enjoyment of sex. Any period of general — not necessarily severe — illness, the few weeks of recovery that are likely to follow an operation, or the flare-up of a chronic condition such as arthritis, will all probably reduce the desire for sex temporarily. However, as health improves, sexual interest usually returns, and apart from being patient, no special treatment is needed. If return to normal health is not accom-panied by a corresponding return of the sex drive, or if there are complications, there is, in most cases, no need to suffer in silence; the family doctor can very often be of great help.

Sometimes emotional rather than physical prob-lems can affect an older person's sex life. Worry, depression, or the grief that follows the death of a relative or close friend can cause the loss of the sex drive. Anxiety and grief usually disappear of their own accord over time, but if emotional problems do continue, counselling can often be helpful. Again, unless a friend can recommend a sympath-etic relationship counsellor, the family doctor will usually be able to help.

As they grow older, both men and women have problems exclusive to their sex. Difficulties can generally be resolved, but if they are not tackled, they may cause deep unhappiness for the couple.

Sexual worries in older men

As a man grows older, there are likely to be changes in his sexuality, though these need not affect either his own or his partner's enjoyment of love-making. Erections are less likely to occur spontane-ously, or without some manual stimulation, and will not return so soon after orgasm. Orgasm itself does not usually happen as quickly or easily — which of course makes for greater 'staying power' — and indeed, on some occasions, may not occur at all. Perhaps surprisingly to some younger men, these natural changes do not make lovemaking any less enjoyable or fulfilling for either the older lover or his partner.

Most men, of any age, occasionally have difficulty in getting or keeping an erection. This is quite normal and does not require treatment. However, if an older man 'fails' he is much more likely to believe it is the end of his sex life. Unfortunately, belief in impotence is usually the reason why the condition continues: when the man next tries to make love his lack of confidence means that he is beaten before he starts. In all too many cases, his feelings of shame and humiliation mean that the man never risks making love again.

In most cases, all that is necessary to 'cure' im-

potence is the courage to try again in as relaxed a state of mind as possible with a sympathetic partner, though in a number of cases, psychosexual therapy may prove to be necessary. There are some instances, however, in which impotence is caused by a decrease in the sex hormones. This can sometimes be made good by taking the male sex hormone (testosterone) or a sexual stimulant, though it is for the family doctor to decide whether these would help his patient.

The most common physical problems affecting older men's sexuality are the illnesses of the prostate gland. Fortunately, however, treatment available today is very effective and in a large number of cases there need be no long-term ill effects on a man's virility and sex life.

Sexual worries in older women

Unlike a man, a woman's desire for satisfaction in lovemaking does not depend on anything so temperamental as an erection, and the pattern of her sexuality usually does not change very much with age. The end of child-bearing at the menopause does not mean the end of lovemaking, and the right man at the right time is likely to have much the same effect on a woman at 70 as he did when she was 20.

However, the menopause does cause changes in a woman's body, and in some cases these changes can be worrying. Some women find that the vagina does not become as moist during love-making as when they were younger. This may affect both partners since, if the vagina is too dry, inter-course will be painful, difficult or even impossible.

This problem can often be solved very easily if the woman uses a non-greasy, water-based jelly (available from chemists) as a lubricant. In more severe cases a hormone cream may be needed. Before a woman decides to use this, or any other kind of hormone replacement treatment, she should consult her doctor (see pages 205–208).

Operations to remove a breast (mastectomy) or the womb (hysterectomy) are quite common in older women. These operations not only require a period of convalescence, but may also adversely affect a woman's sex life. The womb and breasts are uniquely female organs and their loss means that some women may feel somehow less feminine. Sometimes, partners genuinely do not understand these feelings and may unintentionally be very hurtful. If this happens, it is helpful for men to imagine how they would feel if their testicles were removed. If a woman is seriously depressed, doc-tors may prescribe drugs, but in most cases, a reassuring partner and sympathetic counselling will restore sexual confidence.

Relationships in old age

Whatever the physical and emotional problems which may arise in older men and women, the quality of a couple's relationship will play the

---

HOW TO ENJOY SEX AFTER 60

People often find that sex improves as they grow older because the confidence and experience of age make for very fulfilling and uninhibited love-making. However, aging brings with it physical and emotional changes which may affect a couple's sex life, so it is especially important for older people to look after their health.

Try to eat a balanced diet — many common illnesses last longer if you don't eat properly, and excess weight may interfere with lovemaking. Your doctor will advise on the right diet.

Take regular, gentle exercise. Not only will you look and feel better, but a stronger, more supple body makes for more exciting love-making and greater pleasure.

Keep your mind active and your partner inter-ested — start a new hobby, go to an evening class, or join a club or society together.

Don't accept illness as a necessary part of old age. Modern treatments can improve many conditions, and in severe cases your doctor can give something to lessen any pain.

Use the freedom of retirement to vary your sex life — make love at home wherever and whenever you wish.

Lovemaking between couples who have been together for some time is often very fulfilling because they understand each other's responses, but if a partnership shows signs of staleness, try sharing or acting out each other's fantasies, or looking at erotic books or pictures together.

If one partner finds it difficult to become excited, don't be afraid to try new ways of caressing — for instance, both men and women often find oral sex particularly arousing.

If a physical ailment, such as arthritis, makes lovemaking difficult, don't be afraid to experi-ment with new positions — 'spoons' (ie both partners lying on their sides, the man entering from behind) is often easier for older people than the traditional man-on-top position.

Remember that lovemaking is not just about penetration, and that skilled and loving caresses can be just as fulfilling as intercourse itself.

If sexual problems do occur, don't accept them as inevitable. If you feel embarrassed about consulting your family doctor, go to one of the psychosexual clinics run by large hospitals, where you can be treated without having to get a letter from your doctor.

greatest part in deciding the nature of their sex lives. If they are still happy and continue to be fascinated by each other, then clearly sex will be better than if the couple have little mutual liking or respect, are bored with their relationship, or discover that it was only their children who kept them together. For these couples, retirement may lead to many tensions and arguments, though happier couples will welcome the chance to spend more time together as they grow older.

In their later years, some people find themselves divorced, widowed or just not married. Old age for a single person may be lonely, and, not surprisingly, he or she may develop a new relationship late in life. This is entirely natural, and there is nothing ridiculous or undignified about older people falling in love. Some such relationships will be primarily for company and security, but there is no reason why sex should not play its part (though it is wise, to avoid painful misunderstandings, to discuss the subject before deciding on a permanent relationship).

The advantages of older lovers

Because of the calm and wisdom of old age, older lovers may also be more experienced, confident and considerate in their lovemaking. For the woman, fear of pregnancy has disappeared, while the older man is often a better lover in the purely physical sense: because of his slower rate of arousal, he can concentrate on pleasing his partner. Not having to go to work, and being alone in the house mean that a couple, without fear of interruption, can experiment with new ways of making love whenever they wish.

Perhaps older people who envy the sexuality of the young should remember that some younger men and women, who find relationships with their own age group shallow and unsatisfying, turn to older lovers for full sexual, as well as intellectual and emotional satisfaction. As one couple in their seventies, who were happily celebrating their fortieth wedding anniversary, said, 'Love and sex are too good to be the monopoly of the young'.

Index